FORMAL LANGUAGES

FORMAL LANGUAGES

ARTO SALOMAA

Department of Mathematics
University of Turku
Turku, Finland

A C A D E M I C   P R E S S   New York and London   1973

A Subsidiary of Harcourt Brace Jovanovich, Publishers

ACADEMIC PRESS, INC.
111 Fifth Avenue, New York, New York 10003

United Kingdom Edition published by
ACADEMIC PRESS, INC. (LONDON) LTD.
24/28 Oval Road, London NW1

LIBRARY OF CONGRESS CATALOG CARD NUMBER: 72-88356

PRINTED IN THE UNITED STATES OF AMERICA

To Kaarina, Kai, and Kirsti

Contents

PART ONE

Chapter I   Language and Grammar

Chapter II   Regular and Context-Free Languages

Chapter III   Context-Sensitive and Type-0 Languages

PART TWO

Chapter IV   **Abstract Families of Languages**

Chapter V   **Regulated Rewriting**

Chapter VI   **Context-Free Languages Revisited**

Chapter VII   **Some Further Classes of Generative Devices**

PART THREE

Chapter VIII   Solvability and Unsolvability

Chapter IX   Complexity

Preface

This book develops a theory of formal languages from the point of view of generative devices, mainly grammars. Recognition devices, automata, are introduced only as a secondary tool and are themselves presented within the framework of rewriting systems.

The main emphasis is on mathematical aspects of formal languages rather than applications. People interested only in applications to programming languages (resp. natural languages) would certainly prefer a more comprehensive discussion on topics such as $LR(k)$ grammars (resp. transformational grammars). Such discussions lie outside the scope of this book.

Unnecessary abstractions are avoided because no advanced mathematical background is assumed on the part of the reader. The reader is supposed to be familiar only with the very basic notions of algebra and logic. No previous knowledge about formal languages is required. The level of presentation corresponds to that of beginning graduate or advanced undergraduate work.

The book is self-contained in the sense that no other sources are needed for the proofs of the results stated as theorems. Some additional results are sometimes mentioned without proofs, mainly as propositions or in the notes following some sections. Of course, these results are not used in the proofs of later theorems. An attempt has also been made to cover the most recent developments.

Acknowledgments

Parts of the manuscript for this book were used as notes for lectures given at the Universities of Aarhus (Denmark), Turku (Finland), Uppsala (Sweden), and Western Ontario (London, Canada). I want to thank the participants in these courses. The 1971 summer program in formal languages at the Computer Science Department of the University of Western Ontario was especially helpful as regards many details and sharpening of the proofs. I want to thank the Head of the Department, Dr. John Hart, for making this program possible. I am grateful to (at the least) the following people for useful discussions concerning various details: A. Aho, G. Beckhoff, R. Book, B. Brodda, J. Brzozowski, S. Ginsburg, M. Harrison, G. Herman, G. Hotz, Neil Jones, E. Latikka, J. van Leeuwen, A. Lindenmayer, M. Linna, B. Mayoh, R. Newkirk, M. Nivat, P. Palomäki, A. Paz, M. Penttonen, A. Phalén, R. Rosebrugh, G. Rozenberg, M. Steinby, A. Szilard, P. Turakainen, D. Wood. Special thanks are due to Lauri Pimiä for planning the figures, Hannu Velmala for useful comments concerning the manuscript, and Leena Leppänen for careful typing of the script. Finally, I wish to thank Academic Press for excellent editorial work with both the manuscript and proofs.

Note to the Reader

Each of the Chapters IV–IX constitutes (apart from minor points) a separate entity which can be studied after the basic Chapters I–III. The difference between "theorems" and "propositions" is that the latter are not proved in this book (and also not used in subsequent proofs).

We use customary set-theoretic notation. In particular, $\{x|P_1,...,P_k\}$ denotes the set of all elements x which possess each of the properties $P_1,...,P_k$.

The symbol ∎ is used to mark the end of a proof. Throughout the book, the expression "if and only if" is abbreviated as "iff".

PART ONE

Chapter I

Language and Grammar

A language, whether a natural language such as English or a programming language such as ALGOL, can be considered to be a set of sentences, that is, finite strings of elements of some basic vocabulary. The definition of a language introduced in this chapter is based on this notion and is, consequently, general enough to include both natural and programming languages. The syntactic specification of a language with finitely many sentences can be given, at least in principle, by listing the sentences. This is not possible for languages with infinitely many sentences. The main problem of formal language theory is to develop finite representations for infinite languages. As can be seen in this chapter, such a representation may be accomplished by a generative device or by a recognition device. By imposing restrictions on the devices, different language families are obtained.

1. REWRITING SYSTEMS

An *alphabet* is a finite nonempty set. The elements of an alphabet V are called *letters*. A *word* over an alphabet V is a finite string consisting of zero or more letters of V, whereby the same letter may occur several times. The string consisting of zero letters is called the *empty word*, written λ. Thus, $\lambda, 0, 1, 001,$ 1111 are words over the alphabet $V = \{0, 1\}$. The set of all words over an alphabet V is denoted by $W(V)$. For any V, $W(V)$ is infinite.

The basic set V, its elements, and strings of its elements could also be called a vocabulary, words and sentences, or an instruction set, instructions and programs, respectively. This would reflect an approach aiming at applications only in the field of natural languages or only in the field of programming languages. In this book, we use the terminology introduced above.

If P and Q are words over an alphabet V, then their *catenation* PQ is also a word over V. Catenation is an associative operation and the empty word λ is an identity with respect to catenation: $P\lambda = \lambda P = P$ for any word P. For a word P and natural number i, the notation P^i means the word obtained by catenating i copies of the word P; P^0 denotes the empty word λ.

The *length* of a word P, in symbols $lg(P)$, means the number of letters in P when each letter is counted as many times as it occurs. By definition, $lg(\lambda) = 0$. A word P is a *subword* of a word Q iff there are words P_1 and P_2 such that $Q = P_1 P P_2$. If $P_1 = \lambda$ (resp. $P_2 = \lambda$), then P is termed an *initial* (resp. a *final*) subword of Q. A subword P of Q is *proper* iff $P \neq \lambda, Q$. Subsets of $W(V)$ are referred to as *languages* over the alphabet V.

For instance, the following sets are languages over the alphabet $V = \{a, b\}$:

$$L_1 = \{\lambda\},$$
$$L_2 = \{a, ba, aaba, bbbbb\},$$
$$L_3 = \{a^p | p \text{ prime}\},$$
$$L_4 = \{a^i b^i | i \text{ natural number}\},$$
$$L_5 = \{P \in W(V) | N_a(P) = N_b(P)\},$$

where $N_\alpha(P)$ denotes the number of occurrences of the letter α in P for $\alpha = a, b$. The languages L_1 and L_2 are *finite*, that is, contain only a finite number of words, whereas the languages L_3 to L_5 are *infinite*. We consider also the *empty language* $\varnothing$ which contains no words. Note that $\varnothing$ is not the same as the language L_1 above.

A finite language can always be defined by listing all of its words. Such a procedure is not possible for infinite languages and, consequently, other devices for the representation of infinite languages in a finitary manner have to be developed. The infinite languages L_3–L_5 above were characterized by specifying a property and then considering the language to be the set of words obeying this property. Such a *property specification* is one of the basic devices for defining infinite languages. Regular expressions and rudimentary predicates discussed in Sections 5 and 12 are such property-specifying devices. Another approach for defining an infinite language is to introduce a *generative* device and consider the language to consist of words produced by the device. Finally, we may construct a *recognition* device. In this approach the language consists of all words recognized by the device.

In this book we discuss various hierarchies of generative devices. For many classes of generative devices, we exhibit a class of recognition devices defining the same family of languages. The basic generative and recognition devices introduced in this chapter can be defined in terms of *rewriting systems*. We first consider some simple examples before the general definitions.

Example 1.1. Let L be the language over the alphabet $\{a, b\}$ defined as follows:

   (i) $\lambda \in L$.
  (ii)   If $X \in L$, then also $aXb \in L$.
 (iii)   No other words belong to L.

We claim that

$$L = \{a^i b^i | i = 0, 1, 2, \ldots\}. \tag{1.1}$$

Indeed, by (i), $a^0 b^0 \in L$. Assuming that $a^i b^i \in L$, we conclude by (ii) that $a^{i+1} b^{i+1} \in L$. Consequently, the right side of (1.1) is included in L. Conversely, $a^0 b^0$ is the only word of length 0 in L. Assuming that $a^i b^i$ is the only word of length $2i$ in L, we conclude by (ii) and (iii) that $a^{i+1} b^{i+1}$ is the only word of length $2(i+1)$ in L. Since L does not contain any words of odd length, we conclude that L is included in the right side of (1.1). Note that (i)–(iii) constitute a generative device for L, whereas (1.1) is a property-specifying definition.

Example 1.2. Let L be defined as follows:

   (i) $\lambda \in L$.
  (ii)   If $X \in L$, then also $aXb \in L$ and $bXa \in L$.
 (iii)   If $X_1 \in L$ and $X_2 \in L$, then also $X_1 X_2 \in L$.
 (iv)   No other words belong to L.

Now we claim that L consists of words with an equal number of a's and b's; that is, L is the language L_5 introduced above. Indeed, since λ has this property and (ii)–(iii) preserve it, L contains only words with this property. Clearly, L contains all words of length 0 with equally many a's and b's. Proceeding inductively, we assume that L contains all words of length no greater than $2i$ with this property. Let P be an arbitrary word of length $2(i+1)$ with this property. Without loss of generality, we assume that the first letter of P is a (because, otherwise, we can interchange the roles of a and b). If the last letter of P is b, we have $P = aP_1 b$ where P_1 is a word of length $2i$ with equally many a's and b's. By (ii) and the inductive hypothesis, we conclude that $P \in L$. If the last letter of P is a, we have $P = P_1 P_2$ where P_1 and P_2 are words of length no greater than $2i$ with equally many a's and b's. In fact, in this case P must have a proper initial subword with equally many a's and b's, and we may choose P_1 to be the first of such subwords. By (iii) and the inductive hypothesis, we conclude that $P \in L$. This completes the induction and, consequently, L contains all words with equally many a's and b's.

Example 1.3. Let L be the language consisting of all words which can be reduced to λ by a sequence of replacements of subwords ab by λ. Thus, the words λ, $aabb$, and $aabbab$ belong to L. Clearly, L is a subset of the language considered in the previous example. It is a proper subset because, for instance, none of the words ba, $abba$, or $abbaab$ belongs to L. If the letters a and b are understood as the left and the right parenthesis, respectively, then it is easily verified that L consists of all strings of correctly nested parentheses. Our original definition of L can be considered as a recognition device.

In each of our examples, some subwords of given words were rewritten. In Example 1.3, the subword ab was rewritten as λ. The language L of Example 1.1 consists of such words over the alphabet $\{a,b\}$ which can be obtained from the word X using the following rewriting rules: X can be rewritten as λ or aXb. Thereby, X is an auxiliary letter not belonging to the alphabet of the terminal language. The language L of Example 1.2 is obtained similarly from X by the following rewriting rules: X can be rewritten as λ, aXb, bXa, or XX. According to the following definition, a finite set of rewriting rules determines a *rewriting system*.

Definition. A *rewriting system* is an ordered pair $\mathrm{RW} = (V, F)$ where V is an alphabet and F a finite set of ordered pairs of words over V. The elements (P, Q) of F are referred to as *rewriting rules* or *productions* and denoted by $P \to Q$.

A word P over V *generates directly* a word Q, in symbols, $P \Rightarrow_{\mathrm{RW}} Q$ or in short $P \Rightarrow Q$, iff there are words P', P_1, P'', Q_1 such that $P = P' P_1 P''$, $Q = P' Q_1 P''$, and $P_1 \to Q_1$ belongs to F. A word P *generates* Q, in symbols, $P \Rightarrow^*_{\mathrm{RW}} Q$ or $P \Rightarrow^* Q$ iff there is a finite sequence of words over V

$$P_0, P_1, ..., P_k, \qquad k \geq 0, \tag{1.2}$$

where $P_0 = P$, $P_k = Q$, and P_i generates directly P_{i+1} for $0 \leq i \leq k-1$. The sequence (1.2) is referred to as a *derivation* of Q from P according to RW. The number k is the *length* of the derivation. Derivations are written also

$$P_0 \Rightarrow P_1 \Rightarrow \cdots \Rightarrow P_k.$$

Thus, $\Rightarrow$ is a binary relation on the set $W(V)$ and $\Rightarrow^*$ is the reflexive transitive closure of $\Rightarrow$. In general, if ρ is a binary relation on a set W, then the *reflexive transitive closure* ρ^* of ρ is defined as follows:

(i) $P\rho^* P$ for all $P \in W$.

(ii) If $P_1 \rho^* P_2$ and $P_2 \rho P_3$, then $P_1 \rho^* P_3$.

(iii) $P\rho^* Q$ only if it can be established by (i) and (ii).

A rewriting system RW can be converted to a generative device by specifying a subset AX of $W(V)$, a so-called *axiom set*, and considering the language

$$L_g(RW, AX) = \{Q | P \Rightarrow^* Q, \ P \in AX\}. \tag{1.3}$$

Similarly, RW can be converted to a recognition device by considering the language

$$L_a(RW, AX) = \{P | P \Rightarrow^* Q, \ Q \in AX\}. \tag{1.4}$$

The set in (1.3) is referred to as the language *generated* by the pair (RW, AX), and that in (1.4) as the language *recognized* or *accepted* by (RW, AX).

In most of our considerations, the axiom set AX consists of one element, and in the remaining cases, its structure is still very simple. We also consider certain modifications of the languages (1.3) and (1.4). The most common of them is to divide the alphabet V into two parts V_T and V_N, referred to as the *terminal* and the *nonterminal* alphabet, and to restrict the attention to the subsets of (1.3) and (1.4) consisting of words over V_T.

The languages defined in Examples 1.1–1.3 are represented in terms of rewriting systems as follows. The language of Example 1.3 can be defined as $L_a(RW, \{\lambda\})$, where

$$RW = (\{a, b\}, \{ab \rightarrow \lambda\}).$$

The language of Example 1.1 is given by

$$L_g(RW, \{X\}) \cap W(\{a, b\}), \tag{1.5}$$

where

$$RW = (\{a, b, X\}, \{X \rightarrow \lambda, \ X \rightarrow aXb\}).$$

The language of Example 1.2 is defined by (1.5) where now

$$RW = (\{a, b, X\}, \{X \rightarrow \lambda, \ X \rightarrow aXb, \ X \rightarrow bXa, \ X \rightarrow XX\}).$$

Rewriting systems are also called *semi-Thue systems* in the literature. In the subsequent two notes, we describe briefly certain widely used modifications which we do not discuss further in this book.

Note 1.1. A *Markov normal algorithm* is a rewriting system $RW = (V, F)$ where the elements of F are given in a linear order

$$P_1 \rightarrow Q_1, ..., P_k \rightarrow Q_k. \tag{1.6}$$

Furthermore, a subset F_1 of the set of productions (1.6) is given. The elements of F_1 are called *final* productions and denoted by $P \rightarrow . Q$. At each step of the rewriting process, the first applicable production from (1.6) must be chosen and, furthermore, the leftmost occurrence of its left side must be rewritten. Thus, normal algorithms possess a property not possessed by rewriting systems in general: They are *monogenic* in the sense that, for any word P, there is at most one word that can be produced from P in one step.

Formally, P *generates* Q *directly*, in symbols $P \Rightarrow Q$, iff each of the following conditions is satisfied:

(i)   There is a number i, $1 \leq i \leq k$, and words P' and P'' such that $P = P' P_i P''$ and $Q = P' Q_i P''$.

(ii)   None of the words P_j, where $j < i$, is a subword of P.

(iii) P_i occurs as a subword of $P' P_i$ only once.

(iv) $P_i \to Q_i$ is not an element of F_1, and one of the words $P_1, \ldots, P_k$ is a subword of Q.

The rewriting process terminates with an application of a final production or when none of the productions (1.6) is applicable. Formally, we write $P \Rightarrow Q$ iff conditions (i)–(iii) are satisfied but condition (iv) is not satisfied (i.e., either $P_i \to Q_i$ is an element of F_1 or none of the words $P_1, \ldots, P_k$ is a subword of Q). Furthermore, $P \Rightarrow^* Q$ iff there is a finite sequence $P = R_0$, $R_1, \ldots, R_u, Q$ such that $R_j \Rightarrow R_{j+1}$, $0 \leq j \leq u-1$, and $R_u \Rightarrow Q$, or else $P = Q$ and none of the words $P_1, \ldots, P_k$ is a subword of P.

It is an immediate consequence of the definitions that for any word P, there is at most one word Q such that $P \Rightarrow^* Q$. If such a Q exists, we say that the normal algorithm *halts* with P and *translates* P into Q. Otherwise the normal algorithm *loops* with P. For instance, the normal algorithm with the alphabet $\{a, b\}$ and productions

$$a \to \lambda, \qquad b \to \lambda, \qquad \lambda \to aba$$

translates every word over the alphabet $\{a, b\}$ into the word aba. All letters a and b are first erased according to the first two productions and, finally, λ is rewritten as aba. A normal algorithm can be converted into a recognition device by specifying a set of axioms and then considering the totality of words which the algorithm translates into one of the axioms.

The verification of the following facts is left to the reader. The normal algorithm with the alphabet $\{a, X, Y, \#\}$ and productions (in this order)

$$Ya \to aY, \qquad Xa \to aYX, \qquad X \to \lambda, \qquad a\# \to \#X,$$

$$\#a \to \#, \qquad \# \to \lambda, \qquad Y \to a$$

translates every word

$$a^i \# a^j, \qquad i, j \geq 0 \tag{1.7}$$

into the word a^{ij}. Hence, this normal algorithm multiplies two numbers. The normal algorithm with the alphabet $\{a, X, Y, Z, \#\}$ and productions

$$aX \to Xa, \qquad a\#a \to X\#, \qquad a\# \to \#Y, \qquad Y \to a,$$

$$X \to Z, \qquad Z \to a, \qquad \# \to \lambda$$

translates every word (1.7) into the word a^k where k is the greatest common divisor of i and j.

Note 1.2. A *Post normal system* is a rewriting system (V, F) where the elements (P, Q) of F are denoted by $PX \to XQ$, X being an operational variable. (It is assumed that $X \in V$ and neither P nor Q has X as a subword.) The yield relation $\Rightarrow$ is now defined as follows: $P_1 \Rightarrow Q_1$ iff there are words P, R, and Q over the alphabet $V - \{X\}$ such that $P_1 = PR$, $Q_1 = RQ$, and $PX \to XQ$ is an element of F. Again, $\Rightarrow^*$ is the reflexive transitive closure of $\Rightarrow$. We may now specify a set of axioms and consider the generated and accepted languages, defined exactly as (1.3) and (1.4).

2. GRAMMARS

We now define a generative device which plays the main role in all of our subsequent discussions.

Definition. A *generative grammar* is an ordered quadruple $G = (V_N, V_T, X_0, F)$ where V_N and V_T are disjoint alphabets, $X_0 \in V_N$, and F is a finite set of ordered pairs (P, Q) such that Q is a word over the alphabet $V = V_N \cup V_T$ and P is a word over V containing at least one letter of V_N. The elements of V_N are called *nonterminals* and those of V_T *terminals*; X_0 is called the *initial* letter. Elements (P, Q) of F are called *rewriting rules* or *productions* and are written $P \to Q$.

A generative grammar G determines a rewriting system (V, F) referred to as the rewriting system *induced* by G. In connection with G, the expressions "generates (directly)" and "derivation," as well as the notations $\Rightarrow$ and $\Rightarrow^*$, mean the corresponding things in the induced rewriting system. The language $L(G)$ *generated* by G is defined by

$$L(G) = \{P \mid P \in W(V_T), \ X_0 \Rightarrow^* P\}.$$

We now introduce the concept dual to a generative grammar. An *analytic grammar* is an ordered quadruple $G = (V_N, V_T, X_0, F)$ where V_N, V_T, and X_0 are exactly as above but now F is a finite set of ordered pairs (P, Q) such that P is a word over the alphabet $V = V_N \cup V_T$ and Q is a word over V containing at least one letter of V_N. An analytic grammar also determines a rewriting system, and this defines the relations $\Rightarrow$ and $\Rightarrow^*$. The language $L(G)$ *recognized* or *accepted* by an analytic grammar G is defined by

$$L(G) = \{P \mid P \in W(V_T), P \Rightarrow^* X_0\}.$$

Thus, for a generative grammar G, $L(G)$ denotes the language generated by G and, for an analytic grammar G, $L(G)$ denotes the language recognized by G.

Two grammars G and G_1, whether generative or analytic, are termed *equivalent* iff $L(G) = L(G_1)$. We are dealing mostly with generative grammars, and make the convention that the short expression "grammar" always means a generative grammar.

Returning to our examples in Section 1, we note that the language of Example 1.1 is generated by the grammar

$$(\{X\}, \{a,b\}, X, \{X \to \lambda, X \to aXb\}) \tag{2.1}$$

and recognized by the analytic grammar

$$(\{X\}, \{a,b\}, X, \{\lambda \to X, aXb \to X\}). \tag{2.2}$$

The language of Example 1.2 is generated by the grammar

$$(\{X\}, \{a,b\}, X, \{X \to \lambda, X \to aXb, X \to bXa, X \to XX\}) \tag{2.3}$$

and recognized by the analytic grammar

$$(\{X\}, \{a,b\}, X, \{\lambda \to X, aXb \to X, bXa \to X, XX \to X\}). \tag{2.4}$$

The language of Example 1.3 is generated by the grammar

$$(\{X\}, \{a,b\}, X, \{X \to \lambda, X \to aXb, X \to XX\}) \tag{2.5}$$

and recognized by the analytic grammar

$$(\{X\}, \{a,b\}, X, \{\lambda \to X, aXb \to X, XX \to X\}). \tag{2.6}$$

The following theorem shows that any grammar (generative or analytic) can be included in a pair of equivalent "dual" grammars, such as (2.1)–(2.2), (2.3)–(2.4), and (2.5)–(2.6).

Theorem 2.1. Let $G = (V_N, V_T, X_0, F)$ be a generative or an analytic grammar. Let F_1 consist of all productions $Q \to P$ such that $P \to Q$ is in F. Then $L(G_1) = L(G)$ where $G_1 = (V_N, V_T, X_0, F_1)$.

Proof. Clearly, if G is a generative (an analytic) grammar, then G_1 is an analytic (a generative) grammar. Hence, without loss of generality, we assume that G is generative. We claim that, for any word P over $V_N \cup V_T$,

$$X_0 \Rightarrow^*_G P \qquad \text{iff} \qquad P \Rightarrow^*_{G_1} X_0. \tag{2.7}$$

Indeed, we can show that, for any k,

$$P_0 \Rightarrow P_1 \Rightarrow \cdots \Rightarrow P_k \qquad (2.8)$$

is a derivation according to G iff

$$P_k \Rightarrow \cdots \Rightarrow P_1 \Rightarrow P_0 \qquad (2.9)$$

is a derivation according to G_1. By the definition of F_1, this holds true for $k = 1$. Proceeding inductively, we assume that it holds true for the value $k \geq 1$. Consequently, (2.8) holds according to G iff (2.9) holds according to G_1, and $P_k \Rightarrow P_{k+1}$ holds according to G iff $P_{k+1} \Rightarrow P_k$ holds according to G_1. Combining these results, we see that the assertion holds for the value $k+1$. As a special case, we obtain (2.7) which, in turn, implies the equation $L(G) = L(G_1)$. ∎

For a generative or analytic grammar G, the grammar G_1 is referred to as its *dual*.

We now consider examples of more complicated languages. In general, it is not easy to prove that a given grammar behaves as required (just as it is difficult to be sure in advance that a computer program works). Therefore, we do not try to give grammars with as few nonterminals or productions as possible but rather grammars such that the derivations leading to terminal words can be easily characterized.

Example 2.1 (due to M. Soittola). We claim that the grammar

$$G = (\{X_0, X_1, X_2\}, \{a, b, c\}, X_0, \{X_0 \to abc, X_0 \to aX_1 bc, X_1 b \to bX_1,$$

$$X_1 c \to X_2 bcc, bX_2 \to X_2 b, aX_2 \to aaX_1, aX_2 \to aa\})$$

generates the language

$$\{a^n b^n c^n | n \geq 1\}. \qquad (2.10)$$

In fact, consider any derivation D from the word $a^i X_1 b^i c^i$, where $i \geq 1$, leading to a word over the terminal alphabet; D must begin with i applications of the third production and then continue with an application of the fourth production, yielding the word $a^i b^i X_2 bc^{i+1}$. Now the only possibility is to apply the fifth production i times, yielding $a^i X_2 b^{i+1} c^{i+1}$. This word generates directly one of the two words $a^{i+1} X_1 b^{i+1} c^{i+1}$ or $a^{i+1} b^{i+1} c^{i+1}$. The former is of our original form, with the exponents increased by 1. Taking into account the fact that any derivation according to G begins with an application of the first or second production, we have established our assertion.

The reader may verify that also each of the following four grammars G_1–G_4 generates the language (2.10). For simplicity, we list the productions only. In each case, X_0 is the initial letter and capital letters are nonterminals.

$G_1:$ $X_0 \to aX_1 X_2,$ $aX_1 \to aaX_1 b,$ $X_1 b \to bX_1 X_3,$
$X_3 b \to bX_3,$ $X_3 X_2 \to X_2 c,$ $X_1 X_2 \to bc.$

$G_2:$ $X_0 \to aX_0 X_1 X_2,$ $X_0 \to abX_2,$ $X_2 X_1 \to X_1 X_2,$
$bX_1 \to bb,$ $bX_2 \to bc,$ $cX_2 \to cc.$

$G_3:$ $X_0 \to aX_0 X_1,$ $X_0 \to aX_2,$ $X_2 X_1 \to bX_2 c,$
$cX_1 \to X_1 c,$ $X_2 \to bc.$

$G_4:$ $X_0 \to X_0 Z_1,$ $X_0 \to X_1 Z_1,$ $X_1 \to aY_1,$
$X_1 \to aX_1 Y_1,$ $Y_1 Z_1 \to Y_1 Z_3,$ $Y_1 Z_3 \to YZ_3,$
$YZ_3 \to YZ,$ $Y_1 Y \to Y_1 Y_2,$ $Y_1 Y_2 \to YY_2,$
$YY_2 \to YY_1,$ $ZZ_1 \to Z_2 Z_1,$ $Z_2 Z_1 \to Z_2 Z,$
$Z_2 Z \to Z_1 Z,$ $Y \to b,$ $Z \to c.$

Example 2.2. We now present a grammar G generating the language

$$\{PP | P \in W(\{0, 1\})\}. \tag{2.11}$$

The productions of G are as follows:

$$X_0 \to X_1 X_2 X_3, \tag{2.12}$$

$$X_1 X_2 \to iX_1 Y_i, \qquad Y_i j \to jY_i, \qquad Y_i X_3 \to X_2 iX_3, \qquad iX_2 \to X_2 i, \tag{2.13}$$

$$X_1 X_2 \to \lambda, \qquad X_3 \to \lambda, \tag{2.14}$$

where i and j independently assume the values 0 and 1.

Consider derivations D from $PX_1 X_2 PX_3$ leading to a terminal word. [After an application of the initial (2.12), $P = \lambda$.] If one of the productions (2.14) is used, then also the other must be used, and the word PP results. If D begins with an application of the first production (2.13), the only possibility is to continue the derivation to the words $PiX_1 PY_i X_3$ and $PiX_1 PX_2 iX_3$. This leads to one of the words $PiX_1 X_2 PiX_3$ or $PiX_1 X_2 Pi$. The former is of our original form, and the latter necessarily leads to the word $PiPi$. We conclude that (2.11) is the generated language.

Example 2.3 (due to M. Soittola). Consider the grammar G determined by the productions

$$X_0 \to a, \qquad X_0 \to aXX_2 Z, \tag{2.15}$$

$$X_2 Z \to aa, \tag{2.16}$$

$$Xa \to aa, \qquad Ya \to aa, \tag{2.17}$$

$$X_2 Z \to Y_1 YXZ, \tag{2.18}$$

$$XX_1 \to X_1 YX, \qquad YX_1 \to Y_1 YX, \tag{2.19}$$

$$XY_1 \rightarrow X_1 Y, \qquad YY_1 \rightarrow Y_1 Y, \tag{2.20}$$

$$aX_1 \rightarrow aXXYX_2, \tag{2.21}$$

$$X_2 Y \rightarrow XY_2, \qquad Y_2 Y \rightarrow YY_2, \qquad Y_2 X \rightarrow YX_2. \tag{2.22}$$

We prove that

$$L(G) = \{a^{n^2} | n \geq 1\}. \tag{2.23}$$

The construction of G is based on the identity

$$n^2 = 1 + 3 + \cdots + (2n - 1).$$

The initial productions (2.15) yield one of the two words a and $aXX_2 Z$. Consider derivations from

$$P_i = aXQ_i X_2 Z, \qquad Q_i \in W(\{X, Y\}), \tag{2.24}$$

leading to a terminal word. At first only (2.16) or (2.18) is applicable. If (2.16) is applied, then the only possibility to continue is to apply (2.17) until a terminal word of length $1 + 3 + lg(Q_i)$ is obtained. (Since the terminal alphabet consists of one letter, any word is uniquely determined by its length.) If (2.18) is applied, we obtain the word $aXQ_i Y_1 YXZ$. The only possibility of continuing is to send the index 1 to the left by (2.19) and (2.20), until (2.21) becomes applicable. After applying (2.21), we obtain the word $aXXYX_2 Q_i' YYXZ$, where Q_i' results from Q_i by writing the letter Y in front of every occurrence of X. Now the only possibility is to send the index 2 to the right by (2.22), yielding

$$P_{i+1} = aXQ_{i+1} X_2 Z, \qquad Q_{i+1} = XYXQ_i' YY.$$

[Note that productions (2.22) suffice to send the index 2 to the right. $X_2 X \rightarrow XX_2$ is not needed because there are no two consecutive X's.] We have, thus, a new word of the form (2.24), and a new loop begins by applying (2.16) or (2.18). Furthermore,

$$lg(Q_{i+1}) = lg(Q_i) + N_X(Q_i) + 5.$$

where $N_X(Q_i)$ denotes the number of occurrences of X in Q_i. Since clearly $N_X(Q_{i+1}) = N_X(Q_i) + 2$, we conclude that the lengths of the generated terminal words are the elements of the sequence

$$1, 1 + 3, 1 + 3 + 5, 1 + 3 + \cdots + (2n - 1), \ldots.$$

This proves (2.23).

Example 2.4. The grammar

$$G = (\{X_0, X, Y, Z\}, \{a\}, X_0, \{X_0 \rightarrow YXY, YX \rightarrow YZ, ZX \rightarrow XXZ,$$

$$ZY \rightarrow XXY, X \rightarrow a, Y \rightarrow \lambda\})$$

generates the language

$$\{a^{2^n} | n \geq 0\}.$$

Terminating derivations from $YX^{2^i}Y$ lead to one of the words a^{2^i} or $YX^{2^{i+1}}Y$; Y acts as a boundary marker. If one of the last two productions is used prematurely, no terminal word results.

Example 2.5 (due to M. Penttonen). This grammar is quite complicated, the generated language being

$$\{a^p | p \text{ prime}\}.$$

The productions are listed below. Again, capital letters are nonterminals and X_0 is the initial letter. In (2.27), i ranges over the letters A and B, and in (2.29) j ranges over the numbers 0, 1, and 2:

$$X_0 \to a^2, \qquad\qquad X_0 \to a^3, \qquad\qquad X_0 \to a^5, \tag{2.25}$$
$$X_0 \to a^7,$$

$$X_0 \to Y_1 A^6 X_3, \qquad Y_1 \to Y_1 A^2, \qquad Y_1 A^3 \to X_1 A^3 X_2, \tag{2.26}$$

$$iAX_2 A \to DY_2 Y_i E, \quad iDY_2 \to DY_2 i, \qquad X_1 DY_2 \to X_1 BY_3,$$
$$Y_3 i \to iY_3, \qquad\qquad Y_3 Y_i E \to Y_i Y_3 E, \qquad Y_3 Ei \to iY_3 E, \tag{2.27}$$
$$Y_3 EX_3 \to Y_4 CX_3, \qquad iY_4 \to Y_4 i, \qquad\quad Y_i Y_4 \to iX_2,$$

$$X_1 B \to X_1 Y_5, \qquad\quad Y_5 B \to BY_5, \qquad\quad Y_5 X_2 A \to Y_6 X_2 A, \tag{2.28}$$
$$BY_6 \to Y_6 A, \qquad\qquad X_1 Y_6 \to X_1 A,$$

$$CX_3 \to Y_7 X_3, \qquad\quad CY_7 \to Y_7 A, \qquad BA^j X_2 Y_7 \to Y_8 A^{j+1} X_2,$$
$$A^4 X_2 Y_7 \to Y_8 A^4 X_2, \quad AY_8 \to Y_8 A, \qquad\quad BY_8 \to Y_8 A, \tag{2.29}$$
$$X_1 Y_8 \to X_1 A,$$

$$X_2 X_3 \to Y_9 a, \qquad\quad AY_9 \to Y_9 a, \qquad\quad X_1 Y_9 \to aa. \tag{2.30}$$

Productions (2.26) generate, for any odd $n \geq 9$, the word $X_1 A^3 X_2 A^{n-6} X_3$. Productions (2.27)–(2.29) test whether or not n is divisible by 3 and, if not, yield the word $X_1 A^4 X_2 A^{n-7} X_3$. Now a divisibility test by 4 is performed. A negative answer always causes X_2 to move one step to the right. A positive answer causes the derivation to terminate without producing a terminal word. If all divisibility tests fail, the word $X_1 A^{n-3} X_2 X_3$ is obtained and productions (2.30) become applicable, yielding a^n. This informal description of the grammar can be replaced by an inductive proof. The details are left to the reader.

Grammars are now classified by imposing restrictions on the form of productions. The resulting hierarchy of grammars and languages is the object of detailed study in subsequent chapters of this book.

Definition. For $i = 0, 1, 2, 3$, a grammar $G = (V_N, V_T, X_0, F)$ is of the *type i* iff the restrictions (i) on F, as given below, are satisfied.

(0)   No restrictions.

(1)   Each production in F is of the form $Q_1 X Q_2 \rightarrow Q_1 P Q_2$, where Q_1 and Q_2 are words over the alphabet $V = V_N \cup V_T$, $X \in V_N$, and P is a *non-empty* word over V, with the possible exception of the production $X_0 \rightarrow \lambda$ whose occurrence in F implies, however, that X_0 does not occur on the right side of any production in F.

(2)   Each production in F is of the form $X \rightarrow P$ where $X \in V_N$ and $P \in W(V)$.

(3)   Each production is of one of the two forms $X \rightarrow YP$ or $X \rightarrow P$ where $X, Y \in V_N$ and $P \in W(V_T)$.

For $i = 0, 1, 2, 3$, a language is of the *type i* iff it is generated by a grammar of type i. The family of all languages of type i is denoted by $\mathscr{L}_i$.

Thus, according to grammars of type 1, a single nonterminal X may be replaced by a word P, but only in the context $Q_1 X Q_2$. Therefore, type-1 languages are called *context-sensitive*. According to type-2 grammars, a nonterminal X may be rewritten as P, no matter what the letters adjacent to X are, that is, independently of the context. Therefore, type-2 languages are called *context-free*. The expressions "context-sensitive" and "context-free" are extended to concern grammars too. Type-3 grammars and languages are often referred to as *finite-state* or *regular*. The motivation of these terms becomes apparent in Sections 4 and 5.

It is obvious by the definition that every grammar is of type 0 and, furthermore that every type-3 grammar is of type 2. Consequently $\mathscr{L}_0$ includes all of our families $\mathscr{L}_i$ and $\mathscr{L}_2$ includes $\mathscr{L}_3$. It will be seen that

$$\mathscr{L}_3 \subset \mathscr{L}_2 \subset \mathscr{L}_1 \subset \mathscr{L}_0,$$

where every inclusion is proper.

A grammar is *length-increasing* iff every production $P \rightarrow Q$ satisfies the condition $lg(P) \leq lg(Q)$, with the possible exception of the production $X_0 \rightarrow \lambda$ whose occurrence in the production set implies, however, that X_0 does not occur on the right side of any production. Clearly, every type-1 grammar is length-increasing. It is shown in Section 9 that, for every length-increasing grammar, there is an equivalent type-1 grammar.

The definitions given above deal with generative grammars. For analytic grammars, the types are defined in exactly the same way, with the left and right sides of the productions interchanged. By Theorem 2.1, the family of languages recognized by analytic type-i grammars equals the family $\mathscr{L}_i$ for $i = 0, 1, 2, 3$. The dual notion of a length-increasing generative grammar is a *length-decreasing* analytic grammar.

Each of the grammars (2.1)–(2.6) is context-free. The grammars G and G_1–G_3 of Example 2.1 are length-increasing and G_4 is, moreover, context-sensitive. The grammars of Examples 2.3 and 2.5 are length-increasing, whereas those of Examples 2.2 and 2.4 are type 0. It is seen in Chapters II and III that each of the languages considered in Examples 2.1–2.5 is context-sensitive but none of them is context-free. We conclude this section with three simple examples.

Example 2.6. From the point of view of linguistics, grammars are used for parsing sentences. Consider the following analytic context-free grammar. The alphabet of nonterminals is $\{S, V_p, N_p, V, N, A\}$ where the letters mean, intuitively, "sentence," "verb phrase," "noun phrase," "verb," "noun," and "article." The terminal alphabet is {the, cat, mouse, ate} where each of the items is considered to be an indivisible object. The initial letter is S. The productions are

$$\text{the} \to A, \quad \text{cat} \to N, \quad \text{mouse} \to N, \quad \text{ate} \to V,$$

$$AN \to N_p, \quad VN_p \to V_p, \quad N_p V_p \to S.$$

One recognized sequence of terminals is

the cat ate the mouse.

The recognition is illustrated in Fig. 1.

Example 2.7. For a word P, the *mirror image* of P, in symbols $\text{mi}(P)$, is the word obtained by writing P backward. By definition, $\text{mi}(\lambda) = \lambda$. The language

$$\{P\,\text{mi}(P)\,|\,P \in W(V_r)\} \tag{2.31}$$

over the alphabet $V_r = \{a_1, \ldots, a_r\}$ is generated by the context-free grammar

$$(\{X\},\, V_r,\, X,\, \{X \to \lambda,\, X \to a_1\,Xa_1, \ldots, X \to a_r\,Xa_r\}).$$

The language (2.31) is a subset of the set of *palindromes*, that is, words which remain the same when read backward. Comparing languages (2.11) and (2.31), we see that it is much more difficult to generate (or recognize) the former than the latter. This is an intrinsic feature of our generative devices because, from the point of view of property specification, (2.11) and (2.31) are of the same complexity.

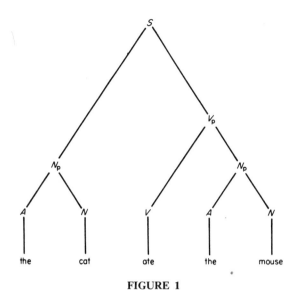

FIGURE 1

Example 2.8. Assume that $n \geq 1$ and $P_1, ..., P_n$ are words over V_T. The grammar

$$(\{X\}, V_T, X, \{X \to P_1, ..., X \to P_n\})$$

generates the finite language $\{P_1, ..., P_n\}$. The grammar $(\{X\}, V_T, X, \{X \to X\})$ generates the empty language. Both of the grammars are of type 3 (and of any of our types i).

3. CLOSURE UNDER BASIC OPERATIONS

A mathematical structure can be imposed on a family of languages by introducing *operations* which yield new languages from given ones. A family of languages $\mathscr{L}$ is *closed* under an operation ω iff a language in $\mathscr{L}$ results whenever ω is applied to languages of $\mathscr{L}$. One of our main problems is the study of the closure of various language families under various operations.

Since languages are sets, we may define the set-theoretic operations of union, intersection, difference, and complement in the usual fashion:

$$L_1 \cup L_2 = \{P | P \in L_1 \text{ or } P \in L_2\}, \qquad L_1 \cap L_2 = \{P | P \in L_1 \text{ and } P \in L_2\},$$

$$L_1 - L_2 = \{P | P \in L_1 \text{ and } P \notin L_2\}, \qquad \sim L = W(V) - L$$

where L is over the alphabet V.

The *catenation* (or *product*) of two languages L_1 and L_2, in symbols $L_1 L_2$, is defined by

$$L_1 L_2 = \{P_1 P_2 | P_1 \in L_1 \text{ and } P_2 \in L_2\}.$$

Catenation of languages is associative because catenation of words is associative. Consequently, we may define L^i, $i \geq 1$, to be the language obtained by catenating i copies of L. Furthermore, we define L^0 to be the language $\{\lambda\}$ consisting of the empty word λ. The languages $\varnothing$ and $\{\lambda\}$ are zero and unit elements with respect to catenation: For any language L,

$$L\varnothing = \varnothing L = \varnothing, \qquad L\lambda = \lambda L = L.$$

(Note that we have written λ instead of $\{\lambda\}$. In general, we may identify an element with its unit set if there is no danger of confusion.)

The *catenation closure* (or *iteration*) of a language L, in symbols L^*, is defined to be the union of all powers of L:

$$L^* = \bigcup_{i=0}^{\infty} L^i.$$

The *λ-free catenation closure* of L, in symbols L^+, is defined to be the union of all positive powers of L:

$$L^+ = \bigcup_{i=1}^{\infty} L^i.$$

Clearly, L^+ equals either L^* or $L^* - \lambda$, depending whether $\lambda \in L$ or $\lambda \notin L$.

The *left quotient* of a language L_1 by a language L_2 is defined by

$$L_2 \backslash L_1 = \{Q | PQ \in L_1 \text{ for some } P \in L_2\}.$$

The *left derivative* of a language L with respect to a word P is obtained as a special case:

$$\partial_P L = \{P\} \backslash L = \{Q | PQ \in L\}.$$

Right quotient and *right derivative* are defined similarly:

$$L_1 / L_2 = \{Q | QP \in L_1 \text{ for some } P \in L_2\},$$

$$\partial_P^r L = L / \{P\} = \{Q | QP \in L\}.$$

The *mirror image* of a language is the collection of the mirror images of its words, that is,

$$\text{mi}(L) = \{\text{mi}(P) | P \in L\}.$$

We now define the operations of *substitution* and *homomorphism*. For each letter a of an alphabet V, let $\sigma(a)$ be a language over an alphabet V_a. Define, furthermore,

$$\sigma(\lambda) = \lambda, \qquad \sigma(PQ) = \sigma(P)\sigma(Q) \qquad \text{for} \quad P, Q \in W(V).$$

Such a mapping σ of $W(V)$ into $2^{W(V')}$, where V' is the union of the alphabets V_a, is called a *substitution*. For a language L over V, we define

$$\sigma(L) = \{Q|Q \in \sigma(P) \text{ for some } P \in L\}.$$

A substitution σ is *regular* iff each of the languages $\sigma(a)$ is regular. A substitution σ is *λ-free* iff none of the languages $\sigma(a)$ contains the empty word. A family of languages is closed under substitution iff, whenever L is in the family and σ is a substitution such that each $\sigma(a)$ is in the family, then $\sigma(L)$ is also in the family.

A substitution σ such that each $\sigma(a)$ consists of a single word P_a is called a *homomorphism*. Thus, a homomorphism is a mapping of $W(V)$ into $W(V')$. A homomorphism is *λ-free* iff none of the words P_a is λ.

[Algebraically, $W(V)$ is the free semigroup with identity λ generated by V. The notion of homomorphism introduced above agrees with the customary definition of homomorphism of one semigroup into another. Since h is determined by its values for the elements of V, it is also referred to as a homomorphism of V.]

We now prove results concerning the closure of the families $\mathscr{L}_i$, $i = 0, 1, 2, 3$, under various operations. The following theorem is a useful lemma in many constructions involving grammars.

Theorem 3.1. For any grammar $G = (V_N, V_T, X_0, F)$, one may construct an equivalent grammar $G' = (V_N', V_T, X_0, F')$ such that every production of F' containing letters of V_T is of the form $X \to a$ where $X \in V_N'$ and $a \in V_T$. Furthermore, if G is type 0, type 1, type 2, or length-increasing, then G' is also type 0, type 1, type 2, or length-increasing, respectively.

Proof. For each letter $a \in V_T$, we introduce a new nonterminal letter A_a. The alphabet V_N' is formed by adding all of the letters A_a to V_N. (In general, we make the *convention* that whenever new letters are introduced in a construction, they are distinct from the letters introduced previously. Thus, none of the letters A_a belongs to V_N.) The production set F' is obtained from F by replacing each of the letters a everywhere by A_a, and finally adding the productions

$$A_a \to a, \qquad a \in V_T. \tag{3.1}$$

Clearly, F' has the required property, and the second sentence of the theorem is satisfied.

To show that $L(G) = L(G')$, we prove first that

$$L(G) \subseteq L(G'). \tag{3.2}$$

Assume that a nonempty word $P = a_1 \cdots a_n \in L(G)$. Then we may first derive, according to G', the word $A_{a_1} \cdots A_{a_n}$ and hence, by (3.1), the word P. If

$\lambda \in L(G)$, the same derivation can be carried out also according to G', with every a replaced by A_a. Thus, (3.2) holds.

To establish the converse inclusion

$$L(G') \subseteq L(G), \tag{3.3}$$

we first define a homomorphism h of $W(V_N' \cup V_T)$ into $W(V_N \cup V_T)$ by

$$h(A_a) = a \quad \text{for} \quad a \in V_T; \qquad h(x) = x \quad \text{for} \quad x \in V_N \cup V_T.$$

Assume that $P \Rightarrow_{G'} Q$. If thereby some of the productions (3.1) have been applied, we have $h(P) = h(Q)$. Otherwise, $h(P) \Rightarrow_G h(Q)$. Thus, in both cases,

$$h(P) \Rightarrow_G^* h(Q).$$

This implies that whenever $P \in L(G')$, then also

$$X_0 = h(X_0) \Rightarrow_G^* h(P) = P.$$

Thus, $P \in L(G)$. This proves the inclusion (3.3). ∎

It is customary to call the three operations of union, catenation, and catenation closure *regular* operations. Our first closure theorem deals with regular operations.

Theorem 3.2. Each of the families $\mathscr{L}_i$, $0 \leq i \leq 3$, contains all finite languages and is closed under regular operations.

Proof. The first assertion follows by Example 2.8. To prove the second assertion, we assume that L and L' are generated by the grammars

$$G = (V_N, V_T, X_0, F) \qquad \text{and} \qquad G' = (V_N', V_T', X_0', F')$$

of type i where $0 \leq i \leq 3$. By Theorem 3.1, we may assume that terminals do not occur on the left side of any production in F or F'. We may assume, furthermore, that V_N and V_N' are disjoint (because this situation can always be reached by renaming the elements of V_N').

Closure under union is established first. For $i \neq 1$, the language $L \cup L'$ is generated by the type-i grammar

$$(V_N \cup V_N' \cup \{Y_0\}, \; V_T \cup V_T', \; Y_0, \; F \cup F' \cup \{Y_0 \to X_0, \; Y_0 \to X_0'\}) \tag{3.4}$$

where Y_0 is a new nonterminal. The same grammar is suitable also for $i = 1$, provided neither L nor L' contains λ (and consequently neither $X_0 \to \lambda$ nor $X_0' \to \lambda$ is among the productions). If $i = 1$ and $\lambda \in L \cup L'$, we first consider languages $L - \lambda$ and $L' - \lambda$, and form the grammar (3.4). Then we add a new initial letter Y_1 and productions $Y_1 \to Y_0$ and $Y_1 \to \lambda$.

As regards catenation and catenation closure, we consider different values of i separately.

Assume first that $i = 2$. The language LL' is generated by the type-2 grammar

$$(V_N \cup V_N' \cup \{Y_0\}, \; V_T \cup V_T', \; Y_0, \; F \cup F' \cup \{Y_0 \to X_0 X_0'\}).$$

The language L^* is generated by the type-2 grammar

$$(V_N \cup \{Y_0\}, \; V_T, \; Y_0, \; F \cup \{Y_0 \to \lambda, \; Y_0 \to Y_0 X_0\}).$$

Assume next that $i = 3$. Replace in F' each production of the form

$$X \to P, \qquad X \in V_N', \quad P \in W(V_T') \tag{3.5}$$

by the production $X \to X_0 P$. Denote the resulting set of productions by F_1. Then the type-3 grammar

$$(V_N \cup V_N', \; V_T \cup V_T', \; X_0', \; F_1 \cup F)$$

generates the language LL'. Replace in F' each production of the form (3.5) by the production $X \to X_0' P$, and denote the resulting set by F_2. The type-3 grammar

$$(V_N' \cup \{Y_0\}, \; V_T', \; Y_0, \; \{Y_0 \to \lambda, \; Y_0 \to X_0'\} \cup F' \cup F_2)$$

generates the language $(L')^*$. Hence we have shown that the families $\mathscr{L}_2$ and $\mathscr{L}_3$ are closed under catenation and catenation closure.

Assume, finally, that $i = 0$ or $i = 1$. We consider first catenation and suppose that for $i = 1$, $\lambda \notin L \cup L'$. Then the type-i grammar

$$(V_N \cup V_N' \cup \{Y_0\}, \; V_T \cup V_T', \; Y_0, \; F \cup F' \cup \{Y_0 \to X_0 X_0'\}) \tag{3.6}$$

generates the language LL'. In fact, it is obvious that each word in LL' can be generated according to (3.6). On the other hand, if

$$Y_0 \Rightarrow Q_1 \Rightarrow \cdots \Rightarrow Q_u$$

is a derivation according to (3.6), then each Q_j is the form $Q_j = P_j P_j'$ where $X_0 \Rightarrow_G^* P_j$ and $X_0' \Rightarrow_G^* P_j'$. This is seen inductively. Clearly, $Q_1 = X_0 X_0'$ is of this form. If Q_j is of this form, then the same holds for Q_{j+1} since no terminals appear on the left sides of the productions and the alphabets V_N and V_N' are disjoint. Consequently, only words in LL' can be generated according to (3.6).

Suppose now that $i = 1$ and $\lambda \in L \cup L'$. Denote

$$L_1 = L - \lambda \qquad \text{and} \qquad L_1' = L' - \lambda.$$

By the obvious distributive laws, it is seen that LL' is one of the three languages

$$L_1 L_1' \cup L_1, \qquad L_1 L_1' \cup L_1', \qquad L_1 L_1' \cup L_1 \cup L_1' \cup \lambda.$$

Because we have shown that $\mathcal{L}_1$ is closed under union and that a type-1 grammar can be constructed for $L_1 L_1'$, we conclude that a type-1 grammar can be constructed for LL'. Thus, we have shown that $\mathcal{L}_0$ and $\mathcal{L}_1$ are closed under catenation.

To show that $\mathcal{L}_0$ and $\mathcal{L}_1$ are closed under catenation closure, we note first that for any language L,

$$(L \cup \lambda)^* = L^*.$$

Moreover, for any type-1 or type-0 grammar G_1, we may construct a grammar G_1' such that $L(G_1') = L(G_1) - \lambda$. If G_1 is of type 1, we simply remove the production $Y_0 \to \lambda$ (where Y_0 is the initial letter). If G_1 is of type 0, we replace each production of the form $P \to \lambda$ by the productions $xP \to x$ and $Px \to x$ where x ranges over the letters in the nonterminal and terminal alphabets. By these remarks, we conclude that the closure of $\mathcal{L}_0$ and $\mathcal{L}_1$ under $*$-operation follows if we prove that L^* is of type i, $i = 0, 1$, whenever L is of type i and $\lambda \notin L$.

Thus, without loss of generality, we assume that $\lambda \notin L$. Then the type-i grammar

$$(V_N \cup \{Y_0, Y_1\}, V_T, Y_0, F \cup \{Y_0 \to \lambda, Y_0 \to X_0, Y_0 \to Y_1 X_0\}$$

$$\cup \{Y_1 a \to Y_1 X_0 a | a \in V_T\} \cup \{Y_1 a \to X_0 a | a \in V_T\}) \qquad (3.7)$$

generates the language L^*. It is easy to see, namely, that every word in L^* is generated by (3.7). On the other hand, consider an arbitrary derivation

$$Y_0 \Rightarrow Q_1 \Rightarrow \cdots \Rightarrow Q_u, \qquad u \geqq 1$$

according to (3.7). If $Q_1 = \lambda$ or $Q_1 = X_0$, then $Q_1 \in L^*$ or the derivation can lead only to terminal words in L. Otherwise, $Q_1 = Y_1 X_0$ and each Q_j is of one of the two forms

(i) $Y_1 R_1 \cdots R_v$, where $v \geqq 1$, the first letter in the words $R_2, \ldots, R_v$ is terminal, and $X_0 \overset{*}{\underset{G}{\Rightarrow}} R_v$ for $v = 1, \ldots, v$; or

(ii) $R_0 R_1 \cdots R_v$, where $v \geqq 1$, the first letter in the words $R_1, \ldots, R_v$ is terminal, and $X_0 \overset{*}{\underset{G}{\Rightarrow}} R_v$ for $v = 0, \ldots, v$.

This is seen inductively. [Q_1 is of form (i). Assume that Q_j is of form (i) or (ii). By checking through the productions of (3.7) and remembering that terminals do not occur on the left sides of the productions in F, we see that also Q_{j+1} is of the form (i) or (ii).] This implies that only words in L^* can be derived according to (3.7). ∎

The proof of Theorem 3.2 gives, in each case, an effective procedure of constructing the required grammar. This is true of almost all results in this book: Although not stated separately in each case, an effective procedure is involved.

Our next theorem is an immediate corollary of Theorem 3.2. In fact we only have to remove productions $Y_0 \to \lambda$ from the grammars generating the language L^*.

Theorem 3.3. If the language L is of type i, $0 \leq i \leq 3$, then also the language L^+ is of type i.

We now prove a result about the families $\mathscr{L}_0 - \mathscr{L}_2$. The result is extended in Section 5 to concern the family $\mathscr{L}_3$.

Theorem 3.4. Each of the families $\mathscr{L}_0 - \mathscr{L}_2$ is closed under mirror image.

Proof. Let L be generated by the type-i $(0 \leq i \leq 2)$ grammar $G = (V_N, V_T, X_0, F)$. Consider the grammar

$$G' = (V_N, V_T, X_0, F'), \qquad F' = \{\mathrm{mi}(P) \to \mathrm{mi}(Q) | P \to Q \text{ in } F\}.$$

Clearly, G' is of type i. We claim that

$$L(G') = \mathrm{mi}(L).$$

Indeed,

$$X_0 \Rightarrow Q_1 \Rightarrow \cdots \Rightarrow Q_u \tag{3.8}$$

is a derivation according to G iff

$$X_0 \Rightarrow \mathrm{mi}(Q_1) \Rightarrow \cdots \Rightarrow \mathrm{mi}(Q_u) \tag{3.9}$$

is a derivation according to G'. For $u = 1$, this follows by the definition of F'. Assume the equivalence of (3.8) and (3.9) for the value u. By the definition of F',

$$Q_u \Rightarrow_G Q_{u+1} \qquad \text{iff} \quad \mathrm{mi}(Q_u) \Rightarrow_{G'} \mathrm{mi}(Q_{u+1}).$$

Consequently, the equivalence of (3.8) and (3.9) holds for the value $u+1$. ∎

Theorem 3.5. The families $\mathscr{L}_0$ and $\mathscr{L}_2$ are closed under substitution. Consequently, they are closed under arbitrary homomorphisms.

Proof. Consider first the family $\mathscr{L}_2$. Assume that $L = L(G)$ where

$$G = (V_N, V_T, X_0, F), \qquad V_T = \{a_1, \ldots, a_r\}, \tag{3.10}$$

is of type 2. Let σ be a substitution such that $\sigma(a_i)$ is generated by the type-2 grammar

$$G_i = (V_N^i, V_T^i, X_0^i, F^i), \tag{3.11}$$

for $i = 1, \ldots, r$. Without loss of generality, we assume that the nonterminal alphabets in these $r + 1$ grammars are pairwise disjoint and, by Theorem 3.1, that no terminals occur on the left side of any production. [This assumption is used later when we assume that (3.11) is of type 0.] Denote by F_1 the set of productions obtained from F by replacing in each production every letter a_i, $i = 1, \ldots, r$, by the letter X_0^i. Then the type-2 grammar

$$(V_N \cup V_N^1 \cup \cdots \cup V_N^r, V_T^1 \cup \cdots \cup V_T^r, X_0, F_1 \cup F^1 \cup \cdots \cup F^r)$$

generates the language $\sigma(L)$.

This method is not directly applicable for type-0 grammars. This is due to the fact that "illegitimate contexts" may arise for the use of productions. For instance, if L is generated by the grammar with the only production $X_0 \rightarrow a_1^2$ and

$$G_1 = (\{X_0^1\}, \{a_1\}, X_0^1, \{X_0^1 \rightarrow a_1^2, X_0^1 X_0^1 \rightarrow a_1\}),$$

then the construction above would yield $\sigma(L) = \{a_1, a_1^4\}$ although the correct result is $\sigma(L) = \{a_1^4\}$. To avoid this situation, we modify our earlier construction.

Thus assume that L is generated by a type-0 grammar (3.10) and that the grammars (3.11) defining the substitution σ are of type 0. We assume again that the sets of nonterminals in these $r + 1$ grammars are pairwise disjoint. Then the language $\sigma(L)$ is generated by the following grammar G_σ. The nonterminal alphabet of G_σ equals the union

$$V_N \cup V_N^1 \cup \cdots \cup V_N^r \cup \{Y_0, Y, A_{a_1}, \ldots, A_{a_r}\}.$$

The initial letter is Y_0, and the terminal alphabet is

$$V_T^1 \cup \cdots \cup V_T^r.$$

Denote by F_2 the set of productions obtained from F by replacing in each production every letter a_i, $i = 1, \ldots, r$, by the letter A_{a_i}, and denote

$$F_3 = \{YA_{a_i} \rightarrow YX_0^i | 1 \leq i \leq r\}, \qquad F_4 = \{Ya \rightarrow aY | a \in V_T^1 \cup \cdots \cup V_T^r\}.$$

The production set of G_σ is

$$F_2 \cup F_3 \cup F_4 \cup F^1 \cup \cdots \cup F^r \cup \{Y_0 \rightarrow YX_0, Y \rightarrow \lambda\}.$$

Let $P \in \sigma(L)$ be arbitrary. Then P is obtained from a word $Q \in L$ by replacing each a_i by a word in $\sigma(a_i)$. We can derive according to G_σ first the word YQ', where Q' results from Q by replacing each a_i by A_{a_i}. Using F_3, the first letter of Q' is converted into the initial letter of the corresponding grammar (3.11), say, X_0^j. Using productions in F^j the appropriate word in $\sigma(a_j)$ is derived and then Y goes to the right by F_4. The procedure is repeated for the second letter of Q' and continued until Y converts the last letter of Q', after which Y can be deleted. Thus every word in $\sigma(L)$ is generated by G_σ. Also the converse holds true, this being due to the fact that Y can convert a new letter only after the derivation beginning from the letter converted previously has been terminated. ∎

Theorem 3.5 is extended to concern the family $\mathscr{L}_3$ in Section 5 and, as regards λ-free substitutions, the family $\mathscr{L}_1$ in Section 10.

The discussion concerning the closure of our language families under Boolean operations other than union is postponed until more sophisticated tools have been developed. However, the following theorem is easily obtained already at this stage.

Theorem 3.6. The family $\mathscr{L}_0$ is closed under intersection.

Proof. Assume that $L = L(G)$ and $L' = L(G')$ where

$$G = (V_N, V_T, X_0, F), \qquad G' = (V_N', V_T', X_0', F')$$

are type-0 grammars. We may assume again that $V_N \cap V_N' = \varnothing$. Consider the grammar

$$G_1 = (V_N \cup V_N' \cup V_N'', V_T \cup V_T', Y_0, F \cup F' \cup F_1),$$

where V_N'' contains, for every element $a \in V_T \cup V_T'$, the element A_a and, furthermore, three additional elements Y_0, Y_1, Y_2, and where F_1 consists of the following productions:

$$Y_0 \rightarrow Y_1 X_0 Y_2 X_0' Y_1, \tag{3.12}$$

$$Y_2 a \rightarrow A_a Y_2 \quad \text{for} \quad a \in V_T \cup V_T', \tag{3.13}$$

$$b A_a \rightarrow A_a b \quad \text{for} \quad a, b \in V_T \cup V_T', \tag{3.14}$$

$$Y_1 A_a a \rightarrow a Y_1 \quad \text{for} \quad a \in V_T \cup V_T', \tag{3.15}$$

$$Y_1 Y_2 Y_1 \rightarrow \lambda. \tag{3.16}$$

Using (3.12) and the productions in $F \cup F'$, all words of the form

$$Y_1 P Y_2 P' Y_1, \qquad P \in L, \quad P' \in L' \tag{3.17}$$

can be derived from Y_0. By (3.13)–(3.15), the word

$$P Y_1 Y_2 Y_1 \tag{3.18}$$

can be derived from (3.17) iff $P = P'$. By (3.16), the word P can be derived from (3.18). Because this is the only case where a derivation leads from Y_0 to a terminal word, we conclude that $L(G_1) = L \cap L'$. ∎

4. HIERARCHY OF AUTOMATA

Automata are mathematical models of devices that process information by giving responses to inputs. From the point of view of formal language theory, automata are considered as recognition devices and sometimes also as devices for translating languages. A hierarchy of automata, corresponding to the hierarchy of the language families $\mathscr{L}_i$, can be introduced.

The simplest automaton in this hierarchy is the *finite deterministic automaton*. It is a recognition device which discriminates between input words over a fixed alphabet V in the following fashion. The device is capable of a finite number of internal states, among which are a specified initial state s_0 and a designated set S_1 of final states. Given a word $a_1 a_2 \cdots a_k$, the device first scans the letter a_1 in the state s_0 (cf. Fig. 2). Then it moves into another state s_1 (eventually $s_1 = s_0$) and scans the letter a_2 in s_1, and so on, until it comes to the right end of the word. At each step, the next state s_{i+1} ($0 \leq i \leq k-1$) is uniquely determined by the state s_i and the scanned letter a_{i+1}. Thus the input word $a_1 a_2 \cdots a_k$ determines uniquely the terminal state s_k. If s_k belongs to the designated set S_1, then the word is accepted by the automaton; otherwise it is rejected. All words accepted by a given finite deterministic automaton constitute a language, called the language *accepted* or recognized by the automaton.

After these heuristic remarks, we now give the formal definitions.

Definition. A rewriting system (V, F) is called a *finite deterministic automaton* iff the following conditions are satisfied:

(i) V is divided into disjoint alphabets S and V_T, referred to as the *state* and the *terminal* alphabet.

(ii)   An element $s_0 \in S$ and a subset $S_1 \subseteq S$ are specified, so-called *initial state* and *final state set*.

(iii)   The productions in F are of the form

$$s_i a_k \rightarrow s_j, \qquad s_i, s_j \in S; \quad a_k \in V_T. \tag{4.1}$$

Furthermore, for each pair (s_i, a_k) where $s_i \in S$ and $a_k \in V_T$, there is exactly one production (4.1) in F.

Let FDA be a finite deterministic automaton, and $\Rightarrow$ the yield-relation of the underlying rewriting system. The language *accepted* or recognized by FDA is defined by

$$L(\text{FDA}) = \{P \in W(V_T) | s_0 P \Rightarrow^* s_1 \text{ for some } s_1 \in S_1\}.$$

A language L is *acceptable* by a finite deterministic automaton iff, for some FDA, $L = L(\text{FDA})$.

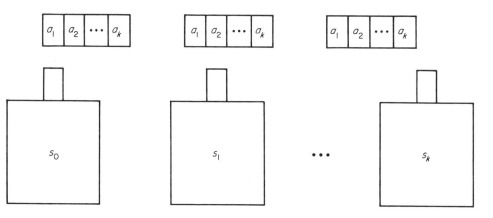

FIGURE 2

Thus, $L(\text{FDA})$ consists of words which move the automaton from the initial state to one of the final states. Clearly, $\lambda \in L(\text{FDA})$ iff $s_0 \in S_1$. Since there is exactly one production (4.1) for each pair (s_i, a_k), we are given a mapping f of the Cartesian product $S \times V_T$ into S. The mapping f is referred to as the transition or *next state* function. A finite deterministic automaton can thus be defined by specifying the quintuple (S, V_T, s_0, S_1, f).

A *finite nondeterministic automaton* FNA is defined as a deterministic one, with the following two exceptions. In (ii), s_0 is replaced by a subset $S_0 \subseteq S$, referred to as the *set of initial states*. In (iii), the second sentence is omitted. The language *accepted* by FNA is the set

$$L(\text{FNA}) = \{P \in W(V_T) | s_0 P \Rightarrow^* s_1 \text{ for some } s_0 \in S_0 \text{ and } s_1 \in S_1\}.$$

A language L is *acceptable* by a finite nondeterministic automaton iff, for some FNA, $L = L(\text{FNA})$.

Since the second sentence is omitted from (iii), we may have for a pair (s_i, a_k) none or several values of j such that the production (4.1) is in F. This can be interpreted to mean that the automaton has several choices for the next state when scanning a_k in state s_i. In this interpretation, a word P may cause several sequences of state transitions beginning from a fixed state. The word P is accepted iff it causes at least one sequence of state transitions leading from an initial state to a final state. Thus if there is one successful sequence of state transitions for P, all failures caused by P are disregarded.

The following theorem connects finite automata with type-3 grammars.

Theorem 4.1. For a language L, the following three conditions are equivalent.

  (i) L is acceptable by a finite deterministic automaton.

  (ii) L is acceptable by a finite nondeterministic automaton.

  (iii) L is of type 3.

Proof. Because a deterministic automaton is a special case of a nondeterministic one, we conclude that (i) implies (ii). Consider the assertion that (ii) implies (iii). A language accepted by a finite nondeterministic automaton FNA equals the union of all languages of the form

$$\{P \in W(V_T)|s_0 P \Rightarrow^* s_1\}, \qquad s_0 \in S_0, \quad s_1 \in S_1, \tag{4.2}$$

where S_0 and S_1 are the initial and final state sets, respectively. Each language (4.2) is recognized by the type-3 analytic grammar whose production set consists of the productions of FNA and of the additional production $\lambda \to s_0$, and whose initial letter is s_1. Since, by Theorem 3.2, the union of two type-3 languages is of type 3, we conclude that $L(\text{FNA})$ is of type 3. Thus, (ii) implies (iii).

To show that (iii) implies (i), we consider a language L recognized by an analytic type-3 grammar $G = (V_N, V_T, X_0, F)$. We prove first that one may construct an equivalent type-3 analytic grammar $G' = (V_N', V_T, X_0, F')$ whose productions are of one of the following two forms:

$$Xa \to Y, \qquad a \in V_T; \quad X, Y \in V_N', \tag{4.3}$$

$$\lambda \to Y, \qquad Y \in V_N'. \tag{4.4}$$

In addition to (4.3) and (4.4), G may contain productions of the following three forms:

$$Ya_1 \cdots a_k \to X, \qquad k \geq 2; \quad a_j \in V_T; \quad X, Y \in V_N, \tag{4.5}$$

$$a_1 \cdots a_k \to Y, \qquad k \geq 1; \quad a_j \in V_T; \quad Y \in V_N, \tag{4.6}$$

$$Y \to X', \qquad X', Y \in V_N. \tag{4.7}$$

Thus, we have to eliminate all productions (4.5)–(4.7) from G.

For each production (4.5), we introduce new nonterminals $X_1, \ldots, X_{k-1}$ and replace (4.5) by the productions

$$Ya_1 \to X_1, \; X_1 a_2 \to X_2, \; \ldots, \; X_{k-1} a_k \to X.$$

For each production (4.6), we introduce new nonterminals $Y_1, \ldots, Y_k$ and replace (4.6) by the productions

$$\lambda \to Y_1, \; Y_1 a_1 \to Y_2, \ldots, \; Y_k a_k \to Y.$$

It is easy to see that the language generated by our grammar is not affected by these replacements. The procedure is carried on until all productions (4.5) and (4.6) have been eliminated. The resulting grammar G'' contains only productions of the forms (4.3), (4.4), (4.7), and $L(G'') = L(G)$.

To eliminate the productions (4.7), we proceed as follows. For each non-terminal Z of G'', we denote by $U(Z)$ the set of all nonterminals Z' such that $Z \Rightarrow^* Z'$. [Clearly, always $Z \in U(Z)$. The set $U(Z)$ can be determined effectively. A method is given in the proof of Theorem 6.3.] We now remove all productions (4.7) from G''. For each production (4.3) [resp. (4.4)], we add to G'' all productions $Xa \rightarrow Y'$ [resp. $\lambda \rightarrow Y'$] satisfying $Y' \in U(Y)$. The generated language is not affected and thus we obtain a grammar G' as required.

The second and final step in our construction is to replace G' by a finite deterministic automaton FDA such that

$$L(\text{FDA}) = L(G'). \tag{4.8}$$

The terminal alphabet of FDA is V_T. The state alphabet S of FDA consists of all subsets (including the empty set) of the set V_N'. The initial state Z_0 is the subset of V_N' consisting of all letters Y such that the production (4.4) is in F'. The final state set consists of those subsets of V_N' which contain the letter X_0. Finally, the production set F_1 of FDA is defined as follows. For each pair (Z, a) where $Z \in S$ and $a \in V_T$, the production $Za \rightarrow Z_1$ is in F_1, where

$$Z_1 = \{Y | Xa \rightarrow Y \text{ is in } F' \text{ for some } X \in Z\}.$$

It can now be verified that (4.8) holds true. Assume that $P = a_1 \cdots a_u \in L(G')$ where each $a_i \in V_T$. Then there is a derivation

$$a_1 a_2 \cdots a_u \Rightarrow Y_1 a_1 a_2 \cdots a_u \Rightarrow Y_2 a_2 \cdots a_u \Rightarrow^* Y_u a_u \Rightarrow X_0 \tag{4.9}$$

according to G'. By the definition of FDA,

$$Z_0 a_1 a_2 \cdots a_u \Rightarrow Z_1 a_2 \cdots a_u \Rightarrow^* Z_u, \tag{4.10}$$

where Z_u contains X_0 and thus is a final state. On the other hand, a derivation of the form (4.9) can be inferred from (4.10). Consequently, (4.8) holds true and we have shown that (iii) implies (i). ∎

Our next two theorems are corollaries of Theorem 4.1.

Theorem 4.2. The family $\mathscr{L}_3$ is closed under intersection and complementation.

Proof. Assume that $L \in \mathscr{L}_3$. By Theorem 4.1, there is a finite deterministic automaton FDA such that $L = L(\text{FDA})$. Let S and S_1 be the state set and final state set of FDA, respectively. Denote by FDA_1 the finite deterministic automaton obtained from FDA by replacing S_1 by $S - S_1$. Then

$$\sim L = L(\text{FDA}_1).$$

By Theorem 4.1, $\sim L$ is of type 3. Consequently, $\mathscr{L}_3$ is closed under complementation. Since the intersection of two languages can be expressed in the form

$$L_1 \cap L_2 = \sim((\sim L_1) \cup (\sim L_2)),$$

Theorem 3.2 implies that $\mathscr{L}_3$ is closed under intersection. ∎

Theorem 4.3. Every type-3 language is generated by a grammar (V_N, V_T, X_0, F) such that every production in F is of one of the two forms $X \to Ya$ and $X \to \lambda$ where $X, Y \in V_N$ and $a \in V_T$.

Proof. The assertion follows immediately by considering the dual of G' in the proof of Theorem 4.1. ∎

In many cases it is useful to be able to reduce the productions of a grammar to certain simple forms. Theorem 4.3 shows that any type-3 grammar can be reduced to an equivalent one which satisfies certain additional conditions. Many results concerning the reduction of grammars to such "normal forms" are presented later on in this book.

The only response which an FDA or FNA can give to an input is "yes" or "no," depending on whether it is in a final or nonfinal state after having scanned the whole input. We now define a device which is otherwise similar to a finite nondeterministic automaton but which can output a word for each input letter.

Definition. A rewriting system (V, F) is called a *generalized sequential machine* iff the following conditions are satisfied:

(i) V is divided into two disjoint alphabets S and $V_1 \cup V_0$. The sets S, V_1, and V_0 are called the *state*, *input*, and *output* alphabet, respectively. The sets V_1 and V_0 are nonempty but not necessarily disjoint.

(ii)   An element $s_0 \in S$ and a subset $S_1 \subseteq S$ are specified, namely, the so-called *initial state* and *final state set*.

(iii)   The productions in F are of the form

$$s_i a \to P s_j, \qquad s_i, s_j \in S; \quad a \in V_1; \quad P \in W(V_0). \qquad (4.11)$$

For a generalized sequential machine GSM and a word Q over its input alphabet V_1, we denote

$$\text{GSM}(Q) = \{R \mid s_0 Q \Rightarrow^* R s_1 \text{ for some } s_1 \in S_1\}.$$

Let L be a language over V_1. Then GSM *translates* or *maps* L into the language

$$\text{GSM}(L) = \{P \mid P \in \text{GSM}(Q) \text{ for some } Q \in L\}. \qquad (4.12)$$

We say that the mapping defined by (4.12) is a *gsm mapping*.

Similarly, for $Q \in W(V_0)$, we define

$$\text{GSM}^{-1}(Q) = \{R|Q \in \text{GSM}(R)\}.$$

For a language $L \subseteq W(V_0)$, we define

$$\text{GSM}^{-1}(L) = \{P|P \in \text{GSM}^{-1}(Q) \text{ for some } Q \in L\}. \qquad (4.13)$$

The mapping defined by (4.13) is an *inverse gsm mapping*.

A generalized sequential machine GSM is *deterministic* iff, for every $s_i \in S$ and $a \in V_1$, there is exactly one production (4.11) in F. A deterministic GSM is a *Mealy machine* iff all words P appearing in productions (4.11) consist of one letter of V_0.

Productions (4.11) may be interpreted as follows. When GSM scans the letter a in the state s_i, one possible behavior is to expend a, output P, and move to the state s_j. For a deterministic GSM, there is only one possible behavior in each configuration. The mapping defined by a Mealy machine is *length-preserving*: For every word P,

$$lg(\text{GSM}(P)) = lg(P).$$

If GSM is deterministic, the productions (4.11) determine a mapping f of $S \times V_1$ into S, as well as a mapping φ of $S \times V_1$ into $W(V_0)$, referred to as the *transition* and *output* function, respectively. If GSM is a Mealy machine, then φ is a mapping into V_0.

Example 4.1. Consider the generalized sequential machine GSM, where

$$S = \{s_0, s_1, s_2, s_3, s_4, s_5\}, \qquad V_1 = V_0 = \{a, b\},$$

s_0 is the initial state and $\{s_4\}$ the final state set, and F consists of the productions

$$s_0 a \rightarrow as_1, \qquad s_0 b \rightarrow bs_5,$$
$$s_1 a \rightarrow as_1, \qquad s_1 b \rightarrow as_2,$$
$$s_2 a \rightarrow bs_3, \qquad s_2 b \rightarrow as_2,$$
$$s_3 a \rightarrow bs_3, \qquad s_3 b \rightarrow bs_4,$$
$$s_4 a \rightarrow as_5, \qquad s_4 b \rightarrow bs_4,$$
$$s_5 a \rightarrow as_5, \qquad s_5 b \rightarrow bs_5.$$

Clearly, GSM is a Mealy machine. The transition and output function are illustrated in Fig. 3, where arrows are labeled by letters of V_1, with the corresponding letter of V_0 in parentheses. The following results concerning

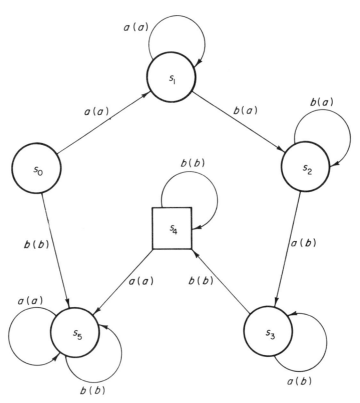

FIGURE 3

translation of languages are easily verified:

$$\text{GSM}\{a^n b^n a^n b^n | n \geq 1\} = \{a^{2n} b^{2n} | n \geq 1\},$$
$$\text{GSM}^{-1}\{a^{2n} b^{2n} | n \geq 1\} = \{a^m b^n a^p b^q | m, n, p, q \geq 1, \ m+n = p+q \text{ is even}\},$$
$$\text{GSM}^{-1}\{a^n | n \geq 1\} = \varnothing.$$

Consequently,

$$\text{GSM}^{-1}(\text{GSM}\{a^n b^n a^n b^n | n \geq 1\}) \neq \{a^n b^n a^n b^n | n \geq 1\},$$
$$\text{GSM}(\text{GSM}^{-1}\{a^n | n \geq 1\}) \neq \{a^n | n \geq 1\}.$$

Thus, GSM^{-1} is not a true inverse in an algebraic sense.

According to the definitions above, generalized sequential machines are devices for translating languages. However, they can be viewed also as recognition devices by considering the language accepted by GSM to consist of those words P over V_1 for which $\text{GSM}(P)$ is nonempty. In this fashion, the language accepted by GSM is affected only by the underlying finite non-deterministic automaton. Consequently, the languages acceptable by generalized sequential machines are the type-3 languages.

We now define recognition devices capable of defining larger language classes. A feature common to these devices or automata is that they have a finite control and an infinite memory whose organization essentially determines the recognition capacity of the automaton.

A *pushdown automaton* reads input words from left to right and is capable of a finite number of internal states. In addition, it has an auxiliary memory called the *pushdown store* which is potentially infinite. The information in the store must be used in the order reverse to the one in which it is inserted into the store, that is, last in—first out. After scanning a letter a in a state s and with z as the topmost letter in the store, the automaton (i) erases z and inserts a word $z_1 \cdots z_k$ (possibly empty) to the store, (ii) goes to another state s', and (iii) either continues scanning a or starts scanning the next letter of the input word (cf. Fig. 4). The automaton is nondeterministic: For each configuration

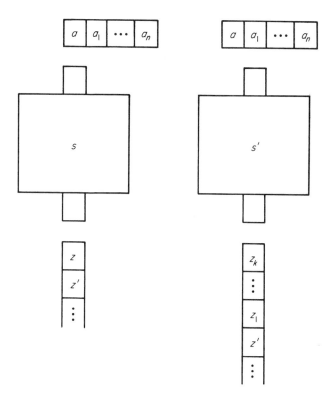

FIGURE 4

(a, s, z) there may be several choices for the behavior (i)–(iii). When the automaton starts scanning an input word, it is in a specified initial state and has a specified start letter in the store. The word is accepted iff the automaton is in a designated final state after scanning the whole word. These notions are formalized in the following.

Definition. A rewriting system (V, F) is called a *pushdown automaton* iff the following conditions are satisfied:

(i) V is divided into two disjoint alphabets S and $V_1 \cup V_Z$. The sets S, V_1, and V_Z are called the *state*, *input*, and *pushdown* alphabet, respectively. The sets V_1 and V_Z are nonempty but not necessarily disjoint.

(ii)   Elements $s_0 \in S$ and $z_0 \in V_Z$, and a subset $S_1 \subseteq S$ are specified, namely, the so-called *initial state*, *start letter*, and *final state set*.

(iii)   The productions in F are of the two forms

$$z s_i \to Q s_j, \qquad z \in V_Z; \quad Q \in W(V_Z); \quad s_i, s_j \in S, \tag{4.14}$$

$$z s_i a \to Q s_j, \qquad z \in V_Z; \quad Q \in W(V_Z); \qquad a \in V_1; \quad s_i, s_j \in S. \tag{4.15}$$

The language *accepted* by a pushdown automaton PDA is defined by

$$L(\text{PDA}) = \{ P \in W(V_1) | z_0 s_0 P \Rightarrow^* Q s_1 \text{ for some } Q \in W(V_Z), s_1 \in S_1 \}.$$

A language L is *acceptable* by a pushdown automaton iff there is a PDA such that $L = L(\text{PDA})$.

Productions of the form (4.14) may be interpreted to mean that, after being in state s_i with z topmost in the store, PDA may go to s_j and replace z by Q without changing the position of the reading head scanning the input. Productions (4.15) mean that, after scanning a in state s_i with z topmost in the store, PDA may go to s_j, replace z by Q, and expend a, that is, move the reading head one step to the right.

Pushdown automata bear the same relation to context-free languages as finite automata do to type-3 languages:

Proposition 4.1. A language is acceptable by a pushdown automaton iff it is context-free.

A pushdown automaton PDA is *deterministic* iff

(i)   for each $s_i \in S$ and $z \in V_Z$, F contains either exactly one production (4.14) and no productions (4.15), or no productions (4.14) and exactly one production (4.15) for every $a \in V_1$;

(ii)   whenever $z = z_0$ in (4.14) or (4.15), then the first letter of Q is z_0.

Thus, condition (i) is the actual requirement of determinism, whereas (ii) asserts that the store is never empty. In fact, (ii) can be omitted without reducing the recognition capacity of deterministic pushdown automata. A language is termed *deterministic* iff it is acceptable by a deterministic pushdown automaton.

A *linear bounded automaton* can move in both directions when scanning the input word. Furthermore, it is able to replace the scanned letter by another letter. While doing this it may use as much space only as is occupied by the input word. The automaton is in general nondeterministic: When scanning the letter a in the state s, the automaton may have several choices for its behavior to (i) replace a by another letter, (ii) change state, and (iii) move the position of the reading and writing head. In Fig. 5, a is replaced by b, the next

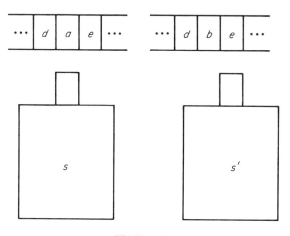

FIGURE 5

state is s', and the head is moved to the right. (In the following formalized version, one step in the action consists of either overprinting or moving the head.) Initial and final states, as well as acceptance, are understood as in connection with finite or pushdown automata.

Definition. A rewriting system (V, F) is called a *linear bounded automaton* iff the following conditions are satisfied:

(i) V is divided into two disjoint alphabets S and V_T, referred to as the *state* and *tape* alphabet. Furthermore, a subalphabet $V_I \subseteq V_T$, called the *input* alphabet, is given.

(ii)   An element $s_0 \in S$ and a subset $S_1 \subseteq S$ are specified, namely, the *initial state* and *final state set*.

(iii)   The productions in F are of the three forms

$$s_i a \to s_j b, \qquad s_i, s_j \in S; \quad a, b \in V_T, \qquad (4.16)$$

$$s_i a \to a s_j, \qquad s_i, s_j \in S; \qquad a \in V_T, \qquad (4.17)$$

$$c s_i a \to s_j c a, \qquad s_i, s_j \in S; \quad a, c \in V_T. \qquad (4.18)$$

Furthermore, for each s_i, a, and s_j, F either contains no production (4.18) or contains (4.18) for every $c \in V_T$.

The language *accepted* by a linear bounded automaton LBA is defined by

$$L(\text{LBA}) = \{ P \in W(V_I) | s_0 P \Rightarrow^* Q s_1 \text{ for some } Q \in W(V_T), s_1 \in S_1 \}.$$

Again, L is *acceptable* by a linear bounded automaton iff there is an LBA such that $L = L(\text{LBA})$.

Productions (4.16)–(4.18) correspond to the moves of LBA where the position of the head is left unchanged, changed one step to the right, or changed one step to the left, respectively. The requirement concerning (4.18) means that the behavior depends on the scanned letter only, and not on the letter to the left of the scanned one.

A result analogous to Theorem 4.1 and Proposition 4.1 holds also for linear bounded automata. The "only if" part of Proposition 4.2 is proved in Section 10.

Proposition 4.2. A language is acceptable by a linear bounded automaton iff it is context-sensitive.

A linear bounded automaton is *deterministic* iff, for each $s_i \in S$ and $a \in V_T$, at most one of the conditions (i)–(iii) is satisfied:

(i)   There is exactly one production of form (4.16) in F.
(ii) There is exactly one production of form (4.17) in F.
(iii) There is exactly one collection of productions (4.18), where c ranges over V_T, in F.

A *Turing machine* differs from a deterministic linear bounded automaton in that it can extend its workspace. When it is about to "go off" the input tape from either end, a new square is automatically added. A Turing machine operates between two boundary markers $\#$ which are moved when the workspace is extended. (It is often convenient to use boundary markers for LBA's, too. The recognition capacity is not thereby altered.)

Definition. A rewriting system (V, F) is called a *Turing machine* iff the following conditions are satisfied:

(i) V is divided into two disjoint alphabets S and V_T, referred to as the *state* and *tape* alphabet.

(ii)   Elements $s_0 \in S$, $\# \in V_T$, and a subset $S_1 \subseteq S$ are specified, namely, the *initial state*, the *boundary marker*, and the *final state set*. The set $V_1 = V_T - \{\#\}$ is not empty. An element $o \in V_1$ and a subset $V_1 \subseteq V_1$ are specified.

(iii)   The productions in F are of the forms

$$s_i a \rightarrow s_j b \quad \text{(overprint)}, \tag{4.19}$$

$$s_i ac \rightarrow as_j c \quad \text{(move right)}, \tag{4.20}$$

$$s_i a\# \rightarrow as_j o\# \quad \text{(move right and extend workspace)}, \tag{4.21}$$

$$cs_i a \rightarrow s_j ca \quad \text{(move left)}, \tag{4.22}$$

$$\# s_i a \rightarrow \# s_j oa \quad \text{(move left and extend workspace)}, \tag{4.23}$$

where $s_i, s_j \in S$ and $a, b, c \in V_1$. Furthermore, for each $s_i, s_j \in S$ and $a \in V_1$, F either contains no productions (4.20) and (4.21) [resp. (4.22) and (4.23)] or else contains both (4.21) and (4.20) for every $c \in V_1$ [resp. contains both (4.23) and (4.22) for every $c \in V_1$]. For no $s_i \in S$ and $a \in V_1$, the word $s_i a$ is a subword of the left side in two productions of the forms (4.19), (4.21), and (4.23).

We say that a word sP, where $s \in S$ and $P \in W(V_T)$, is *final* iff P does not begin with a letter a such that sa is a subword of the left side of some production in F. The language *accepted* by a Turing machine TM is defined by

$$L(\text{TM}) = \{P \in W(V_1) | \# s_0 P\# \Rightarrow^* \# P_1 s_1 P_2 \# \text{ for some } s_1 \in S_1,$$

$$P_1, P_2 \in W(V_1) \text{ such that } s_1 P_2 \# \text{ is final}\}.$$

A language L is *acceptable* by a Turing machine iff $L = L(\text{TM})$ for some TM. It is to be noted that TM is monogenic: At each step of the rewriting process, at most one production is applicable.

Turing machines bear the same relation to type-0 languages as our other automata do to our other language families.

Theorem 4.4. If a language is acceptable by a Turing machine, then it is of type 0.

Proof. Assume that $L = L(\text{TM})$ where in connection with TM we use the notations of the definition. We define a type-0 analytic grammar G which recognizes L. The terminal alphabet of G is V_1. The nonterminal alphabet consists of the letters in $V - V_1$ and of the additional letters X_0, X_1, and X_2.

The initial letter is X_0. The production set of G consists of the productions of TM and of the productions

$$\lambda \to \#s_0, \qquad \lambda \to \#, \qquad s_1 a \to X_1, \qquad X_1 b \to X_1,$$
$$X_1 \# \to X_2, \qquad s_1 \# \to X_2, \qquad bX_2 \to X_2, \qquad \#X_2 \to X_0,$$

where s_1 ranges over S_1, b ranges over V_1, and for each s_1, a ranges over such elements of V_1 that $s_1 a$ is final. It can now be verified that $L(G) = L(TM)$. If $P \in L(TM)$, there is a derivation according to G

$$P \Rightarrow \#s_0 P \Rightarrow \#s_0 P \# \Rightarrow^* \#P_1 s_1 aP_2 \# \Rightarrow \#P_1 X_1 P_2 \# \Rightarrow^* \#P_1 X_2 \Rightarrow^* X_0$$

or, if $P = \lambda$,

$$P \Rightarrow \#s_0 \Rightarrow \#s_0 \# \Rightarrow \#X_2 \Rightarrow X_0.$$

Consequently, $P \in L(G)$. Assume, conversely, that $P \in L(G)$. If $P = \lambda$, there is a derivation according to G from $\#s_1 \#$ to X_0 where $s_1 \in S_1$ and $s_1 = s_0$. This implies that $\lambda \in L(TM)$. If $P \neq \lambda$, there is a derivation according to G from

$$\#P_1 s_1 aP_2 \#, \qquad s_1 \in S_1; \quad a \in V_1; \quad P_1, P_2 \in W(V_1); \quad s_1 a \text{ final}, \quad (4.24)$$

to X_0, and also a derivation from P to (4.24). This implies that $P \in L(TM)$. ∎

Also the converse of Theorem 4.4 holds true.

Proposition 4.3. Every type-0 language is acceptable by a Turing machine. Hence, a language is acceptable by a Turing machine iff it is of type 0.

Note 4.1. All types of automata in the hierarchy introduced in this section can be defined to behave deterministically or nondeterministically. (A nondeterministic Turing machine is obtained from TM by relaxing the condition that the underlying rewriting system is monogenic.) Since deterministic automata are special cases of nondeterministic ones, the family of languages acceptable by the former devices is a subfamily of the family of languages acceptable by the latter. Theorem 4.1 shows that, for finite automata, the subfamily is not proper. The same holds true for Turing machines but not for pushdown automata, for which the subfamily is proper, as is seen in Chapter VI. Whether or not nondeterministic linear bounded automata accept more languages than do deterministic ones is an unsolved problem (perhaps the most famous one in the field of automata).

EXERCISES

1. Give a context-free grammar for each of the following languages:

$$L_1 = \{a^{3i}b^i | i \geq 1\}, \qquad L_2 = \{a^i b^j | i \geq j \geq 0\},$$
$$L_3 = \{P \in W\{a, b\} | N_a(P) = 2N_b(P)\},$$

where $N_a(P)$ [resp. $N_b(P)$] is the number of a's [resp. b's] in P. Give then a context-free grammar for the language $(L_1 L_2 \cup L_2)^*$.

2. Which of the following equations are valid for all languages L_1, L_2, L_3 and all homomorphisms h? Give reasons in each case.

$$L_1 \cap L_2 = L_2 \cap L_1, \qquad\qquad L_1 L_2 = L_2 L_1,$$

$$L_1(L_2 \cup L_3) = L_1 L_2 \cup L_1 L_3, \qquad L_1(L_2 \cap L_3) = L_1 L_2 \cap L_1 L_3,$$

$$(L_1{}^*)^* = L_1{}^*, \qquad\qquad (L_1 \cup L_2)^* = L_1{}^* \cup L_2{}^*,$$

$$(L_1 \cap L_2)^* = L_1{}^* \cap L_2{}^*, \qquad (L_1 L_2)^* L_1 = L_1(L_2 L_1)^*,$$

$$(L_1 \cup L_2)^* = L_2{}^*(L_1 L_2{}^*)^*, \qquad L_2(L_2 \backslash L_1) = L_1,$$

$$h(h(L_1)) = h(L_1), \qquad\qquad h(L_1 \cup L_2) = h(L_1) \cup h(L_2),$$

$$h(L_1 \cap L_2) = h(L_1) \cap h(L_2), \qquad h(L_1 L_2) = h(L_1) h(L_2).$$

3. Construct a finite deterministic automaton accepting the language L over the alphabet $\{a, b\}$, consisting of all words P that satisfy each of the following conditions: (i) The length of P is divisible by 3; (ii) P begins with the letter a and ends with b; (iii) aaa is not a subword of P.

4. A type-2 grammar G with the initial letter X_0 is *reduced* iff, for each non-terminal $X \neq X_0$, (i) X_0 generates a word containing X and (ii) X generates some terminal word. Give a method which, for each type-2 grammar, produces an equivalent reduced grammar.

5. Call a nonterminal X *cyclic* iff X generates (in more than 0 steps) a word containing X. Assume that G is a type-2 reduced grammar (in the sense of Exercise 4) which has no productions $Y \to \lambda$ or $Y \to Z$ where Y and Z are nonterminals. Prove that $L(G)$ is infinite iff G has a cyclic nonterminal. [The trivial case of $L(G)$ being empty is excluded.]

6. Give a method which, for each context-free grammar, produces an equivalent context-free grammar where every nonterminal distinct from the initial letter generates infinitely many terminal words.

7. Consider the Markov normal algorithm with the alphabet $V \cup \{X, Y, Z\}$ and productions

$$\alpha\beta X \to \beta X \alpha, \qquad Y\alpha \to \alpha X \alpha Y, \qquad X \to Z, \qquad Z \to \lambda, \qquad Y \to . \lambda, \qquad \lambda \to Y,$$

where α and β independently range over V. (It is assumed that none of the letters X, Y, or Z belongs to V. The mutual order of productions in the first two schemas is immaterial.) Prove that this normal algorithm translates every word P over V into PP.

8. Define a homomorphism h of $W\{a, b\}$ by $h(a) = b$, $h(b) = ab$. Determine the values of the function

$$f(n) = lg(h^n(a)), \qquad n \geq 1,$$

where h^n stands for n applications of h.

9. Let R be a type-3 language and L an arbitrary language. Prove that the left quotient $L\backslash R$ is of type 3.

10. Consider the following infinite sequence

$$T = 0110100110010110\cdots = a_1 a_2 a_3 \cdots$$

of letters of the alphabet $\{0, 1\}$, defined as follows. The first letter a_1 equals 0. If the first 2^k ($k \geq 0$) have already been defined and are equal to $a_1 a_2 \cdots a_{2^k}$, then the next 2^k letters are $a_1' a_2' \cdots a_{2^k}'$ where $a_i' = 1 - a_i$. Prove that T contains no finite subword of the form P^3 where $P \neq \lambda$. See Morse and Hedlund (1938) for related problems.

11. Change the definition of a grammar in such a way that the initial letter is replaced by a finite set of *axioms*, that is, words over $V_N \cup V_T$. The language generated by the grammar consists now of all terminal words generated by some of the axioms. The four types of restrictions of the form of productions remain unaltered. Prove that the families $\mathscr{L}_i$, $i = 0, 1, 2, 3$, remain invariant under this change.

12. Instead of introducing a final state set, one can define acceptance for pushdown automata by making the convention that a word is accepted iff it empties the pushdown store. The family of acceptable languages remains the same in the nondeterministic case but becomes smaller in the case of deterministic pushdown automata. In the deterministic case, it also makes a difference whether or not λ-moves, that is, productions (4.14), are allowed. Prove the following assertions. The language

$$\{a^i b^j c^k a^i | i \geq 1, j \geq k \geq 1\}$$

is deterministic but not acceptable by a deterministic pushdown automaton which does not use λ-moves. The language

$$\{a^i b^j | i \geq j \geq 1\}$$

is acceptable by a deterministic pushdown automaton which does not use λ-moves but not acceptable by such a device by the empty pushdown store. Give examples of languages acceptable by deterministic pushdown automata with no λ-moves and with the empty stack as the mode of acceptance.

BIBLIOGRAPHICAL REMARKS

The notion of a rewriting system was introduced by Thue in a series of papers, of which we mention Thue (1914). For normal algorithms, see Markov (1961) and, for canonical systems, Post (1943). The generative grammars are due to Chomsky (1956, 1957, 1959). Scheinberg (1960) and Bar-Hillel *et al.*

(1961) represent some of the early work on closure operations. Kleene (1956) and Mealy (1955) are the first papers on finite automata and sequential machines. Pushdown automata are due to Chomsky (1962) and Evey (1963), linear bounded automata to Myhill (1960), and Turing machines to Turing (1936). All of these types of automata are discussed extensively in many of the works listed at the end of this book.

BIBLIOGRAPHY

Y. **Bar-Hillel, M. Perles,** and **E. Shamir.** On formal properties of simple phrase structure grammars. *Z. Phonetik Sprachwiss. Kommunikat.* **14** (1961) 143–172; also appears in

Y. **Bar-Hillel.** "Language and Information." Addison-Wesley, Reading, Massachusetts, 1964.

N. **Chomsky.** Three models for the description of language. *IRE Trans. Information Theory* IT-2 (1956) 113–124.

N. **Chomsky.** "Syntactic Structures." Mouton, Gravenhage, 1957.

N. **Chomsky.** On certain formal properties of grammars. *Information Control* 2 (1959) 137–167.

N. **Chomsky.** Context-free grammars and pushdown storage. *M.I.T. Res. Lab. Electron. Quart. Progr. Rep.* **65** (1962).

R. J. **Evey.** The theory and application of pushdown store machines. Mathematical Linguistics and Automatic Translation, Harvard Univ. Computation Lab. Rep. NSF-IO (1963).

S. C. **Kleene.** Representation of events in nerve nets and finite automata. "Automata Studies," Princeton Univ. Press, Princeton, New Jersey, 1956, pp. 3–42.

A. A. **Markov.** "Theory of Algorithms." Israel Program for Scientific Translations, Jerusalem, 1961.

G. H. **Mealy.** A method for synthesizing sequential circuits. *Bell. Syst. Tech. J.* **34** (1955) 1045–1079.

M. **Morse** and G. **Hedlund.** Symbolic dynamics. *Amer. J. Math.* **60** (1938) 815–866.

J. **Myhill.** Linear bounded automata. WADD Tech. Note 60–165 (1960).

E. L. **Post.** Formal reduction of the general combinatorial decision problem. *Amer. J. Math.* **65** (1943) 197–215.

S. **Scheinberg.** Note on the Boolean properties of context-free languages. *Information Control* 3 (1960) 372–375.

A. **Thue.** Probleme über Veränderungen von Zeichenreihen nach gegebenen Regeln. *Skrifter utgit av Videnskapsselskapet i Kristiania I* **10** (1914), 34 pp.

A. M. **Turing.** On computable numbers, with an application to the Entscheidungsproblem. *Proc. London Math. Soc.* **42** (1936) 230–265.

Chapter II

Regular and Context-Free Languages

The next two chapters are devoted to a more detailed study of the language families $\mathscr{L}_i$, $i = 3, 2, 1, 0$. We begin with the families $\mathscr{L}_3$ and $\mathscr{L}_2$, that is, regular and context-free languages; $\mathscr{L}_3$ is the simplest family and $\mathscr{L}_2$ the most important from the point of view of applications. We will return to some more advanced topics concerning context-free languages in Chapter VI.

5. EQUIVALENT CHARACTERIZATIONS OF REGULAR LANGUAGES

It was shown in Theorem 4.1 that $\mathscr{L}_3$ is the family obtained by a class of *recognition* devices, namely, finite (deterministic or nondeterministic) automata. By definition, $\mathscr{L}_3$ is the family corresponding to a class of *generating* devices, namely, type-3 grammars. We now characterize $\mathscr{L}_3$ in terms of *property specification*. This is done by introducing a class of formulas, each of which denotes a language, and proving that the family of languages denoted by these formulas equals $\mathscr{L}_3$.

Definition. Assume that V and $V' = \{\cup, *, \varnothing, (,)\}$ are disjoint alphabets. A word P over $V \cup V'$ is a *regular expression* over V iff

(i) P is a letter of V or the letter $\varnothing$, or else

(ii) P is of one of the forms $(Q \cup R)$, (QR), or Q^* where Q and R are regular expressions over V.

Each regular expression P over V denotes a language $|P|$ over V according to the following conventions:

(i)   The language denoted by $\emptyset$ is the empty language.
(ii)   The language denoted by $a \in V$ consists of the word a.
(iii)   For regular expressions P and Q over V,

$$|(P \cup Q)| = |P| \cup |Q|, \qquad |(PQ)| = |P||Q|, \qquad |P^*| = |P|^*.$$

Example 5.1. $(aa)^*$ is a regular expression over the alphabet $V = \{a\}$. It denotes the language consisting of all words of even length. The same language is denoted also by each of the regular expressions

$$(aa)^* \cup (\emptyset a), \qquad (aa \cup aaaa)^*, \qquad (aa)^*(aa)^*.$$

Note that we have omitted, for convenience, unnecessary parentheses from these regular expressions. The order of strength of the three operations involved in regular expressions is as follows: Catenation is performed before union, and catenation closure before both union and catenation.

We noticed in Section 2 that type-3 languages are also called regular languages. The term refers to regular expressions and is justified by the following.

Theorem 5.1. A language is denoted by a regular expression iff it is of type 3.

Proof. Assume that L is denoted by a regular expression over the alphabet $\{a_1, ..., a_r\}$. This means, by the definition of regular expressions, that L is obtained from the finite languages

$$\emptyset, \{a_1\}, ..., \{a_r\}$$

by finitely many applications of the three regular operations. By Theorem 3.2, L is of type 3.

Assume, conversely, that L is of type 3. By Theorem 4.1, L is accepted by a finite deterministic automaton FDA. Let V_T and $\{s_1, ..., s_n\}$ be the terminal and state alphabets of FDA. Let s_1 be the initial state and S_1 the final state set, and denote the transition function by f. If $S_1 = \{s^1, ..., s^k\}$, then $L(\text{FDA})$ is the union of the languages $L(\text{FDA}(s^i))$, $i = 1, ..., k$, where $\text{FDA}(s^i)$ is obtained from FDA by replacing S_1 by $\{s^i\}$. If S_1 is empty, then $L(\text{FDA})$ is denoted by the regular expression $\emptyset$. Hence, without loss of generality, we assume that S_1 consists of one element, say s_u.

Denote by

$$L_{ij}^k, \qquad 0 \leq k \leq n; \quad 1 \leq i, j \leq n$$

the language consisting of all words P for which there is a derivation

$$s_i P \Rightarrow s_{i_1} P_1 \Rightarrow \cdots \Rightarrow s_{i_t} P_t \Rightarrow s_j,$$

where $i_v \leqq k$ for $v = 1, \ldots, t$. (By definition, $\lambda \in L_{ij}^k$ iff $i = j$.) Thus, for $i \neq j$, L_{ij}^0 either is empty or consists of some letters of V_T. For $i = j$, L_{ij}^0 consists of λ and of zero or more letters of V_T. Since λ is denoted by the regular expression $\varnothing^*$, we conclude that, for each i and j, L_{ij}^0 is denoted by a regular expression.

Proceeding inductively, we assume that for a fixed value k, where $0 \leq k \leq n-1$, each of the languages L_{ij}^k is denoted by a regular expression. Since obviously

$$L_{ij}^{k+1} = L_{ij}^k \cup L_{i(k+1)}^k (L_{(k+1)(k+1)}^k)^* L_{(k+1)j}^k,$$

we conclude that each of the languages L_{ij}^{k+1} is denoted by a regular expression. This completes the induction and consequently all of our languages L_{ij}^k are denoted by regular expressions. Thus also the language $L = L(\text{FDA}) = L_{1u}^n$ is denoted by a regular expression. ∎

Let L be denoted by a regular expression P. Then $\text{mi}(L)$ is denoted by the regular expression P' obtained from P by writing (RQ) everywhere where (QR) occurs in P, that is, by reversing the order of factors in all catenations. It follows immediately from the definitions that the family of languages denoted by regular expressions is closed under substitution. Consequently, we obtain from Theorem 5.1 the following corollary which solves problems left open in Theorems 3.4 and 3.5.

Theorem 5.2. The family $\mathscr{L}_3$ is closed under mirror image, substitution, and arbitrary homomorphisms.

Theorem 5.3. The family $\mathscr{L}_3$ equals the family of languages generated by grammars whose productions are of the two forms $X \to PY$ and $X \to P$ where X and Y are nonterminals, and P is a word over the terminal alphabet.

Proof. Let G be a grammar of type 3. Denote by $\text{mi}(G)$ the grammar obtained from G by replacing the right side of every production by its mirror image. Then the productions of $\text{mi}(G)$ are of the two forms mentioned in Theorem 5.3. Furthermore, $\text{mi}(G)$ generates the language $\text{mi}(L(G))$. Similarly, it is seen that if G is a grammar with productions of the two forms mentioned in Theorem 5.3, then $\text{mi}(G)$ is of type 3 and generates the language $\text{mi}(L(G))$. Since all languages L satisfy the equation $\text{mi}(\text{mi}(L)) = L$, Theorem 5.3 follows by Theorem 5.2. ∎

Definition. A grammar G is termed *linear* iff its productions are of the two forms $X \to P_1 Y P_2$ and $X \to P$ where X and Y are nonterminals and the P's are words over the terminal alphabet. The grammar G is termed *left-linear* (resp. *right-linear*) iff each of the words P_1 (resp. P_2) is λ.

Thus, G being left-linear is equivalent to G being type 3, according to our original definition. By Theorem 5.3, left-linear and right-linear grammars generate the same languages.

Our next characterization of type-3 languages is an algebraic one. Let L be a language over an alphabet V. The *equivalence relation E_L induced* by L is the binary relation on the set $W(V)$ defined by the condition: $PE_L Q$ holds iff there is no word $R \in W(V)$ such that exactly one of the words PR and QR belongs to L.

It is immediately verified that E_L is indeed an equivalence relation. Furthermore, E_L is *right invariant*: Whenever $PE_L Q$ holds, then also $PRE_L QR$ holds for any $R \in W(V)$. By the *index* of E_L we mean the number of its equivalence classes.

Theorem 5.4. L is acceptable by a finite deterministic automaton iff E_L is of finite index.

Proof. Assume first that L is a language over V_T such that E_L is of finite index $n+1$. We choose representatives $P_0 = \lambda$, $P_1, ..., P_n$ from each equivalence class, and denote by $[P]$ the class determined by the word P. We now define a finite deterministic automaton FDA. The state alphabet of FDA consists of the elements $[P_0], [P_1], ..., [P_n]$, where $[P_0]$ is the initial state and $[P_i]$ is a final state iff $P_i \in L$. The terminal alphabet is V_T and the transition function is defined by the equation

$$f([P_i], a) = [P_i a], \qquad a \in V_T; \quad i = 0, ..., n.$$

Since E_L is right invariant, the values of f do not depend on the choice of the representatives P_i. Furthermore, by the definition of E_L, the final state set is independent of the choice of representatives. It is an immediate consequence of the definition of f that, for any word $Q \in W(V_T)$,

$$[P_0] Q \Rightarrow^* [Q].$$

Consequently, $L = L(\text{FDA})$.

Conversely, assume that L is accepted by a finite deterministic automaton FDA with the terminal alphabet V_T, state alphabet S, initial state s_0, final state set S_1, and transition function f. We introduce an equivalence relation E on the set $W(V_T)$ by defining the following: PEQ holds iff there is a state s such that

$$s_0 P \Rightarrow^* s \qquad \text{and} \qquad s_0 Q \Rightarrow^* s, \tag{5.1}$$

that is, P and Q move FDA from s_0 to the same state. Clearly, E is an equivalence relation. We now claim that, for all P and Q, PEQ implies $PE_L Q$.

Assume the contrary: For some P, Q, and R, PEQ holds and exactly one of the words PR and QR, say PR, belongs to L. Hence,

$$s_0 PR \Rightarrow^* s_1, \qquad s_1 \in S_1; \qquad s_0 QR \Rightarrow^* s_2, \qquad s_2 \notin S_1. \tag{5.2}$$

On the other hand, because PEQ holds, (5.1) is satisfied for some s. But FDA cannot satisfy both (5.1) and (5.2). Consequently, our claim is correct, which means that the index of E_L does not exceed that of E which, in turn, does not exceed the number of elements of S. Thus, E_L is of finite index. █

Example 5.2. Theorem 5.4 provides a convenient tool for proving that a given language is not acceptable by a finite deterministic automaton (and, thus, neither is denoted by a regular expression nor is of type 3). Consider the language L of Example 1.1. If E_L were of finite index, we would have $a^m E_L a^n$ for some $m > n$. This is not possible because exactly one of the words $a^m b^m$ and $a^n b^m$, namely the former, belongs to L. Consequently, E_L is not of finite index. Similarly, it is shown that none of the languages of Examples 1.2, 1.3, 2.1–2.5, or 2.7 is acceptable by a finite deterministic automaton. Consider in general languages $L_I = \{a^i | i \in I\}$ where $I = \{i_1, i_2, \ldots\}$ over a one-letter alphabet $\{a\}$. Assume that I is ordered in such a way that $i_j, j = 1, 2, \ldots$, is a monotonically increasing sequence. Consider the differences

$$d_j = i_{j+1} - i_j, \qquad j = 1, 2, \ldots. \tag{5.3}$$

It follows, either by Theorem 5.4 or by the definition of a finite deterministic automaton, that L_I is of type 3 iff the sequence (5.3) is almost periodic.

Our final characterization of $\mathcal{L}_3$ is to specify $\mathcal{L}_3$ as a certain subfamily of $\mathcal{L}_2$.

Definition. A type-2 grammar $G = (V_N, V_T, X_0, F)$ is *self-embedding* iff $X \Rightarrow^* PXQ$ for some $X \in V_N$ and $P, Q \in W(V_N \cup V_T)$ such that $P \neq \lambda$ and $Q \neq \lambda$. A type-2 language L is self-embedding iff all type-2 grammars generating L are self-embedding.

Theorem 5.5. A language is of type 3 iff it is of type 2 and not self-embedding.

Proof. Since no type-3 grammar is self-embedding, we conclude that if a language L is self-embedding, it is not of type 3. Conversely, assume that L is generated by a type-2 grammar $G = (V_N, V_T, X_0, F)$ which is not self-embedding. We may assume without loss of generality that, for each $X \in V_N$, there is a derivation from X_0 to a word containing X [because otherwise X and all productions involving X can be removed without altering $L(G)$]. We now separate two cases.

CASE 1. For each $X \in V_N$, there is a derivation from X to a word containing X_0. Every production in F containing nonterminals on the right side is of one of the four forms (i) $X \to PYQ$, (ii) $X \to PY$, (iii) $X \to YQ$, or (iv) $X \to Y$ where $X, Y \in V_N$, and P and Q are words over $V_N \cup V_T$ distinct from λ. If F contains a production of the form (i) we must have, by the assumtpion of Case 1, a derivation

$$X \Rightarrow PYQ \Rightarrow^* PP_1 X_0 Q_1 Q \Rightarrow^* PP_1 P_2 XQ_2 Q_1 Q,$$

for some words P_1, P_2, Q_1, and Q_2 (possibly empty). Since $P, Q \neq \lambda$, G is self-embedding, which is impossible. The same contradiction arises if F contains productions of both forms (ii) and (iii). Therefore, if F contains a production of the form (ii), then in all productions of the form (ii) contained in F the word P is over V_T [because otherwise F would contain also a production of the form (i) or (iii)]. But this means that G is right-linear. Similarly, we conclude that if F contains a production of the form (iii), then G is left-linear. In both cases, $L(G)$ is of type 3 by Theorem 5.3. Clearly, $L(G)$ is of type 3 if F contains no productions of the forms (i)–(iii).

CASE 2. There is a nonterminal X_1 such that, for no words P and Q, $X_1 \Rightarrow^* PX_0 Q$. The proof of $L(G)$ being of type 3 is in this case by induction on the number n of nonterminals. For $n = 1$, the assertion is vacuous because always $X_0 \Rightarrow^* X_0$. Assume that the assertion holds true for $n = k$. Let the number of nonterminals in V_N be $k + 1$. Consider the grammar

$$G_1 = (V_N - \{X_0\}, V_T, X_1, F'),$$

where F' is obtained from F by removing all productions containing X_0, and the grammar

$$G_2 = (V_N - \{X_1\}, V_T \cup \{X_1\}, X_0, F'')$$

where F'' is obtained from F by removing all productions with X_1 on the left side. (Hence, G_2 is obtained from G by considering X_1 as a terminal.) Both of the languages $L(G_1)$ and $L(G_2)$ are of type 3, either by the inductive hypothesis or by Case 1. Clearly, $L(G)$ is the result of substituting X_1 in $L(G_2)$ by $L(G_1)$. By Theorem 5.2, $L(G)$ is of type 3. Our assertion holds true for $n = k + 1$ which completes the induction. ∎

Summarizing results in Theorems 4.1, 5.1, and 5.3–5.5, we obtain the following.

Theorem 5.6. For a language L, the following seven conditions are equivalent:

(i) L is of type 3.

(ii) L is generated by a right-linear grammar.

(iii) L is denoted by a regular expression.
(iv) L is acceptable by a finite deterministic automaton.
(v) L is acceptable by a finite nondeterministic automaton.
(vi) L is of type 2 and not self-embedding.
(vii)   The equivalence relation induced by L is of finite index.

We now prove one more result about the recognition capacity of finite deterministic automata. Consider subsets N of the set of natural numbers. Each such N can be represented as the language $\{a^i | i \in N\}$ over a one-letter alphabet. It was pointed out in Example 5.2 how one can decide whether or not such languages are regular. It is immediately seen, for instance, that the set of primes and the set of perfect squares are not regular when represented as languages over one letter. The question remains: What happens if other representations, such as binary and decimal, are considered?

In general, we consider the m-ary notation: A word $a_1 a_2 \cdots a_k$ over the alphabet

$$\{0, 1, \ldots, m-1\}, \qquad m \geq 2, \tag{5.4}$$

where the a's are letters of (5.4), is interpreted as the nonnegative integer

$$a_1 m^{k-1} + a_2 m^{k-2} + \cdots + a_{k-1} m + a_k. \tag{5.5}$$

Given a set N and an integer $m \geq 2$, we denote by $L(N, m)$ the language over (5.4) consisting of words $a_1 \cdots a_k$ such that (5.5) belongs to N and $a_1 \neq 0$. Given N and a rational number n, we denote by $\pi(N, n)$ the number of such elements in N which are less than n.

Theorem 5.7. If a set N satisfies the subsequent conditions (5.6) and (5.7), where t ranges over positive rationals, then $L(N, m)$ is not regular for any m:

$$\lim_{x \to \infty} \left(\pi(N, x)/x \right) = 0, \tag{5.6}$$

$$\lim_{x \to \infty} \left(\pi(N, x)/\pi(N, tx) \right) = \alpha_t \quad \text{and} \quad \alpha_t \neq 1 \quad \text{for} \quad t \neq 1. \tag{5.7}$$

Proof. Assume the contrary: A set N satisfies (5.6) and (5.7) but, for some m and FDA,

$$L(N, m) = L(\text{FDA}), \tag{5.8}$$

where FDA is specified by the quintuple (S, V_T, s_0, S_1, f), (5.4) being the alphabet V_T. Without loss of generality, we assume that, for all $s \in S$, there is a word P such that $s_0 P \Rightarrow^* s$. [Obviously, such states s which do not satisfy this condition can be removed without altering $L(\text{FDA})$.] For $s \in S$ and $P \in W(V_T)$, we denote by $f(s, P)$ the unique state s_P such that $sP \Rightarrow^* s_P$.

Since every word in $L(N, m)$ begins with a letter other than 0, the state $f(s_0, 0) = s_1$ must be a "dead state," that is, for no word P, $f(s_1, P) \in S_1$. Suppose there is a dead state s' for which there is a word Q such that $f(s_0, Q) = s'$ and the first letter of Q is not 0. Denote by $\bar{Q}$ the integer represented by Q in m-ary notation. Denote $(\bar{Q} + 1)/\bar{Q} = t_0$. Thus, $t_0 > 1$. Denote $n_i = \overline{Q0^i}$ for $i = 1, 2, \dots$. Hence, $n_i = m^i \cdot \bar{Q}$. By the choice of Q and s', no word QP belongs to the language $L(N, m)$. We let P range over all words of length i and conclude that $L(N, m)$ contains no word R for which

$$n_i = m^i \bar{Q} \leqq \bar{R} < m^i \bar{Q} + m^i = m^i(\bar{Q} + 1) = t_0 n_i.$$

Consequently, for all i,

$$\pi(N, n_i) = \pi(N, t_0 n_i).$$

Thus we conclude that

$$\lim_{i \to \infty} (\pi(N, n_i)/\pi(N, t_0 n_i)) = 1$$

which contradicts (5.7). Consequently, there is no such dead state s'.

Let q be the number of states in FDA. Let u be an arbitrary but fixed nonnegative integer. Consider any word P over (5.4) which does not begin with 0 and satisfies the condition $m^{qu} \leqq \bar{P} < m^{qu+1}$. Because of the nonexistence of dead states s', there is a word Q such that $\overline{PQ} \in N$. Furthermore, Q can be chosen in such a way that $lg(Q) < q$. This implies that $\overline{PQ} < m^{qu+1+(q-1)} = m^{q(u+1)}$. Thus the number of elements n in N satisfying $m^{qu} \leqq n < m^{q(u+1)}$ is not smaller than the number of integers x in the interval $m^{qu} \leqq x < m^{qu+1}$. (Clearly, distinct numbers $\overline{PQ}$ correspond to distinct numbers $\bar{P}$ since $\bar{P}$ is uniquely determined by the first $qu + 1$ digits of $\overline{PQ}$.) This implies that

$$\pi(N, m^{q(u+1)}) \geqq (m-1) m^{qu} \geqq m^{qu},$$

contradicting (5.6). ∎

The facts underlying the proof of Theorem 5.7 are that (i) dead states produce large gaps in the sequence of numbers recognized by the automaton and, thus, (5.7) cannot be satisfied, and (ii) the condition (5.6) is satisfied only if there are dead states.

Example 5.3. For $N = \{n^u | n = 1, 2, \dots\}$, where $u \geqq 2$ is a fixed integer, it is immediately verified that (5.6) and (5.7) are satisfied. Consequently, $L(N, m)$ is never acceptable by a finite automaton. The same holds true if N equals the set of prime numbers. In this case, (5.6) and (5.7) are verified using the fact that $\pi(N, n)$ is asymptotically equal to the ratio $n/\log n$.

Note 5.1. The *star height* of a regular expression over the alphabet V is a nonnegative integer defined recursively as follows.

(i)   The letters of V and $\varnothing$ have star height 0.

(ii)   If P and Q have star heights i and j, then $(P \cup Q)$ and (PQ) have star height $\max(i, j)$.

(iii)   If P has star height i, then P^* has star height $i + 1$.

The star height of a regular language L is the least integer i such that L is denoted by a regular expression with star height i.

If V consists of one letter, then every regular language over V possesses at most star height 1. This is immediately seen by considering finite deterministic automata with V_T consisting of one letter. On the other hand, if V consists of at least two letters, it can be shown that there are languages over V with arbitrarily large star height. No algorithm is known for determining the star height of an arbitrary regular language. One can modify the notion of a regular expression to include also intersection and complement as basic operations, and change point (ii) in the definition of star height accordingly. Then it is an unsolved problem as to whether or not there are languages with arbitrarily large star height.

Note 5.2.   An equation $P = Q$ between regular expressions P and Q means that P and Q denote the same language. There is a great variety of valid equations, some of them describing simple properties of union and catenation, others indicating more involved relations between catenation closure and other operations. For instance, all of the following equations, where P, Q, and R are arbitrary regular expressions, are valid:

$$P \cup (Q \cup R) = (P \cup Q) \cup R, \qquad P(QR) = (PQ)R,$$

$$P \cup Q = Q \cup P, \qquad P(Q \cup R) = PQ \cup PR,$$

$$(P \cup Q)R = PR \cup QR, \qquad \varnothing^* P = P,$$

$$\varnothing P = \varnothing, \qquad P^* = P^* P \cup \varnothing^*,$$

$$P^* = (P \cup \varnothing^*)^*.$$

New valid equations can be obtained from given ones by uniform substitution for the letters. However, it can be shown that no finite set of equations is a sufficient basis for generating all valid equations. This is not the case if rules of inference stronger than substitution are allowed. The nine equations listed above generate all valid equations when the rules of inference are substitution and the following: From the equation $P = PQ \cup R$ one may infer the equation $P = RQ^*$, provided the language denoted by Q does not contain the empty word. (The condition concerning Q can easily be detected by the form of Q.) Furthermore, each of the nine equations and two rules of inference is independent in the sense that it cannot be omitted without losing the ability to generate all valid equations.

Note 5.3. Certain subfamilies of regular languages are of interest. A language L over an alphabet V is *definite* iff it is of the form

$$L = L_1 \cup W(V)L_2,$$

where L_1 and L_2 are finite languages. Consequently, a language L is definite iff there is an integer k such that any word P with length at least k belongs to L iff the final subword of P of length k belongs to L.

For a definite language L, one can decide about a given word P whether or not $P \in L$ by looking at the final subword of P of a previously given length k. This is a special case of a *locally testable* language where the same decision can be made by looking at all subwords of P with length k. More specifically, consider an integer $k \geq 1$ and a word P satisfying $lg(P) \geq k + 1$. Denote by $\text{init}(P, k)$ [resp. $\text{fin}(P, k)$] the initial (resp. final) subword of P with length k. Denote by $\text{int}(P, k)$ the set of all subwords of P with length k which are neither initial nor final subwords (i.e., subwords which are "interior" subwords). A regular language L is *k-testable* iff, for any words P_1 and P_2, the equations

$$\text{init}(P_1, k) = \text{init}(P_2, k), \qquad \text{fin}(P_1, k) = \text{fin}(P_2, k),$$

$$\text{int}(P_1, k) = \text{int}(P_2, k)$$

imply that $P_1 \in L$ exactly in case $P_2 \in L$; L is *locally testable* iff L is k-testable for some k. Clearly, every definite language is locally testable. The language denoted by the regular expression $(10101)^*$ is not definite but is 5-testable.

A further generalization of locally testable languages is obtained by considering *noncounting* languages. By definition, a regular language L over an alphabet V is *noncounting* iff there exists an integer n such that, for all words Q_1, Q_2, and P over the alphabet V, we have $Q_1 P^n Q_2 \in L$ exactly in case $Q_1 P^{n+1} Q_2 \in L$. A simple example of a regular language which is not noncounting is the language denoted by the regular expression $(a^2)^*$. The language denoted by the regular expression $(01 \cup 10)^*$ is noncounting but not locally testable. Basically, one gets the family of noncounting languages from the family of locally testable languages by adding some device to express the order of subwords. A language is noncounting iff it is denoted by a *star-free* generalized regular expression, that is, iff it is obtained from $\emptyset$ and the languages $\{a\}$, where a is a letter, by applying Boolean operations and catenation finitely many times.

6. CONTEXT-FREE DERIVATIONS

Given a grammar G and a word $P \in L(G)$, it is sometimes important to know why P belongs to $L(G)$; that is, one should be able to give some structural description of the derivation of P. For context-free grammars G, derivations are naturally characterized in terms of *generation trees* (sometimes called also *parsing trees* or *parsing diagrams*). In this way one can also define ambiguous and unambiguous grammars and languages.

Example 6.1. Consider the context-free grammar

$$G = (\{X\}, \{a, b\}, X, \{X \to a, X \to b, X \to XX\}).$$

Clearly, $L(G)$ consists of all nonempty words over the alphabet $\{a, b\}$. In Fig. 6, two generation trees are given. They both correspond to the derivation

$$X \Rightarrow XX \Rightarrow XXX \Rightarrow aXX \Rightarrow abX \Rightarrow aba.$$

The first tree corresponds also, for instance, to the derivation

$$X \Rightarrow XX \Rightarrow Xa \Rightarrow XXa \Rightarrow aXa \Rightarrow aba,$$

and the second, to the derivation

$$X \Rightarrow XX \Rightarrow aX \Rightarrow aXX \Rightarrow abX \Rightarrow aba.$$

We now proceed to the general definitions. The notion of a *tree* introduced below is, from the point of view of graph theory, a directed tree from a vertex.

Definition. Let T be a finite nonempty set and U a collection of ordered pairs (t_1, t_2) of elements of T. The elements of T are called *nodes* and those of U, *edges*. The edge (t_1, t_2) is said to *leave* t_1 and *enter* t_2. A finite sequence of edges $e_1, \ldots, e_m$ is a *path* from the first member of e_1 to the second member of e_m iff, for $i = 1, \ldots, m-1$, the second member of e_i equals the first member of e_{i+1}. The pair (T, U) or, in short, T, is said to be a *tree* iff

(i)   there is exactly one node, called the *root*, which no edge enters, and
(ii) for each node t other than the root, there is exactly one path from the root to t.

In figures, the first member of an edge will be lower than the second. It follows by the definition that there are no loops in a tree. Consequently there are nodes, called *leaves*, from which no edges leave.

We now describe a procedure of constructing a generation tree for a given context-free derivation. The nodes of the tree are labeled by terminals, nonterminals, or the empty word. The nodes other than leaves are always labeled by nonterminals.

Let $G = (V_N, V_T, X_0, F)$ be a context-free grammar and let

$$X = P_0 \Rightarrow P_1 \Rightarrow \cdots \Rightarrow P_r, \qquad X \in V_N; \quad r \geqq 1, \tag{6.1}$$

be a derivation according to G. For $i = 0, \ldots, r-1$, let $Y_i \to Q_i$ be a production such that, for some α_i and β_i,

$$P_i = \alpha_i Y_i \beta_i, \qquad P_{i+1} = \alpha_i Q_i \beta_i. \tag{6.2}$$

(Thus, $Y_0 = X$ and $Q_0 = P_1$. Note that there may be more than one of such productions.)

The nodes of the generation tree of (6.1) are certain k-tuples ($k \leq r+1$) of natural numbers which, as well as their labels, are defined inductively as follows. The 1-tuple (1) is the root of the tree and its label is X. Make the inductive hypothesis that, for each $j \leq i$ where $i < r$, every letter in P_j already is a label of some node. Let $(u_1, \ldots, u_t)$ be the node whose label is the occurrence of Y_i indicated in (6.2). If $Q_i = \lambda$, we let $(u_1, \ldots, u_t, 1)$ be a new node and λ be its label. If $Q_i = x_1 \cdots x_m$, where the x's are (terminal or nonterminal) letters, we let $(u_1, \ldots, u_t, u)$ be a new node and x_u its label for $1 \leq u \leq m$. This completes the inductive definition of the nodes. For any two nodes $(u_1, \ldots, u_t)$ and $(u_1, \ldots, u_t, u_{t+1})$, there is an edge

$$((u_1, \ldots, u_t), (u_1, \ldots, u_t, u_{t+1})),$$

and all edges are of this form.

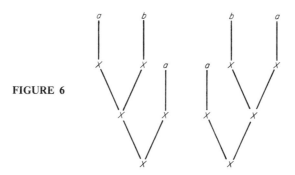

FIGURE 6

For convenience, we often identify nodes with their labels and mark only the labels in figures. The nodes of the first tree in Fig. 6 are

$$(1), (1,1), (1,2), (1,1,1), (1,1,2), (1,2,1), (1,1,1,1), (1,1,2,1).$$

It is obvious by Example 6.1 that the same tree may correspond to several different derivations and, conversely, that one derivation may give rise to several different trees. We now restrict the notion of a derivation in such a way, that any tree is the generation tree of only one derivation.

Definition. The derivation (6.1) according to a context-free grammar G is *leftmost* iff, for each $i = 0, \ldots, r-1$, there is a production $Y_i \to Q_i$ such that (6.2) holds and α_i is a word over the *terminal* alphabet.

Thus, in a leftmost derivation, the leftmost nonterminal is always rewritten. *Rightmost* derivations are defined in an analogous way.

Clearly, all derivations that correspond to a given generation tree are the same except for order of application of productions. Since the order is uniquely determined in a leftmost derivation, there is exactly one leftmost derivation corresponding to any given generation tree.

Definition. A context-free grammar G is *ambiguous* if there is a word in $L(G)$ possessing two leftmost derivations (from the initial letter). Otherwise, G is *unambiguous*. A context-free language L is *unambiguous* if there is an unambiguous context-free grammar G such that $L = L(G)$. Otherwise, L is *(inherently) ambiguous*.

Thus, a grammar G is ambiguous iff there are two generation trees for some word $P \in L(G)$; that is, iff there are two generation trees corresponding to derivations according to G such that P can be read from the leaves of the trees from left to right.

[Formally, we may order the leaves by making the convention that the leaf $(u_1, ..., u_p)$ *precedes* the leaf $(v_1, ..., v_q)$ iff the first of the differences $v_i - u_i$, $i = 1, 2, ...,$ which is distinct from 0, is positive. Let $E_1, ..., E_n$ be all the leaves of a generation tree T where for $i = 1, ..., n-1$, E_i precedes E_{i+1}. Let P be the word obtained by replacing in $E_1 \cdots E_n$ each E_i with its label. Then we say that T *generates* P or is a generation tree *of P*.]

The grammar in Example 6.1 is ambiguous. In fact, Fig. 6 gives two generation trees for the word *aba*, and two distinct leftmost derivations of this word were written down in Example 6.1. We shall return later to the problem of ambiguity of languages. The next theorem is easily obtained at this stage.

Theorem 6.1. Every type-3 language is unambiguous.

Proof. Let L be a type-3 language over an alphabet V_T. By Theorem 5.6,

$$L = L(\text{FDA}) \quad \text{for some} \quad \text{FDA} = (S, V_T, s_0, S_1, f).$$

This implies that L is generated by the grammar

$$(S, V_T, s_0, \{s_i \to as_j | s_i, s_j \in S, a \in V_T, f(s_i, a) = s_j\}$$

$$\cup \{s_i \to \lambda | s_i \in S_1\})$$

which clearly is unambiguous. ∎

Our next theorem is a useful lemma for proofs concerning context-free languages. It also shows that every context-free language is context-sensitive, which is not quite clear by our definition of grammar types. We say that a grammar is *λ-free* iff it has no productions of the form $P \to \lambda$.

Theorem 6.2. For every context-free grammar G, there is a λ-free context-free grammar G_1 such that $L(G_1) = L(G) - \{\lambda\}$. If $\lambda \in L(G)$, there is a context-free grammar $G' = (V_N', V_T, X_0', F')$ such that $L(G') = L(G)$, the only production in G' with λ as the right side is $X_0' \to \lambda$, and X_0' does not appear on the right side of any production of G'.

Proof. For $G = (V_N, V_T, X_0, F)$, we construct the grammar $G_1 = (V_N, V_T, X_0, F_1)$ as follows. Define

$$U_1 = \{X | X \to \lambda \text{ is in } F\},$$

$$U_{i+1} = U_i \cup \{X | X \to P \text{ is in } F \text{ for some } P \in W(U_i)\}, \quad i \geqq 1.$$

Since the sets U_i are monotonically increasing subsets of V_N, there is a natural number k such that $U_k = U_{k+1}$. For this k, $U_k = U_{k+v}$, $v = 1, 2, \ldots$, and furthermore

$$X \Rightarrow_G^* \lambda \quad \text{iff} \quad X \in U_k. \tag{6.3}$$

[Thus, $\lambda \in L(G)$ iff $X_0 \in U_k$.] We now let $X \to P_1$ be a production in F_1 iff $P_1 \neq \lambda$ and there is a production $X \to P$ in F such that P_1 is obtained from P by deleting 0 or more occurrences of elements of U_k. Then $L(G_1) = L(G) - \{\lambda\}$. In fact, the inclusion $L(G_1) \subseteq L(G) - \{\lambda\}$ is obvious by (6.3). The reverse inclusion is established by considering the grammar

$$G_2 = (V_N, V_T, X_0, F \cup F_1).$$

Clearly, $L(G) \subseteq L(G_2)$. If $P \in L(G_2)$ and $P \neq \lambda$, then $P \in L(G_1)$ because all applications of productions $X \to \lambda$ can be replaced by some applications of productions in F_1. Hence, the first part of the theorem follows.

Assume that $\lambda \in L(G)$. Construct first the grammar G_1 as above and let

$$G' = (V_N \cup \{X_0'\}, V_T, X_0', F_1 \cup \{X_0' \to \lambda, X_0' \to X_0\}).$$

Then $L(G') = L(G_1) \cup \{\lambda\} = L(G)$. Furthermore, the required conditions concerning productions of G' are satisfied. ∎

We say that a context-free grammar is in the *Chomsky normal form* iff all productions are of the two forms $X \to YZ$ and $X \to a$ where X, Y, and Z are nonterminals and a is a terminal letter. Clearly, if a grammar is in the Chomsky normal form, then λ does not belong to the generated language. The next theorem shows that, with this exception, every context-free grammar can be brought into the Chomsky normal form.

Theorem 6.3. For every context-free grammar G such that $\lambda \notin L(G)$, there is an equivalent grammar in the Chomsky normal form.

Proof. By Theorem 6.2, we may assume that the given grammar $G = (V_N, V_T, X_0, F)$ is λ-free. We first eliminate productions $X \to Y$, where X and Y are nonterminals, from G. This is done by a method very similar to the one used in the proof of Theorem 6.2.

For $x \in V_N \cup V_T = V$, we consider the following subsets of V:

$$U_1(x) = \{x\},$$

$$U_{i+1}(x) = U_i(x) \cup \{y \in V | \text{for some } z \in U_i(x), z \to y \text{ is in } F\},$$

where $i \geq 1$. Since V is finite, there is a k such that $U_k(x) = U_{k+1}(x)$. For this k, $U_k(x) = U_{k+v}(x)$, $v = 1, 2, \ldots$, and furthermore, for $x \in V_N$ and $y \in V$,

$$x \Rightarrow_G^* y \qquad \text{iff} \quad y \in U_k(x).$$

Consequently, a letter $a \in V_T$ belongs to the language $L(G)$ iff $a \in U_k(X_0)$.

A grammar $G_1 = (V_N, V_T, X_0, F_1)$ is now defined. The production set F_1 consists of (i) all productions $X_0 \to a$ where $a \in V_T \cap U_k(X_0)$, and (ii) all productions $Y \to y_1 y_2 \cdots y_n$ where $Y \in V_N$, $n \geq 2$, and each $y_j \in V$ such that for some production $X \to x_1 x_2 \cdots x_n$ in F, $X \in U_k(Y)$ and $y_j \in U_k(x_j)$, $j = 1, \ldots, n$. (Note that the numbers k may be different for different letters x. Of course, the greatest among them may be chosen.) Clearly, G_1 contains no productions $X \to Y$ where X and Y are nonterminals. It is also easy to verify that G and G_1 are equivalent. In fact, productions (i) in F_1 effect that the same words of length 1 are generated by G and G_1. Otherwise, the use of productions $X \to Y$ is implemented in productions (ii).

We now use the method of Theorem 3.1 to replace G_1 by an equivalent grammar $G_2 = (V_N^2, V_T, X_0, F_2)$ such that every production containing terminals is of the form $X \to a$ where $X \in V_N^2$ and $a \in V_T$. In this process, productions $X \to Y$ are not introduced and, consequently, the productions of G_2 not containing terminals are of the form

$$X \to Y_1 Y_2 \cdots Y_n, \qquad n \geq 2; \quad Y_j \in V_N^2. \tag{6.4}$$

For each production (6.4) where $n > 2$, we introduce new nonterminals $Z_1, \ldots, Z_{n-2}$ and replace (6.4) by the productions

$$X \to Y_1 Z_1, \ Z_1 \to Y_2 Z_2, \ \ldots, \ Z_{n-3} \to Y_{n-2} Z_{n-2}, \ Z_{n-2} \to Y_{n-1} Y_n.$$

The resulting grammar G_3 is in the Chomsky normal form. It is easy to verify that G_3 is equivalent to G_2 and hence to G. ∎

The following theorem, often referred to as Bar-Hillel's lemma, is of fundamental importance in the study of context-free languages.

Theorem 6.4. For any context-free language L, there are natural numbers p and q such that every word $P \in L$ which satisfies $lg(P) > p$ may be written as $P = R_1 Q_1 R Q_2 R_2$ where (i) $lg(Q_1 R Q_2) \leqq q$, (ii) $Q_1 Q_2 \neq \lambda$, and (iii) $R_1 Q_1{}^i R Q_2{}^i R_2 \in L$ for each $i \geqq 0$.

Proof. If $\lambda \in L$, we determine the constants p and q for the language $L - \{\lambda\}$. Clearly, they satisfy (i)–(iii) for L, too. Consequently, by Theorems 6.2 and 6.3, we may assume that L is generated by the context-free grammar $G = (V_N, V_T, X_0, F)$ in the Chomsky normal form.

Consider a derivation (6.1) according to G such that the longest path in the associated generation tree contains k nodes. Then we claim that

$$lg(P_r) \leqq 2^{k-1} \qquad (6.5)$$

This is seen by induction on k. For $k = 2$, (6.5) follows because then $r = 1$ and P_r consists of one or two letters. (Recall that G is in the Chomsky normal form.) Assume that (6.5) holds for a fixed $k \geqq 2$ and consider the case where the longest path contains $k + 1$ nodes. Then the first step in the derivation (6.1) is $X \Rightarrow YZ$ where Y and Z are nonterminals. Our inductive hypothesis is now applicable to the trees whose roots are labeled by Y and Z and consequently

$$lg(P_r) \leqq 2^{k-1} + 2^{k-1} = 2^{(k+1)-1}$$

This completes the induction and thus (6.5) holds.

Assuming that V_N contains u elements, we now choose $p = 2^u$ and $q = 2^{u+1}$. Consider any word $P \in L$ such that $lg(P) > p$. By (6.5), the longest path π in the generation tree T corresponding to a derivation of P (according to G) contains at least $u + 2$ nodes. Since the nodes labeled by terminals must be leaves, π contains at least $u + 1$ nodes labeled by nonterminals. Consequently, π contains two nodes v_1 and v_2 labeled by the same nonterminal, say, X. We assume that v_1 is closer to the root of T than v_2. Clearly, v_1 and v_2 can be chosen in such a way that the subpath of π beginning from v_1 contains at most $u + 2$ nodes. Consider the subtree T_1 of T with root v_1. Since π was the longest path in T, no path in T_1 contains more than $u + 2$ nodes. If Q is the word determined by the leaves of T_1, then by (6.5)

$$lg(Q) \leqq 2^{(u+2)-1} = q. \qquad (6.6)$$

Consider also the subtree T_2 of T with root v_2. If R is the word determined by the leaves of T_2, then $Q = Q_1 R Q_2$ for some Q_1 and Q_2. Furthermore, Q_1 and Q_2 cannot both be the empty word λ because the first production in the derivation of Q from X must be of the form $X \to YZ$ where Y and Z are nonterminals. Thus for some R_1 and R_2, we have the following derivation according to G:

$$X_0 \Rightarrow^* R_1 X R_2 \Rightarrow^* R_1 Q_1 X Q_2 R_2 \Rightarrow^* R_1 Q_1 R Q_2 R_2 = P.$$

Consequently, $R_1 Q_1{}^i R Q_2{}^i R_2 \in L$ for each $i \geqq 0$. We have seen that $Q_1 Q_2 \neq \lambda$ and, by (6.6), also the condition $lg(Q_1 R Q_2) \leqq q$ is satisfied. ∎

Example 6.2. We prove that the language

$$L = \{a^n b^n c^n | n \geq 1\} \tag{6.7}$$

is not context-free. Assume the contrary, and let p and q be integers satisfying the conditions of Theorem 6.4. Choose $k > p/3$ and consider the word $P_1 = a^k b^k c^k$. Hence, P_1 can be written

$$P_1 = R_1 Q_1 R Q_2 R_2$$

where $Q_1 Q_2 \neq \lambda$ and each of the words

$$P_i = R_1 Q_1{}^i R Q_2{}^i R_2, \qquad i = 0, 1, 2, \ldots,$$

belongs to L. By (6.7) the letters a, b, and c always occur in the alphabetical order in the words of L; that is, an occurrence of b never precedes an occurrence of a and an occurrence of c never precedes an occurrence of a or b. Hence, both Q_1 and Q_2 contain at most one of the letters a, b, or c because otherwise P_2 would violate this property of L. Since $Q_1 Q_2 \neq \lambda$, $lg(P_i)$ tends to infinity with i, whereas the number of occurrences of one of the letters a, b, or c is the same in each P_i. Thus, all words P_i cannot belong to L. This contradiction shows that (6.7) is not context-free.

Using Theorem 6.4, it can also be shown that none of the languages considered in Examples 2.2–2.5 is context-free. (In fact, there are no nonregular context-free languages over one letter. This is shown in the next section.) The following corollary of Theorem 6.4 is of interest because it gives rise to an algorithm and, as is seen later on, corresponding algorithms are impossible for context-sensitive languages.

Theorem 6.5. Let L be a context-free language, and p and q integers satisfying the conditions of Theorem 6.4. Then L is infinite iff it contains a word of length t, $p < t \leq p+q$.

Proof. If L contains a word of such a length t, it contains a word of length greater than p and, by property (iii) in Theorem 6.4, L is infinite. Conversely, assume that L is infinite. Then L contains a word P such that $lg(P) > p+q$. Furthermore, we have

$$P = R_1 Q_1 R Q_2 R_2, \qquad Q_1 Q_2 \neq \lambda, \qquad lg(Q_1 R Q_2) \leq q, \qquad R_1 R R_2 \in L.$$

Consequently, we have $p < lg(R_1 R R_2) < lg(P)$. If $lg(R_1 R R_2) \leq p+q$, we have found a word in L with length as required. Otherwise, we repeat the procedure for $R_1 R R_2$ instead of P. After finitely many reductions, we find a word in L of length t where $p < t \leq p+q$. ∎

Theorem 6.5 gives an algorithm for deciding whether or not a given context-free language L is finite. In fact, given a grammar G generating L, we first replace G by an equivalent grammar G_1 in the Chomsky normal form. (We assume without loss of generality that $\lambda \notin L$.) The integers p and q are determined by the number of nonterminals in G_1. To test whether or not L contains a word of length t, where $p < t \leqq p+q$, it suffices to check through finitely many generation trees of G_1.

We note in this connection that, for a given context-free grammar $G = (V_N, V_T, X_0, F)$, there is a simple algorithm of deciding whether or not $L(G)$ is empty. One forms the sets U_i almost as in the proof of Theorem 6.2, with the exception that now

$$U_1 = \{X \mid X \to P \text{ is in } F \text{ for some } P \in W(V_T)\}.$$

Otherwise the definition of the sets U_i, as well as the choice of the number k, remains unaltered. Then $L(G)$ is empty iff $X_0 \notin U_k$.

We now turn to the discussion of some closure properties of the family $\mathscr{L}_2$ left open in Section 3.

Theorem 6.6. The family $\mathscr{L}_2$ of context-free languages is closed neither under intersection nor under complementation.

Proof. Consider the following context-free grammars:

$$G_1 = (\{X_0, X_1\}, \{a, b, c\}, X_0, \{X_0 \to X_0 c, X_0 \to X_1 c, X_1 \to ab, X_1 \to aX_1 b\}),$$

$$G_2 = (\{X_0, X_1\}, \{a, b, c\}, X_0, \{X_0 \to aX_0, X_0 \to aX_1, X_1 \to bc, X_1 \to bX_1 c\}).$$

Clearly,

$$L(G_1) = \{a^n b^n c^m \mid n, m \geqq 1\},$$

$$L(G_2) = \{a^m b^n c^n \mid n, m \geqq 1\}$$

and, consequently,

$$L(G_1) \cap L(G_2) = \{a^n b^n c^n \mid n \geqq 1\}$$

which was shown in Example 6.2 not to be context-free. This proves that $\mathscr{L}_2$ is not closed under intersection. If it were closed under complementation, then, because it is closed under union by Theorem 3.2, the language

$$L(G_1) \cap L(G_2) = \sim\!\big((\sim L(G_1)) \cup (\sim L(G_2))\big)$$

would be context-free, which is absurd. ∎

The following weaker result concerning closure under intersection can be obtained.

Theorem 6.7. The intersection of a context-free language L_1 and a regular language L_2 is context-free. Moreover, if L_1 is unambiguous, then so is $L_1 \cap L_2$.

Proof. Without loss of generality, we may assume that L_1 and L_2 are languages over the same alphabet V_T. We may assume also that $\lambda \notin L_1$ and $\lambda \notin L_2$. For if one of the languages L_1 and L_2 contains the empty word, then we construct first a type-2 grammar (unambiguous if L_1 is unambiguous) with the initial letter X_0 generating the language

$$(L_1 - \{\lambda\}) \cap (L_2 - \{\lambda\})$$

and then, if $\lambda \in L_1$ and $\lambda \in L_2$, add a new initial letter X_0' and the productions $X_0' \to \lambda$ and $X_0' \to X_0$.

Let L_2 be accepted by the finite deterministic automaton FDA $= (S, V_T, s_0, S_1, f)$. By Theorem 6.3, we may assume that L_1 is generated by the grammar $G = (V_N, V_T, X_0, F)$ in the Chomsky normal form. Let $S_1 = \{s^1, \ldots, s^h\}$ and denote

$$L_2^{(i)} = L(\text{FDA}_i), \qquad i = 1, \ldots, h,$$

where FDA_i is obtained from FDA by replacing S_1 by $\{s^i\}$. Clearly,

$$L_1 \cap L_2 = (L_1 \cap L_2^{(1)}) \cup \cdots \cup (L_1 \cap L_2^{(h)}). \tag{6.8}$$

Consider a fixed value of i, $1 \le i \le h$. The language $L_1 \cap L_2^{(i)}$ is generated by the grammar

$$((V_N \cup V_T) \times S \times S, V_T, (X_0, s_0, s^i), F'), \tag{6.9}$$

where F' consists of all productions having one of the following forms:

(i) $(X_1, s, s_1) \to (X_2, s, s_2)(X_3, s_2, s_1)$ where the s's belong to S and the production $X_1 \to X_2 X_3$, $X_j \in V_N$, belongs to F;
(ii) $(X, s, s_1) \to (a, s, s_1)$ where the s's belong to S and the production $X \to a$, $X \in V_N$, $a \in V_T$, belongs to F;
(iii) $(a, s, s_1) \to a$ where $a \in V_T$ and $f(s, a) = s_1$.

Thus, nonterminals are triples whose first component belongs to $V_N \cup V_T$ and whose other two components belong to S. All derivations according to G are preserved by the first component of the productions (i) and (ii), whereas the other two components give an arbitrary sequence of states. By (iii) and the choice of the initial letter, the triples can be eliminated iff the terminal word formed by the first components causes a state transition from s_0 to s^i in FDA. Consequently, $L_1 \cap L_2^{(i)}$ is the language generated by the context-free grammar (6.9). By (6.8) and Theorem 3.2, we conclude that $L_1 \cap L_2$ is context-free.

To prove the second sentence of Theorem 6.7, we assume that L_1 is unambiguous. It is easy to verify that also the grammar G in the Chomsky normal form can be chosen to be unambiguous. Clearly, the union of pair-wise disjoint unambiguous languages is unambiguous, and the languages appearing on the right side of (6.8) are pairwise disjoint. Hence, it suffices to verify that the grammar (6.9) is unambiguous. This again follows because for any

$$P = a_1 \cdots a_m \in L_1 \cap L_2^{(i)}, \qquad a_j \in V_T,$$

there are exactly one word $X_1 \cdots X_m \in W(V_N)$ such that

$$X_0 \Rightarrow_G^* X_1 \cdots X_m \Rightarrow_G^* a_1 \cdots a_m,$$

and exactly one sequence of states $s_1, \ldots, s_{m-1}$ such that

$$f(s_0, a_1) = s_1, f(s_1, a_2) = s_2, \ldots, f(s_{m-1}, a_m) = s^i. \quad \blacksquare$$

The following theorem is an immediate corollary of Theorems 6.7 and 4.2.

Theorem 6.8. The difference $L_1 - L_2$ of a context-free language L_1 and a regular language L_2 is context-free. Moreover, if L_1 is unambiguous, then so is $L_1 - L_2$.

Note 6.1. Syntactic descriptions of programming languages, or parts of them, are often given in terms of systems of equations whose left side is a letter denoting a syntactic class and whose right side is a finite union of words consisting of terminal letters and letters denoting syntactic classes. For instance, the so-called *Backus normal form* for ALGOL constitutes such a description. One particular equation in the description is

$$\langle \text{unsigned integer} \rangle : : = \langle \text{digit} \rangle | \langle \text{unsigned integer} \rangle \langle \text{digit} \rangle. \quad (6.10)$$

The class $\langle \text{digit} \rangle$ consists of the first ten nonnegative integers and, by (6.10), the class $\langle \text{unsigned integer} \rangle$ consists of finite strings of digits. Following our customary notation, we may write (6.10) in the form

$$X = D \cup XD. \quad (6.11)$$

In general, consider two disjoint alphabets V_T and $V_N = \{X_1, \ldots, X_n\}$ and a system of equations

$$X_i = L_i, \qquad i = 1, \ldots, n, \quad (6.12)$$

where each L_i is a *finite* language over the alphabet $V_N \cup V_T$. Such a system (6.12) determines an inductive process for generating words of n languages simultaneously. In (6.11), $n = 1$ and the process generates successively the words in $D, D^2, D^3, \ldots$.

A language L is termed *ALGOL-like* iff there is a system (6.12) such that L is one of the n languages generated by the system. It can be shown that a language is ALGOL-like iff it is context-free.

Note 6.2. The structural description of context-free derivations, which was given above in terms of trees, can also be given in terms of parentheses. Consider a context-free grammar $G = (V_N, V_T, X_0, F)$. For each $X \in V_N$, introduce one new letter $($_X$ and, in addition, the letter $)$, and denote the collection of all these new letters by U. Then the grammar

$$G_1 = (V_N, V_T \cup U, X_0, \{X \to ($_X P) | X \to P \text{ in } F\})$$

is termed the *structural grammar* associated with G. For a derivation of a word $Q \in L(G)$, there corresponds a unique $Q_1 \in L(G_1)$ termed a *structural description* of Q. For instance,

$$\left($_{X_0}($_{X_1} a($_{X_1} ab) b) c\right)$$

is a structural description of $a^2 b^2 c$ obtained from the derivation

$$X_0 \Rightarrow X_1 c \Rightarrow aX_1 bc \Rightarrow a^2 b^2 c.$$

Similarly,

$$\left($_X($_X($_X a)($_X b))($_X a)\right) \quad \text{and} \quad \left($_X($_X a)($_X($_X b)($_X a))\right)$$

are structural descriptions of *aba* obtained from the trees in Fig. 6. A grammar G is unambiguous iff every word $Q \in L(G)$ possesses exactly one structural description.

One can also introduce automata whose inputs are trees or, equivalently, structural descriptions rather than words. Basically, such a *tree automaton* differs from a finite automaton as follows. In a finite automaton (with state set S and transition function f), each letter $a \in V_T$ determines a mapping $\varphi_a : S \to S$ by the convention $\varphi_a(s) = s'$ iff $f(s, a) = s'$. Conversely, a finite automaton can be defined by specifying the mappings φ_a, $a \in V_T$. Thus each φ_a is a function of *one* variable. This condition is omitted in defining tree automata. A tree automaton acts on a generation tree as follows. It first assigns an initial state $s(a)$ to each leaf with label a. At any time when states $s_1, \ldots, s_k$ have been assigned to all "successor" nodes of a node labeled by X, then the latter node is assigned the state $\varphi_X(s_1, \ldots, s_k)$. The tree is accepted iff the state assigned to the root belongs to the designated final state set. [The function φ_X maps the set S^* into S and satisfies the requirement that for $s \in S$, $\varphi_X^{-1}(s)$ is regular.]

One can introduce also nondeterministic tree automata and prove the result corresponding to (i) and (ii) in Theorem 4.1, namely, that a set of trees is acceptable by a nondeterministic tree automaton iff it is acceptable by a deterministic one. Tree automata correspond to context-free grammars in that essentially (with some minor modifications in the definitions) a set of generation trees acceptable by a tree automaton iff it corresponds to the derivations of a context-free grammar.

7. PARIKH MAPPINGS AND HOMOMORPHIC CHARACTERIZATION

In this section we prove two results about context-free languages. Apart from being interesting in their own right they are useful tools in the sequel. We show first that context-free languages are undistinguishable from type-3 languages with respect to the distribution of letters in words. More specifically, we say that two words P and Q over an alphabet V are *letter-equivalent* iff, for each $a \in V$, both P and Q contain the same number of occurrences of a (i.e., P is obtained from Q by a permutation of letters). Two languages L_1 and L_2 over V are termed letter-equivalent iff, for each $P_1 \in L_1$, there is a letter-equivalent $P_2 \in L_2$, and vice versa. For instance, the context-free language $\{a^n b^n | n \geq 1\}$ and the type-3 language $\{(ab)^n | n \geq 1\}$ are letter-equivalent. We prove that for any context-free language, there is a letter-equivalent regular language.

Consider, for some fixed natural number n ordered n-tuples of nonnegative integers. Addition of such n-tuples, as well as multiplication of such an n-tuple by an integer, is carried out termwise. (Thus, we are dealing with the ordinary addition and scalar multiplication of vectors.) A set S of n-tuples is termed *linear* iff there is an integer $k \geq 0$ and n-tuples $v_0, \ldots, v_k$ such that S consists of all n-tuples of the form

$$v_0 + \sum_{i=1}^{k} x_i v_i,$$

where the x's are nonnegative integers. A set of n-tuples is termed *semilinear* iff it is a finite union of linear sets.

Example 7.1. For $n = 3$, the set

$$\{(r, s, t) | s = r \text{ or } s = t\} \tag{7.1}$$

is semilinear. It is the union of two linear sets, determined by the triples

$$v_0 = (0, 0, 0), \qquad v_1 = (1, 1, 0), \qquad v_2 = (0, 0, 1)$$

and

$$v_0' = v_0, \qquad v_1' = (1, 0, 0), \qquad v_2' = (0, 1, 1).$$

Definition. For an alphabet $V = \{a_1, \ldots, a_n\}$, the mapping ψ of $W(V)$ into the set of ordered n-tuples of nonnegative integers, defined by

$$\psi(P) = (N_{a_1}(P), \ldots, N_{a_n}(P)), \qquad P \in W(V),$$

where $N_{a_i}(P)$ denotes the number of occurrences of a_i in P, is termed the *Parikh mapping*. For a language L, the Parikh mapping is

$$\psi(L) = \{\psi(P) | P \in L\},$$

where ψ is defined in $W(V)$ and V is the smallest alphabet such that L is a language over V.

Thus, $\psi(\lambda) = (0, \ldots, 0)$. For the context-free language

$$L = \{a^i b^i c^j | i, j \geqq 0\} \cup \{a^i b^j c^j | i, j \geqq 0\},$$

$\psi(L)$ equals the set (7.1). Also for the language L_1 denoted by the regular expression

$$(ab)^* c^* \cup a^*(bc)^*,$$

$\psi(L_1)$ equals the set (7.1).

The fundamental result concerning the distribution of letters in the words of a context-free language is presented in the following theorem.

Theorem 7.1. For any context-free language L, the set $\psi(L)$ is semilinear.

Proof. Clearly, if $\psi(L-\{\lambda\})$ is semilinear, then also $\psi(L)$ is semilinear. Hence, without loss of generality, we assume that $\lambda \notin L$. By Theorem 6.3, we may assume that L is generated by the grammar $G = (V_N, V_T, X_0, F)$ in the Chomsky normal form. (In fact, in the following proof we only need to know that F does not contain productions of the forms $X \to X$ and $X \to \lambda$.)

For each subset U of the set $V_N - \{X_0\}$, we consider the subset L_U of L consisting of words which possess at least one derivation from X_0 where the occurring nonterminals are exactly the nonterminals in the set $U \cup \{X_0\} = U_0$. Obviously, L is the union of the languages L_U. Since the number of the sets U is finite, we conclude that it suffices to show that each of the sets $\psi(L_U)$ is semilinear.

From now on we consider an arbitrary but fixed language L_U. Assume that the set U_0 contains u elements. In what follows, we investigate generation trees associated with derivations according to G.

Let H be the set consisting of words $P \in W(V_T)$ which are generated by trees such that the following conditions are satisfied: (i) The root is labeled by X_0; (ii) the nodes other than leaves are labeled by elements of U_0 and each element of U_0 occurs at least once as a label; and (iii) there is no path containing more than $u+1$ nodes with the same label X. Clearly, H is a finite subset of L_U. We define

$$H_1 = \{\psi(P) | P \in H\}.$$

For each $Y \in U_0$, we let H_Y be the set consisting of words $P \in W(V_T) \, Y W(V_T)$ which are generated by trees satisfying condition (iii) as above and, in addition, the following conditions: (i)' The root is labeled by Y, and (ii)' the nodes other than leaves are labeled by elements of U_0. (Hence, such a P contains exactly one occurrence of Y, other letters of P being from V_T.)

Clearly, because of condition (iii), H_Y is a finite set. For $P \in H_Y$, we denote by $\gamma(P)$ the word obtained from P by erasing the letter Y. We now define

$$H_2 = \{\psi(\gamma(P))|P \in H_Y \text{ for some } Y \in U_0\}.$$

Thus, both H_1 and H_2 are finite sets. Assume that

$$H_1 = \{h_1, ..., h_\alpha\}, \qquad H_2 = \{k_1, ..., k_\beta\}.$$

Denote by K_i, $i = 1, ..., \alpha$, the set

$$\left\{h_i + \sum_{j=1}^{\beta} x_j k_j | x_j \geq 0 \text{ for } j = 1, ..., \beta\right\},$$

and let K be the union of the sets K_i. By definition, K is semilinear. To prove Theorem 7.1, it suffices to show that

$$\psi(L_U) = K. \tag{7.2}$$

We will prove that each side of (7.2) is included in the other.

Assume that $v \in K$. If v is one of the vectors h_i, then by the definition of the set H_1, $v \in \psi(H)$, and consequently $v \in \psi(L_U)$. Proceeding inductively, we assume that

$$v_1 \in K \cap \psi(L_U) \tag{7.3}$$

and claim that

$$v = v_1 + k_j \in \psi(L_U), \tag{7.4}$$

where j, $1 \leq j \leq \beta$, is arbitrary. By the definition of H_2, there is a letter $Y \in U_0$ and a word $P \in H_Y$ such that $k_j = \psi(\gamma(P))$. Since $P \in H_Y$, there is a generation tree T_Y for P whose root is labeled by Y. Furthermore, Y occurs in P exactly once, and P contains no other nonterminals. The nonterminals occurring as node labels in T_Y belong to U_0. By (7.3) and the definition of L_U, there is a word $Q \in L$ with $v_1 = \psi(Q)$ and a derivation $X_0 \Rightarrow^* Q$ such that the associated generation tree T_1 has exactly the elements of U_0 as labels of the nodes other than leaves. Hence, there is a node in T_1 labeled by Y. (In fact, we introduced the languages L_U only to be able to make this conclusion.) This node is replaced by the tree T_Y (cf. Fig. 7). The resulting generation tree T_2 gives a word $Q_1 \in L_U$ such that

$$\psi(Q_1) = \psi(Q) + \psi(\gamma(P)) = v_1 + k_j = v.$$

Consequently, (7.4) holds true and we have completed the induction. Hence, the right side of (7.2) is included in the left side.

Conversely, assume that $v \in \psi(L_U)$. Thus, there is a word $P \in L_U$ such that $v = \psi(P)$. Let T be the generation tree associated with the derivation $X_0 \Rightarrow^* P$. By the definition of L_U, we assume that exactly the elements of U_0

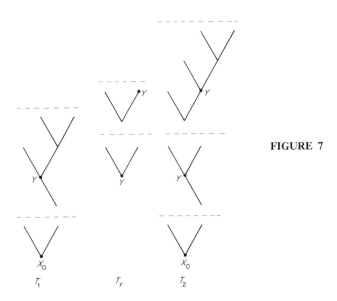

FIGURE 7

occur as labels of the nodes (other than leaves) of T. If there is no path in T containing more than $u+1$ nodes with the same label, then $P \in H$. This implies that $v \in H_1$ and hence $v \in K$.

Thus, we assume that there is a path in T containing at least $u+2$ nodes with the same label X. We choose $u+2$ nodes $g_0, \ldots, g_{u+1}$ with the same label

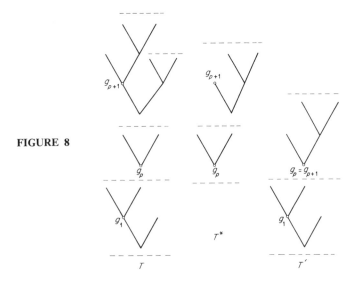

FIGURE 8

X in such a way that (i) for each $i = 0, ..., u$, g_{i+1} is in the tree with root g_i, and (ii) there is no path containing more than $u+1$ nodes with the same label in the tree T_{g_1} with root g_1. (Such nodes g_i are found by checking through T, beginning from the leaves.) There is a number p, $1 \leqq p \leqq u$, such that the same nonterminals occur as node labels in the trees T_{g_p} and $T_{g_{p+1}}$ with roots g_p and g_{p+1}. This follows because there are at most u nonterminals as node labels in the tree T_{g_1}, and at least one nonterminal as a node label in the tree $T_{g_{u+1}}$. We now form a new tree T' by replacing in T the tree T_{g_p} by the tree $T_{g_{p+1}}$. Denote by T^* the tree obtained from T_{g_p} by replacing the tree $T_{g_{p+1}}$ by the single node g_{p+1} (cf. Fig. 8). There is no path in T^* containing more than $u+1$ nodes with the same label since there is no such path in the tree T_{g_1}. The word generated by T^* belongs to the set H_X (by the definition of this set). Consequently, if P' is the word generated by T', we obtain

$$v = \psi(P) = \psi(P') + k_j, \qquad (7.5)$$

for some j, $1 \leqq j \leqq \beta$.

Clearly, T' has fewer nodes than T. If there is a path in T' containing more than $u+1$ nodes with the same label, we repeat the procedure above for the tree T' and obtain a tree T'' generating a word P''. The equation corresponding to (7.5) is now

$$\psi(P') = \psi(P'') + k_{j'}$$

where $1 \leqq j' \leqq \beta$. Continuing in this fashion, we finally obtain a tree where there is no path containing more than $u+1$ nodes with the same label. Thus we can write v in the form

$$v = h_i + \sum_{j=1}^{\beta} x_j k_j, \qquad 1 \leqq i \leqq \alpha; \quad x_j \geqq 0 \quad \text{for} \quad 1 \leqq j \leqq \beta.$$

But this means that $v \in K$, and consequently the left side of (7.2) is included in the right side. ∎

The result mentioned at the beginning of this section can now be established easily.

Theorem 7.2. For every context-free language, there is a letter-equivalent type-3 language.

Proof. Let L be a context-free language over the alphabet $V = \{a_1, ..., a_n\}$. By Theorem 7.1, $\psi(L)$ is semilinear. Hence there is a finite number r of linear sets $S_1, ..., S_r$ such that $\psi(L)$ equals their union. Assume that, for some $v_0, ..., v_k$,

$$S_j = \left\{ v_0 + \sum_{i=1}^{k} x_i v_i \,\middle|\, x_i \geq 0 \text{ for all } i = 1, ..., k \right\},$$

where $1 \leq j \leq r$. Assume, furthermore, that

$$v_i = (\alpha_{1i}, \ldots, \alpha_{ni}), \qquad i = 0, \ldots, k.$$

Let L_1^{j} be the language denoted by the regular expression

$$a_1^{\alpha_{10}} \cdots a_n^{\alpha_{n0}} (a_1^{\alpha_{11}} \cdots a_n^{\alpha_{n1}})^* \cdots (a_1^{\alpha_{1k}} \cdots a_n^{\alpha_{nk}})^*.$$

Then $\psi(L_1^{j}) = S_j$. Thus, the union L_2 of the languages L_1^{j}, $j = 1, \ldots, r$, is letter-equivalent to L. By Theorems 5.6 and 3.2, L_2 is of type 3. ∎

Clearly, two languages over a one-letter alphabet $\{a\}$ are letter-equivalent iff they are equal. Hence, the following theorem is an immediate corollary of Theorem 7.2.

Theorem 7.3. A language over one letter is context-free iff it is regular.

We now turn to the discussion of the second main result in this section. We are going to show how every context-free language can be represented as a homomorphic image of the intersection of a regular language and a simple context-free language, so-called *Dyck language*. This is a part of the general reduction process which is completed in Chapter III and which shows how every type-0 language can be expressed in terms of regular and Dyck languages by using intersections and homomorphisms.

Consider alphabets

$$V_n = \{a_1, a_1', \ldots, a_n, a_n'\}, \qquad n \geq 1.$$

(Thus, V_n consists of an even number of letters which are grouped into pairs.) The context-free language D_n generated by the grammar

$$(\{X\}, V_n, X, \{X \to \lambda, X \to XX, X \to a_1 X a_1', \ldots, X \to a_n X a_n'\}) \qquad (7.6)$$

is termed the *Dyck language* over the alphabet V_n.

Thus, the language considered in Example 1.3 (the language of properly nested parentheses) is the Dyck language D_1. In general, D_n consists of all such words that can be reduced to λ by replacing subwords $a_i a_i'$, $i = 1, \ldots, n$, with λ. It is obvious by the form of the productions in (7.6) that D_n possesses the following properties: (i) If $P_1 \in D_n$ and $P_2 \in D_n$, then also $P_1 P_2 \in D_n$. (ii) If $P_1 \in D_n$, then also $a_i P_1 a_i' \in D_n$ for $i = 1, \ldots, n$. (iii) Each word $P \neq \lambda$ in D_n is of the form $P = a_i P_1 a_i' P_2$ for some i and $P_1, P_2 \in D_n$. (iv) If $a_i a_i' P \in D_n$, then also $P \in D_n$.

We are now in the position to prove the theorem about homomorphic characterization. The proof bears a close resemblance to structural descriptions discussed in Note 6.2.

Theorem 7.4. Every context-free language equals a homomorphic image of the intersection of a regular language and a Dyck language.

Proof. Let L be a given context-free language. If $\lambda \in L$ and the language $L - \{\lambda\}$ can be expressed in the form $h(D \cap R)$, where R is a regular and D a Dyck language and h a homomorphism, then we have $L = h(D \cap (R \cup \{\lambda\}))$. Consequently, we assume without loss of generality that $\lambda \notin L$ and, by Theorem 6.3, we make the further assumption that $G = (V_N, V_T, X_0, F)$ is a grammar in the Chomsky normal form generating L. Let V_T consist of the letters $a_1, \ldots, a_m$ and let

$$X_i \to Y_i Z_i, \qquad i = 1, \ldots, r, \tag{7.7}$$

be all the productions in F having nonterminals on the right side. [Clearly, some of the X's, Y's and Z's appearing in (7.7) may be equal.] We introduce new letters $a_{m+1}, \ldots, a_{m+r}$ and a_i', $i = 1, \ldots, m+r$, and consider the alphabet

$$V_{m+r} = \{a_1, a_1', \ldots, a_{m+r}, a_{m+r}'\}.$$

Let D_{m+r} be the Dyck language over V_{m+r}. Define a homomorphism h of $W(V_{m+r})$ onto $W(V_T)$ by

$$h(a_i) = a_i \qquad \text{for} \quad i = 1, \ldots, m,$$

$$h(a_i) = h(a_j') = \lambda \qquad \text{for} \quad i = m+1, \ldots, m+r \quad \text{and} \quad j = 1, \ldots, m+r.$$

Finally, consider the language R generated by the grammar

$$G_1 = (V_N, V_{m+r}, X_0, F_1),$$

where

$$F_1 = \{X \to aa' | a \in V_T, X \to a \text{ in } F\}$$

$$\cup \{X \to aa'a_{m+i}' Z_i | a \in V_T, X \to a \text{ in } F, 1 \le i \le r\}$$

$$\cup \{X_i \to a_{m+i} Y_i | 1 \le i \le r\}.$$

[Thereby, X_i, Y_i, and Z_i are as in (7.7).] Since G_1 is right-linear, R is regular, by Theorem 5.6. To prove Theorem 7.4, it suffices to show that

$$L = h(D_{m+r} \cap R). \tag{7.8}$$

The equation (7.8) is established by showing inclusion in both directions. We prove first that the left side is included in the right side. To do this, it suffices to show that whenever

$$X = P_0 \Rightarrow P_1 \Rightarrow \cdots \Rightarrow P_t = P, \qquad X \in V_N, \quad P \in W(V_T),$$

is a derivation according to G, then there is a word $Q \in D_{m+r}$ such that $X \Rightarrow_{G_1}^* Q$ and $P = h(Q)$. If $t = 1$, then $P \in V_T$ and the production $X \to P$ is in F. Consequently, the production $X \to PP'$ is in F_1. We may choose $Q = PP'$, since then $Q \in D_{m+r}$ and $P = h(Q)$. We now make the inductive hypothesis that the assertion has been established for numbers less than or equal to a fixed value of $t \geq 1$ and consider a derivation

$$X \Rightarrow P_1 \Rightarrow \cdots \Rightarrow P_{t+1}, \qquad X \in V_N, \quad P_{t+1} \in W(V_T), \qquad (7.9)$$

according to G. Since G is in the Chomsky normal form, there is a number i, $1 \leq i \leq r$, such that $X = X_i$ and $P_1 = Y_i Z_i$. Furthermore, by (7.9), there are words Q_1 and Q_2 such that $P_{t+1} = Q_1 Q_2$, and Q_1 (resp. Q_2) has a derivation from Y_i (resp. Z_i) according to G with length less than t. By our inductive hypothesis, there are words Q_3 and Q_4 in D_{m+r} such that

$$Q_1 = h(Q_3), \qquad Q_2 = h(Q_4), \qquad (7.10)$$

$$Y_i \Rightarrow^*_{G_1} Q_3, \qquad Z_i \Rightarrow^*_{G_1} Q_4. \qquad (7.11)$$

Since $X_i \to Y_i Z_i$ is in F, the production $X_i \to a_{m+i} Y_i$ is in F_1. Consequently,

$$X_i \Rightarrow_{G_1} a_{m+i} Y_i \Rightarrow^*_{G_1} a_{m+i} Q_3 a'_{m+i} Z_i \Rightarrow^*_{G_1} a_{m+i} Q_3 a'_{m+i} Q_4.$$

[At the second step, we replace in the first derivation (7.11) the final application of a production $Y \to aa'$, $a \in V_T$, by an application of the production $Y \to aa'a'_{m+i} Z_i$ which, by definition, is in F_1. The last step follows by the second derivation in (7.11).] We now choose $Q = a_{m+i} Q_3 a'_{m+i} Q_4$. By (7.10) and the definition of h,

$$h(Q) = h(Q_3) h(Q_4) = Q_1 Q_2 = P_{t+1}.$$

By properties (i) and (ii) of Dyck languages, $Q \in D_{m+r}$. This completes the induction, and we conclude that the left side of (7.8) is included in the right side.

To establish the reverse inclusion, it suffices to prove that whenever

$$X = Q_0 \Rightarrow Q_1 \Rightarrow \cdots \Rightarrow Q_u = Q, \qquad X \in V_N, \quad Q \in D_{m+r},$$

is a derivation according to G_1, then also $X \Rightarrow^*_G h(Q)$. For $u = 1$, this is obvious because $Q_1 = Q = aa'$ for some $a \in V_T$, and the production $X \to a$ is in F. Proceeding inductively, we assume that the assertion has been established for numbers less than or equal to a fixed value of $u \geq 1$ and consider a derivation

$$X \Rightarrow Q_1 \Rightarrow \cdots \Rightarrow Q_{u+1} = Q, \qquad X \in V_N, \quad Q \in D_{m+r}, \qquad (7.12)$$

according to G_1. Since $u + 1 \geq 2$, the first production applied in (7.12) is not of the form $X \to aa'$, $a \in V_T$. It is also not of the form $X \to aa'a'_{m+i} Z_i$ because otherwise we would have $Q = aa'a'_{m+i} Q_\alpha$ for some Q_α. By property (iv) of Dyck languages, we would have $a'_{m+i} Q_\alpha \in D_{m+r}$, which contradicts property (iii).

Consequently, there is a number i, $1 \leqq i \leqq r$, such that in (7.12) $X = X_i$, $Q_1 = a_{m+i} Y_i$. This implies that there is a derivation

$$Y_i \Rightarrow_{G_1} Q_2^{\alpha} \Rightarrow_{G_1} \cdots \Rightarrow_{G_1} Q_{u+1}^{\alpha} \qquad (7.13)$$

such that $Q = a_{m+i} Q_{u+1}^{\alpha}$. By property (iii) of Dyck languages, there are words Q^{α} and Q^{β} in D_{m+r} such that $Q = a_{m+i} Q^{\alpha} a'_{m+i} Q^{\beta}$. Considering the productions in F_1, it is seen that there is a number k, $2 \leqq k \leqq u$, such that in (7.13)

$$Q_k^{\alpha} = Q^{\alpha} a'_{m+i} Z_i.$$

Furthermore, the $(k-1)$th production used in (7.13) is

$$Y \to aa' a'_{m+i} Z_i, \qquad a \in V_T, \quad Y \in V_N, \qquad (7.14)$$

and the production $Y \to a$ is in F and thus the production

$$Y \to aa' \qquad (7.15)$$

is in F_1. By replacing at the $(k-1)$th step in (7.13) the application of (7.14) by an application of (7.15), we obtain a derivation

$$Y_i \Rightarrow_{G_1}^* Q^{\alpha} \qquad (7.16)$$

of length less than u. By considering the part of (7.13) beginning with Q_k^{α}, we obtain a derivation

$$Z_i \Rightarrow_{G_1}^* Q^{\beta} \qquad (7.17)$$

of length less than u. By our inductive hypothesis, (7.16), and (7.17),

$$Y_i \Rightarrow_G^* h(Q^{\alpha}), \qquad Z_i \Rightarrow_G^* h(Q^{\beta}).$$

Hence,

$$X = X_i \Rightarrow_G Y_i Z_i \Rightarrow_G^* h(Q^{\alpha}) h(Q^{\beta}) = h(a_{m+i} Q^{\alpha} a'_{m+i} Q^{\beta}) = h(Q).$$

This completes the induction and, thus, the right side of (7.8) is included in the left side. ∎

In the proof of Theorem 7.4 given above, the alphabet V_{m+r} and the Dyck language D_{m+r} depend on the grammar G and thus on the language L. However, it is easy to modify the proof in such a way that the Dyck language depends on the alphabet V_T alone. To do this, it suffices to consider the alphabet

$$V_T' = \{a_1, a_1', \ldots, a_m, a_m', b, b', c, c'\}$$

instead of V_{m+r}. The "left parenthesis" a_{m+i} is replaced by $bc^i b$ and the "right parenthesis" a'_{m+i} by $b'(c')^i b'$. Hence, we obtain the following stronger version of Theorem 7.4.

Theorem 7.5. For an alphabet V_T of m letters, there exist an alphabet V_T' of $2m+4$ letters, a Dyck language D over V_T', and a homomorphism h of $W(V_T')$ onto $W(V_T)$ such that, for every context-free language L over V_T, there is a regular language R over V_T' with the property

$$L = h(D \cap R).$$

8. SUBFAMILIES OF CONTEXT-FREE LANGUAGES

The purpose of this section is to introduce some special cases of context-free grammars which are needed later on.

The notion of a *linear* grammar was defined in Section 5. A language is termed *linear* iff it is generated by a linear grammar. Clearly, all linear languages are context-free. Our next definition generalizes the concept of linearity.

Definition. For an integer $k \geq 2$, a grammar $G = (V_N, V_T, X_0, F)$ is termed *k-linear* iff each production in F is of one of the three forms $X \to P_1 Y P_2$, $X \to P_1$, or $X_0 \to Q$ where $X, Y \in V_N$, $P_1, P_2 \in W(V_T)$, and Q contains at most k nonterminals, and X_0 does not appear on the right side of any production. A grammar is 1-*linear* iff it is linear. A grammar G is *metalinear* iff there is an integer k such that G is k-linear. A language is *k-linear* (resp. *metalinear*) iff it is generated by a k-linear (resp. metalinear) grammar.

Example 8.1. The language $\{a^i b^i | i \geq 1\}$ is linear. The language $\{a^i b^i a^j b^j | i, j \geq 1\}$ is 2-linear and hence metalinear since it is generated by the 2-linear grammar

$$(\{X, Y\}, \{a, b\}, X, \{X \to YY, Y \to aYb, Y \to ab\}).$$

We now study closure properties of the new language families under regular and Boolean operations as well as substitution. The families are also compared with each other and with type-3 and type-2 languages.

Theorem 8.1. The family of metalinear languages is closed under union and catenation. For each $k \geq 1$, the family of k-linear languages is closed under union.

Proof. Assume that L and L' are linear languages generated by the grammars

$$G = (V_N, V_T, X_0, F) \qquad \text{and} \qquad G' = (V_N', V_T', X_0', F'). \tag{8.1}$$

Without loss of generality, we assume that V_N and V_N' are disjoint. Then $L \cup L'$ is generated by the linear grammar

$$(V_N \cup V_N' \cup \{Y\}, V_T \cup V_T', Y, F \cup F' \cup \{Y \to X_0, Y \to X_0'\}).$$

Assume that $k \geqq 2$ and that L and L' are k-linear languages generated by the grammars (8.1) where $V_N \cap V_N' = \varnothing$. Let F_1 be obtained from F' by replacing every production of the form $X_0' \to P$ with the production $X_0 \to P$. Then the k-linear grammar

$$(V_N \cup V_N', V_T \cup V_T', X_0, F \cup F_1)$$

generates the language $L \cup L'$. Furthermore, the $2k$-linear grammar $(V_N \cup V_N' \cup \{Y\}, V_T \cup V_T', Y, F_2)$, where

$$F_2 = \{X \to P \,|\, X \neq X_0, X_0'; X \to P \text{ in } F \cup F'\}$$

$$\cup \{Y \to PP' \,|\, X_0 \to P \text{ in } F, X_0' \to P' \text{ in } F'\},$$

generates the language LL'.

Thus we have shown that (i) for all $k \geqq 1$, the union of two k-linear languages is k-linear, and (ii) for all $k \geqq 2$, the catenation of two k-linear languages is $2k$-linear. To establish Theorem 8.1, it suffices to note that whenever a language L is k-linear, it is also n-linear for any $n \geqq k$. This again follows by definition for $k \geqq 2$ and, for $k = 1$, by replacing a linear grammar of L with an equivalent linear grammar where the initial letter does not occur on the right side of any production. ∎

The next theorem is a useful lemma for establishing inclusion relations between the different linear language families, as well as for showing non-closure of these families under certain operations.

Theorem 8.2. Denote $L_1 = \{a^i b a^i c \,|\, i \geqq 1\}$ and let k be an integer greater than or equal to 2. If a language L is a subset of L_1^* and contains all words of the form

$$(a^n b a^n c)^k, \qquad n \geqq 1, \tag{8.2}$$

then L is not $(k-1)$-linear.

Proof. The idea behind the proof is to use c as a boundary marker and show that, for sufficiently large values of n, the word (8.2) cannot be generated by linear productions from words containing less than k nonterminals.

We assume the contrary: L is generated by the $(k-1)$-linear grammar $G = (V_N, \{a, b, c\}, X_0, F)$. We first replace G by an equivalent $(k-1)$-linear grammar $G_1 = (V_N, \{a, b, c\}, X_0, F_1)$ which contains no productions $X \to Y$ where X and Y are nonterminals. This is done exactly as in the proof of Theorem 6.3. Without loss of generality, we also assume that each nonterminal in V_N generates according to G_1 at least one terminal word and, for $k = 2$, that X_0 does not appear on the right side of any production. We may also assume that, for any $X \in V_N$, there are words P_X and Q_X such that $X_0 \Rightarrow^* P_X X Q_X$.

We now divide the set V_N into subclasses. We say that a nonterminal $X \in V_N$ is *looping* iff there are words P_1 and P_2 such that

$$X \Rightarrow \cdots \Rightarrow P_1 X P_2. \qquad (8.3)$$

Clearly, X_0 is not looping. Because of the linearity of the productions, (8.3) implies that P_1 and P_2 are words over the terminal alphabet. Furthermore, at least one of them is distinct from λ since there are no productions $X \rightarrow Y$. If (8.3) holds, then also

$$X \Rightarrow^* P_1{}^i X P_2{}^i, \qquad i = 1, 2, \ldots. \qquad (8.4)$$

Assume that at least one of the words P_1 and P_2 contains a letter other than a. Then it has to contain both of the letters b and c. Otherwise, we could choose in (8.4) $i = 2$ and thus obtain a subword of a word in L which contains either two occurrences of b without an intermediate occurrence of c or two occurrences of c without an intermediate occurrence of b. But this is impossible since L is a subset of $L_1{}^*$.

We say that X is a *bc-nonterminal* iff (8.3) is satisfied and P_1 or P_2 contains b or c (and, consequently, both b and c); X is an *a-nonterminal* iff (8.3) is satisfied and both P_1 and P_2 are of the form a^i. We now claim (i) an a-nonterminal X generates no terminal words other than words of the form $a^i b a^j$, $i, j \geqq 0$. For assume an a-nonterminal X generates a word $Q_1 c Q_2$. By (8.4), we conclude that there is a word $P \in L$ of the form

$$P = Q_3 P_1 Q_1 c Q_2 P_2 Q_4, \qquad P_1 = a^\alpha, \quad P_2 = a^\beta, \qquad (8.5)$$

and furthermore, that all of the words

$$Q_3 P_1{}^i Q_1 c Q_2 P_2{}^i Q_4, \qquad i \geqq 0, \qquad (8.6)$$

also belong to L. By our remarks concerning looping nonterminals, at least one of the numbers α and β is greater than 0. Thus, in the transition from (8.5) to (8.6), for $i \geqq 2$, we increase the number of a's either in one sequence a^j or in two such sequences separated by at least one c. No other changes are made. But this is impossible because L is a subset of $L_1{}^*$. The same contradiction arises if X generates a terminal word containing no b's or at least two b's. Hence, the assertion (i) is true.

Since bc-nonterminals generate terminal words containing both b and c, assertion (i) implies that no nonterminal is both an a-nonterminal and a bc-nonterminal. Hence, the set of looping nonterminals is partitioned into two disjoint subsets, a-nonterminals and bc-nonterminals. Let u_{bc} be the number of bc-terminals. Let u be the number of those nonterminals which are not looping.

We consider now generation trees of G_1. Let M be any path containing at least $u + u_{bc} + 2 = v$ nodes in any such tree. If no node in M is labeled by an

a-nonterminal, then some bc-nonterminal occurs twice in M and consequently there is an edge from some node in M to a leaf labeled by c. There is only a finite number of trees where the longest path possesses at most $2v$ nodes and the root is labeled by X_0. Let v_1 be the length of the longest terminal word generated by these trees.

Then no word (8.2), where $n > v_1$, is generated by G_1. This follows by assertion (i) and the fact that there are at most $k - 1$ edges from the root to nodes labeled by nonterminals in any generation tree T. Consequently, in any T there are two leaves labeled by c such that their intermediate word cannot be of length $> v_1$ (cf. also Fig. 9). ∎

Results concerning inclusion relations and nonclosure under certain operations now follow as immediate corollaries of Theorem 8.2. The next theorem shows that there is an infinite hierarchy of language families between the family of type-3 languages and the family of metalinear languages.

Theorem 8.3. The family $\mathscr{L}_3$ is contained properly in the family of linear languages. For every $k \geqq 1$, the family of k-linear languages is contained properly in the family of $(k + 1)$-linear languages, and hence the family of k-linear languages is contained properly in the family of metalinear languages. The family of metalinear languages is contained properly in the family $\mathscr{L}_2$.

Proof. The asserted inclusions, apart from being proper, follow by

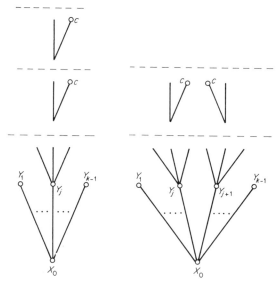

FIGURE 9

definitions. The first sentence follows because the linear language $\{a^i b^i | i \geq 1\}$ is not of type 3. The second sentence is due to the fact that for any $k \geq 1$, the language

$$L_{k+1} = \{a^{n_1} b a^{n_1} c \cdots a^{n_{k+1}} b a^{n_{k+1}} c | n_1 \geq 1, \ldots, n_{k+1} \geq 1\} \qquad (8.7)$$

generated by the $(k+1)$-linear grammar

$$(\{X_0, X\}, \{a, b, c\}, X_0, \{X_0 \to (Xc)^{k+1}, X \to aXa, X \to aba\}) \qquad (8.8)$$

is not k-linear, by Theorem 8.2. The last sentence is established by considering the language L_1 of Theorem 8.2. It is generated by the grammar (8.8) where $k = 0$. By Theorem 3.2, L_1^* is context-free. On the other hand, L_1^* contains, for any k, all words of the form (8.2). Consequently, by Theorem 8.2, there is no such k that L_1^* is $(k-1)$-linear. This implies that L_1^* is not metalinear. ∎

Theorem 8.4. Neither the family of k-linear languages, $k \geq 1$, nor the family of metalinear languages is closed under any of the following operations: intersection, complementation, catenation closure, substitution. The family of k-linear languages, $k \geq 1$, is not closed under catenation.

Proof. Nonclosure of the families under intersection is seen by noting that the languages $L(G_1)$ and $L(G_2)$ considered in the proof of Theorem 6.6 are linear. Nonclosure under complementation now follows indirectly because the families are closed under union by Theorem 8.1. The linear language L_1 of Theorem 8.2 shows that our families are not closed under catenation closure. Consider next the linear language $K = \{d^i | i \geq 0\}$. Let σ be the substitution defined by $\sigma(d) = L_1$. Then $\sigma(K) = L_1^*$ is not metalinear, which shows that none of our families is closed under substitution. Finally, the last sentence of the theorem is due to the fact that the language L_{k+1} of (8.7) is the catenation of the languages L_k and L_1 for any $k \geq 1$. ∎

We finally discuss briefly some other subfamilies of context-free languages. An important subfamily, *deterministic* languages, was introduced in Section 4 and is discussed more closely later on.

A *minimal linear* grammar is a linear grammar with the initial letter X_0 as the only nonterminal and with $X_0 \to a$, for some terminal letter a, as the only production with no nonterminal on the right side. Furthermore, it is assumed that a does not occur in any other production. For instance,

$$(\{X\}, \{a, b\}, X, \{X \to aXa, X \to b\})$$

is a minimal linear grammar generating the language $\{a^i b a^i | i \geq 0\}$.

An *even linear* grammar is a linear grammar where all productions with a nonterminal Y on the right side are of the form $X \to PYQ$, $lg(P) = lg(Q)$.

Although not obvious by definition, one can show that type-3 languages form a proper subfamily of the languages generated by even linear grammars.

A linear grammar $G = (V_N, V_T, X_0, F)$ is *deterministic linear* iff all productions in F are of the two forms

$$X \to aYP, \qquad X \to a, \qquad a \in V_T, \quad Y \in V_N, \quad P \in W(V_T),$$

and furthermore for any $X \in V_N$ and $a \in V_T$, there is at most one production $X \to aP$, $P \in W(V_N \cup V_T)$, in F. Deterministic linear grammars play an important role in the theory of probabilistic automata and grammars.

A context-free grammar $(\{X_1, ..., X_n\}, V_T, X_1, F)$ is *sequential* iff, for all productions $X_i \to P$ in F, we have $P \in W(V_T \cup \{X_j | i \leq j \leq n\})$. For instance, any context-free grammar possessing only one nonterminal is sequential.

Proposition 8.1. The family of languages generated by sequential grammars includes properly $\mathcal{L}_3$ and is properly included in $\mathcal{L}_2$.

EXERCISES

1. Give a type-3 grammar for the language denoted by the regular expression $(aa \cup bb^*a \cup abb^*a)^*$.

2. Give a regular expression for the language generated by the grammar

$$X_0 \to abX_1, \qquad X_1 \to aaX_0, \qquad X_2 \to aX_1,$$
$$X_0 \to aX_2, \qquad X_1 \to bX_1, \qquad X_2 \to b.$$

(X_0 is the initial letter; a and b are terminals.)

3. What is the star height of the language denoted by the regular expression $(ab^*a)^*$?

4. A language L consists of all words P over the alphabet $\{a, b, c, d\}$ which satisfy each of the following conditions:

(i) $N_a(P) + N_b(P) = 2(N_c(P) + N_d(P))$. (For the definition of the function N, compare Exercise 1 to Chapter I.)

(ii) aaa is a subword of P but abc is not a subword of P.

(iii) The third letter of P is not c.

Prove that L is context-free.

5. Give a star-free generalized regular expression for the language denoted by $(10101)^*$.

6. Which of the grammars (2.1), (2.3), and (2.5) are ambiguous?

7. Prove that every regular language is a homomorphic image of a 2-testable language. [Begin with an alphabet whose letters are triples (s, a, s') where s and s' are states and a is a terminal.]

8. Prove that every context-free language L can be expressed in the form $L = h(D \cap K)$ where D is a Dyck language, h is a homomorphism, and K is a 2-testable language.

9. Prove that, for each $k \geq 1$, there exists a regular language L_k that is generated by a one-sided linear grammar with k nonterminals but that is generated by no one-sided linear grammar with less than k nonterminals.

10. Prove that if a language L is acceptable by a finite deterministic automaton with n states, then $mi(L)$ is acceptable by a finite deterministic automaton with 2^n states. Can you give examples where no fewer than 2^n states suffice for accepting $mi(L)$?

11. Define a "normal form" for regular expressions over the alphabet $\{a\}$ such that (i) every regular expression can be reduced effectively to a normal form, and (ii) two different normal forms denote different languages. (No such normal forms are known for regular expressions over a two-letter alphabet.)

12. Let L be any language whatsoever over the alphabet $\{a\}$. Prove that L^* is regular.

13. Compare the family of minimal linear languages with the family $\mathscr{L}_3$. Characterize the languages belonging to the intersection of these two families.

14. Prove that there is a linear language which is not generated by any deterministic linear grammar.

15. State and prove a result corresponding to Bar-Hillel's lemma for type-3 languages. (Consider the automaton accepting the language and note that if the length of a word exceeds the number of states, then the same state must have been visited twice.)

16. What are the equivalence classes of E_L if L is (i) the language denoted by the regular expression $(a^2 \cup a^5)^*$; (ii) the language $\{a^i b^i | i \geq 1\}$? (In general, very little is known about the structure of E_L if L is nonregular. For instance, it is not known for what languages the equivalence classes consitute a group.)

17. A Parikh mapping ψ depends on the enumeration of the basic alphabet; another enumeration gives a different mapping ψ'. Prove that if $\psi(L)$ is semilinear for some ψ, then $\psi'(L)$ is semiiinear for any ψ'.

18. Consider languages over a fixed alphabet V_T. Prove that, for any natural number n, there is a context-free language L_n which is generated by no type-2 grammar containing fewer than n nonterminals.

19. Consider the grammar G determined by the productions

$$X_0 \to adX_1 da, \qquad X_0 \to aX_0 a, \qquad X_0 \to aca,$$

$$X_1 \to bX_1 b, \qquad X_1 \to bdX_0 db.$$

Prove that $L(G)$ is not sequential. This shows that all linear languages are not sequential. Conversely, give an example of a sequential language which is not metalinear.

BIBLIOGRAPHICAL REMARKS

The analysis method of Theorem 5.1 is due to McNaughton and Yamada (1960) and the results concerning the equivalence relation induced by a language are to be found in Rabin and Scott (1959). Theorem 5.7 is from Minsky and Papert (1965). Axiomatic characterizations for the set of valid equations between regular expressions are developed in Salomaa (1964, 1966, 1969), and an independent system is given by Urponen (1971). These matters are discussed in detail by Ginzburg (1968), Starke (1969), and Conway (1971). McNaughton and Papert (1971) is an extensive work about noncounting languages. Ginsburg (1966) covers the properties of context-free languages developed up to the middle 1960s and also gives references to the original work. We mention here only the following facts. The notion of ambiguity is defined explicitly by Parikh (1961). Ambiguity and inherent ambiguity are treated more extensively in Chapter VI. The reference by Parikh also contains the results on Parikh mappings developed in Section 7. The original version of Theorem 7.4 appears in Chomsky (1962). The results on linear and metalinear languages established in Section 8 are due to Chomsky and Schützenberger (1963). For a generalized version of Bar-Hillel's lemma, see Ogden (1968). More information about the subsequent topics can be obtained as follows: tree automata (from the point of view discussed in Note 6.2), see Thatcher (1967); sequential grammars and ALGOL-like languages, see Ginsburg and Rice (1962); deterministic languages, see Ginsburg (1966) and Hopcroft-Ullman (1969); probabilistic automata and deterministic linear grammars, see Paz (1971). The notion of a deterministic linear grammar is due to Nasu and Honda (1969). (This notion is somewhat different from the ordinary notions of deterministic and linear. It is not true that a language is generated by a deterministic linear grammar iff it is deterministic and linear.)

BIBLIOGRAPHY

N. **Chomsky.** Context-free grammars and pushdown storage. *M.I.T. Res. Lab. Electron. Quart. Prog. Rep.* **65** (1962).

N. **Chomsky** and M. P. **Schützenberger.** The algebraic theory of context-free languages. *In* P. Braffort and D. Hirschberg (eds.), "Computer Programming and Formal Systems." North Holland Publ., Amsterdam, 1963, pp. 118–161.

J. H. **Conway.** "Regular Algebra and Finite Machines." Chapman and Hall, London, 1971.

S. **Ginsburg.** "The Mathematical Theory of Context-Free Languages." McGraw-Hill, New York, 1966.

S. **Ginsburg** and H. G. **Rice.** Two families of languages related to ALGOL. *J. Assoc. Comput. Mach.* **9** (1962) 350–371.

A. Ginzburg. "Algebraic Theory of Automata." Academic Press, New York, 1968.

J. E. Hopcroft and J. D. Ullman. "Formal Languages and Their Relation to Automata." Addison-Wesley, Reading, Massachusetts, 1969.

R. McNaughton and S. Papert. "Counter-Free Automata," Research Monograph no. 65. M.I.T. Press, Cambridge, Massachusetts, 1971.

R. McNaughton and H. Yamada. Regular expressions and state graphs for automata. *IRE Trans. Electron. Comput.* EC-9 (1960) 39–47.

M. Minsky and S. Papert. Unrecognizable sets of numbers. *J. Assoc. Comput. Mach.* 13 (1966) 281–286.

M. Nasu and N. Honda. Mappings induced by PGSM-mappings and some recursively unsolvable problems of finite probabilistic automata. *Information Control* 15 (1969) 250–273.

W. Ogden. A helpful result for proving inherent ambiguity. *Math. Systems Theory* 2 (1968) 191–194.

R. J. Parikh. Language generating devices. *M.I.T. Res. Lab. Electron. Quart. Prog. Rep.* 60 (1961) 199–212.

A. Paz. "Introduction to Probabilistic Automata." Academic Press, New York, 1971.

M. Rabin and D. Scott. Finite automata and their decision problems. *IBM J. Res. Develop.* 3 (1959) 114–125.

A. Salomaa. Axiom systems for regular expressions of finite automata. *Ann. Univ. Turku. Ser. AI* 75 (1964).

A. Salomaa. Two complete axiom systems for the algebra of regular events. *J. Assoc. Comput. Mach.* 13 (1966) 158–169.

A. Salomaa. "Theory of Automata." Pergamon, Oxford, 1969.

P. H. Starke. "Abstrakte Automaten." VEB Deutscher Verlag der Wissenschaften, 1969.

J. W. Thatcher. Characterizing derivation trees of context-free grammars through a generalization of finite automata theory. *J. Comput. System Sci.* 1 (1967) 317–322.

T. Urponen. On axiom systems for regular expressions and on equations involving languages. *Ann. Univ. Turku. Ser. AI* 145 (1971).

Chapter III

Context-Sensitive and Type-0 Languages

The purpose of this chapter is to study properties of type-1 and type-0 languages and thus complete our look at the basic hierarchy of type-i, $i = 0, 1, 2, 3$, languages. Indeed, it has become customary in formal language theory to regard this hierarchy as fundamental, and consequently to compare any new generating devices first with type-i grammars. Why, then, have we chosen such a basic hierarchy and not something else? The motivation for type-3 grammars is very clear: They are models for strictly finite generation (or recognition) devices. Type-0 grammars are equivalent to Turing machines which, in turn, are the formal equivalent of the intuitive notion of an effective process. Indeed, it is a widely accepted contention (known as Church's thesis) that Turing machines can perform any effective process, that is, any mechanically or automatically executable process. Thus, type-0 grammars are the most general effective generating devices. The importance of type-1 and type-2 grammars is not as unquestionable as that of type-0 and type-3 grammars, although it is natural to study how in a derivation dependence on and independence from context affect the generation process. Type-2 grammars have also turned out to be most fruitful from the point of view of applications to natural and programming languages.

9. RECURSIVELY ENUMERABLE AND RECURSIVE LANGUAGES. HIERARCHY OF FOUR LANGUAGE FAMILIES

We first establish two basic results concerning type-1 grammars, beginning with a result which is significant because it is not true of type-0 grammars.

Theorem 9.1. There is an algorithm for deciding whether or not a word P belongs to the language $L(G)$ generated by a type-1 grammar $G = (V_N, V_T, X_0, F)$.

Proof. By the definition of type-1 grammars, it is obvious that $\lambda \in L(G)$ iff the production $X_0 \to \lambda$ belongs to F. Thus we may assume that $P \neq \lambda$ and $P \in W(V_T)$. Consider sequences of the form

$$P_0 = X_0, P_1, \ldots, P_{n-1}, P_n = P, \tag{9.1}$$

where $n \geq 1$, P_i are pairwise distinct words over $V_N \cup V_T$, and, for $0 \leq i \leq n-1$, $lg(P_i) \leq lg(P_{i+1})$. Clearly, the number of such sequences is finite. It is also obvious that $P \in L(G)$ iff, for some sequence (9.1),

$$X_0 = P_0 \Rightarrow P_1 \Rightarrow \cdots \Rightarrow P_{n-1} \Rightarrow P_n = P. \tag{9.2}$$

Thus it suffices to check, for each of the finitely many sequences (9.1), whether or not (9.2) is satisfied. This, in turn, can be accomplished because for any two words Q_1 and Q_2 and a grammar G, we can decide by checking through the productions in G whether or not $Q_1 \Rightarrow_G Q_2$ holds. ∎

The essential point in the proof is that for type-1 grammars, we may assume that the derivation (9.2) satisfies the condition $lg(P_i) \leq lg(P_{i+1})$ for $i = 0, \ldots, n-1$. This again is true because every type-1 grammar is length-increasing in the sense defined in Section 2. The next theorem shows that also the converse holds true as far as the generative capacity is concerned.

Theorem 9.2. For every length-increasing grammar, there is an equivalent type-1 grammar.

Proof. We first show how to replace one length-increasing production by type-1 productions. Theorem 9.2 then easily follows by induction.

Consider a type-1 grammar $G_1 = (V_N, V_T, X_0, F)$, which does not contain the production $X_0 \to \lambda$, and two words P and Q over V_N such that $2 \leq lg(P) \leq lg(Q)$, that is,

$$P = X_1 \cdots X_m, \qquad Q = Y_1 \cdots Y_n, \qquad 2 \leq m \leq n,$$

where X's and Y's are letters of V_N. Define

$$G_2 = (V_N, V_T, X_0, F \cup \{P \to Q\}).$$

Then G_2 is equivalent to the type-1 grammar

$$G_2' = (V_N \cup \{Z_1, ..., Z_m\}, V_T, X_0, F \cup F')$$

where F' consists of the productions

$$X_1 X_2 \cdots X_m \to Z_1 X_2 \cdots X_m,$$

$$Z_1 X_2 \cdots X_m \to Z_1 Z_2 X_3 \cdots X_m,$$

$$\vdots$$

$$Z_1 Z_2 \cdots Z_{m-1} X_m \to Z_1 Z_2 \cdots Z_{m-1} Z_m Y_{m+1} \cdots Y_n,$$

$$Z_1 Z_2 \cdots Z_m Y_{m+1} \cdots Y_n \to Y_1 Z_2 \cdots Z_m Y_{m+1} \cdots Y_n,$$

$$\vdots$$

$$Y_1 \cdots Y_{m-1} Z_m Y_{m+1} \cdots Y_n \to Y_1 \cdots Y_m Y_{m+1} \cdots Y_n.$$

Indeed, G_2' is obviously of type 1 and it is also clear that $L(G_2) \subseteq L(G_2')$. The reverse inclusion follows because the Z's are introduced in such a way that the whole sequence of productions in F' always has to be applied.

Now let G be an arbitrary length-increasing grammar. We are going to construct an equivalent type-1 grammar G'. If G possesses the production $X_0 \to \lambda$ (which implies that X_0 does not occur on the right side of any production), then we (i) remove this production, (ii) perform the construction for the grammar thus obtained, and (iii) add a new initial symbol X_0' and productions $X_0' \to \lambda$ and $X_0' \to X_0$ to the resulting grammar. Thus we assume that G does not possess the production $X_0 \to \lambda$. By Theorem 3.1, we also assume that the only productions in G containing terminal letters are of the form $X \to x$ where X is a nonterminal and x a terminal.

We first remove from G all productions which are not of type 1 and obtain, thus, a type-1 grammar G_1. We then add to G_1 one of the productions $P \to Q$ removed from G. For the resulting grammar G_2, an equivalent type-1 grammar G_2' is constructed by the procedure indicated above. This process is repeated by adding to G_2' another one of the productions removed from G, and continued until all productions removed from G have been added. ∎

We note here that in proofs concerning context-sensitive grammars the productions $X_0 \to \lambda$ have to be treated separately and thus cause an awkward special case. Some authors exclude these productions from context-sensitive grammars. The exclusion has serious disadvantages. For instance, the language hierarchy breaks down because a context-free language is not necessarily context-sensitive. We emphasize that if the productions $X_0 \to \lambda$ are allowed, as we have done, then it is necessary to make the additional assumption that X_0 does not appear on the right side of any production. Otherwise, the generative capacity will be altered. (See Exercise 2.)

We call a language L *recursively enumerable* iff there is an effective procedure of listing only the words in L with or without repetitions. By an effective procedure (equivalently, algorithm or mechanically executable process) we mean a finite set of instructions which describe in an unambiguous and detailed way how the task is performed. There are no restrictions on space or time needed to carry out the procedure, although the amount of information available at each step of the procedure is finite.

A language L is called *recursive* iff there is a terminating algorithm which decides, for any word P, whether or not P belongs to L.

It is obvious that this is not a mathematical definition of recursive and recursively enumerable languages. For an adequate definition, the intuitive notion of an effective procedure must be replaced by a formalized notion such as a Turing machine or a Markov normal algorithm. On the other hand, our intuitive definition *is* adequate for purposes where we only have to show the existence of an effective procedure.

Example 9.1. Consider ordered quadruples (x, y, z, n) of natural numbers satisfying the conditions

$$x^n + y^n = z^n, \qquad n \geqq 3. \tag{9.3}$$

Associate with each such quadruple the word $P = x \# y \# z \# n$ where x, y, z, and n are in binary form. Let L be the language over the alphabet $\{0, 1, \#\}$ consisting of all such words P. (Clearly, L is empty iff the celebrated Fermat's last theorem is true.) Then L is recursive because, given any word P, we can first determine whether or not P is of the form $x \# y \# z \# n$ where x, y, z, and n are nonempty words over the alphabet $\{0, 1\}$, and if it is of this form, determine whether or not the integers represented by x, y, z, and n satisfy (9.3). The language L is also recursively enumerable. To list the words in L, we consider words over $\{0, 1, \#\}$ in some specified order. (For instance, we may order them according to their length, and order words of the same length alphabetically.) For each word, we apply the algorithm described above for deciding whether or not the word is in L. The word is added to the list iff it is in L, after which the next word is considered. Clearly, this procedure does not terminate.

Theorem 9.3. Every context-sensitive language is recursive. Every type-0 language is recursively enumerable.

Proof. The first sentence follows by Theorem 9.1. Assume that G is a type-0 grammar. For each k, there is only a finite number of derivations according to G beginning from the initial symbol and having length k. Hence, we may check through all derivations of length k for $k = 1, 2, \ldots$. Whenever the last word in a derivation is over the terminal alphabet, it is listed in $L(G)$. This constitutes an effective listing procedure. (Note that repetitions may occur.) ∎

We may know that a language is recursive without knowing an algorithm for deciding whether a word is in the language. This is illustrated by the following.

Example 9.2. Let L be as in Example 9.1, and let L_1 be the language over the alphabet $\{a\}$ defined as follows: $L_1 = \varnothing$ if $L = \varnothing$. If $L \neq \varnothing$, then $L_1 = \{a\}$. Although L_1 is finite, an algorithm for deciding whether or not $P \in L_1$ (in particular, for $P = a$) would also decide whether or not Fermat's last theorem is true. Hence, it is not easy to give such a decision method.

The next theorem, together with Theorem 9.3, shows that the family of context-sensitive languages is properly included in the family of recursive languages. The proof is by a *diagonalization* argument which was first used by Cantor in his proof that the set of real numbers is nondenumerable and has, since the famous work of Gödel, become a standard tool in mathematical logic and related areas.

Theorem 9.4. There exists a recursive language which is not context-sensitive.

Proof. Consider context-sensitive grammars with the terminal alphabet $V = \{a, b\}$, initial letter X_0, and the nonterminal alphabet consisting of some letters X_i, $i \geq 0$. Since the nonterminals can always be renamed, any context-sensitive language over V is generated by such a grammar. Moreover, if the productions in such a grammar are $P_1 \to Q_1, \ldots, P_n \to Q_n$, then the grammar is completely specified by the word

$$P_1 \to Q_1 \# \cdots \# P_n \to Q_n, \tag{9.4}$$

the nonterminal alphabet being implicitly defined by (9.4). The words (9.4) are now encoded in the alphabet V by the homomorphism φ defined as follows:

$$\varphi(a) = bab, \qquad \varphi(b) = ba^2b, \qquad \varphi(\to) = ba^3b,$$

$$\varphi(\#) = ba^4b, \qquad \varphi(X_i) = ba^{i+5}b \qquad \text{for} \quad i \geq 0.$$

For instance, if the productions are

$$X_0 \to \lambda, \qquad X_0 \to X_1 X_2, \qquad X_2 \to a, \qquad X_1 X_2 \to bX_2,$$

then the corresponding encoded word is

$$ba^5bba^3bba^4bba^5bba^3bba^6bba^7bba^4b$$

$$ba^7bba^3bbabba^4bba^6bba^7bba^3bba^2bba^7b.$$

Thus for each grammar G of the kind considered, there corresponds a word over the alphabet V. Conversely, given any word over V, we can tell by analyzing it whether or not it corresponds to a context-sensitive grammar. We now number all words over V in the following way. The empty word λ is assigned the number 1. Assume that $k \geqq 0$ and that all words of length k have been assigned numbers, the greatest of them being m. Then the 2^{k+1} words of length $k+1$ are assigned, in the alphabetical order, the numbers $m+1,...,m+2^{k+1}$. This numbering also induces a numbering of context-sensitive grammars: The ith grammar G_i corresponds to the ith word which defines a context-sensitive grammar. (We may have $G_i = G_j$ although $i \neq j$, since the permuting of the productions causes a change in the corresponding word.)

Now let L be the language over V defined by the condition: For each i, the ith word P_i is in L iff $P_i \notin L(G_i)$. (For instance, $\lambda \notin L$ since λ is the first word, and the grammar G_1 consists of the production $X_0 \to \lambda$.) By Theorem 9.1, L is recursive because, given any P over V, we may compute its number i and then determine the grammar G_i. We claim that L is not context-sensitive. Assume the contrary. Then there is a number j such that $L = L(G_j)$. Consider the jth word P_j. If $P_j \in L$, then P_j is not generated by G_j and hence $P_j \notin L$. If $P_j \notin L$, then, since $L = L(G_j)$, P_j is not generated by G_j, which implies, by the definition of L, that $P_j \in L$. Thus, in both cases, a contradiction arises. Consequently, L is a recursive language which is not context-sensitive. ∎

Theorem 9.5. A language L is recursive iff L and its complement $\sim L$ are both recursively enumerable.

Proof. Clearly any recursive language L is recursively enumerable. To enumerate the words in L, we consider words P over the alphabet of L in some order. For each P, we apply the algorithm for deciding whether or not $P \in L$ and, if it does, we list it as a word in L.

Assume that L is recursive. Since for any word P over the alphabet of L, $P \in \sim L$ iff $P \notin L$, we conclude that $\sim L$ is recursive. Hence, both L and $\sim L$ are recursively enumerable.

Conversely, assume that L and $\sim L$ are recursively enumerable. If either L or $\sim L$ is finite, then both are evidently recursive. Let both L and $\sim L$ be infinite. Since we have procedures for listing both L and $\sim L$, we can combine the procedures by alternately choosing elements from L and $\sim L$ to make a single list, beginning with the first element of L. To decide whether or not $P \in L$, we need only observe whether P occurs in an odd or even position on our combined list. ∎

Theorem 9.6. There is a recursively enumerable language whose complement is not recursively enumerable. Consequently, there is a recursively enumerable language which is not recursive.

Proof. Indeed, the second sentence is a consequence of the first sentence, by Theorem 9.5. To establish the first sentence, we consider recursively enumerable languages over the one-letter alphabet $V = \{a\}$. Obviously there is an alphabet V' such that every effective procedure of listing a language over V can be expressed as a word over V'. By considering words over V', we obtain a sequence $E_0, E_1, E_2, \ldots$, which contains every effective procedure of listing a language over V. We now define a language L over V as follows. For every $n \geq 0$, the word a^n belongs to L iff a^n is generated by the procedure E_n.

We prove first that the complement of L, $\sim L$, is not recursively enumerable. Assume that $\sim L$ is recursively enumerable. Hence, there is a number k such that $\sim L$ is generated by the procedure E_k. For every $n \geq 0$, the word a^n belongs to $\sim L$ iff a^n is not generated by the procedure E_n. Hence, a^k belongs to $\sim L$ iff a^k is not generated by the procedure E_k. But this is impossible, since $\sim L$ is generated by E_k. Consequently, $\sim L$ is not recursively enumerable.

To complete the proof, it suffices to show that L is recursively enumerable. Every effective procedure can be broken down into discrete steps so that we can speak about the ith step ($i \geq 0$) in the procedure E_j or, in short, the (i, j)th step. [We make the convention that if E_j terminates at the ith step, then steps (i_1, j), $i_1 > i$, mean doing nothing.] We perform these steps in the order

$$(0,0), \ (1,0), \ (0,1), \ (2,0), \ (1,1), \ (0,2), \ (3,0), \ \ldots \ .$$

In general, if the (i, j)th step is kth ($k \geq 1$) in our order, then

$$k = \tfrac{1}{2}((i+j)^2 + 3j + i) + 1. \tag{9.5}$$

Clearly, (9.5) defines a function which assumes each natural number as its value exactly once for i and j nonnegative integers. Thus, for each $k \geq 1$, there is exactly one pair (i, j) such that (9.5) holds. An effective procedure for listing the words in L is now obvious: Whenever the (i, j)th step adds the word a^j to the language generated by E_j, we list a^j as a word of L. ∎

As we have pointed out, the notion of an effective procedure is not mathematically adequate. Although some things may undoubtedly be called "effective procedures" like the ones we have used in the proofs above, we still have no way of distinguishing between effective procedures and things which are not effective procedures. It has become customary to replace the intuitive notion of an effective procedure by the formalized notion of a Turing machine. Turing machines were defined in Section 4 as recognition devices: They are capable of giving "yes" or "no" answers to inputs. An effective procedure might be required to produce more general outputs as, for instance, Euclid's algorithm produces the greatest common divisor of two numbers. However, this requirement is easily taken care of as regards Turing machines: We may define the response of the machine to the given input to be the final outcome, where $\#$, o, and elements of S are ignored, of the rewriting process. Thus, we obtain mappings analogous to gsm mappings.

Clearly, the computing process of a Turing machine constitutes an effective procedure in the intuitive sense. Thus, this formalized version of the intuitive idea is not too broad. But is it too narrow? According to the widely accepted Church's thesis it is not: Every effective procedure can be carried out by a Turing machine. In order to prove Church's thesis, we would have to compare effective procedures and Turing machines and consequently we would have to formalize the notion of an effective procedure. But we would then again face the problem: Is the introduced formalization equivalent to the intuitive notion? The solution of this problem would require another Church's thesis. Evidently, only a proof for the negation of Church's thesis is conceivable—to describe an effective procedure which cannot be carried out by a Turing machine.

That Church's thesis is widely accepted is due to two main lines of reasoning. First, the class of mappings computable by Turing machines (the class of languages acceptable by Turing machines) has very strong closure properties. For instance, all extensions considered (such as machines with more than one tape or machines working nondeterministically or in dimensions higher than one) have been shown equivalent to the original Turing machine. Second, very diverse alternate formalizations of the class of effective procedures have all turned out to be equivalent to the Turing machine formalization. These alternate formalizations include Markov normal algorithms, Post normal systems, and type-0 grammars, which we have already considered, as well as recursive functions and existentially definable predicates, which are considered later.

In the sequel, by *Church's thesis* we mean the following statement: Every recursively enumerable language is acceptable by a Turing machine. The theorems which are established using Church's thesis could also be proved without it. This would mean very tedious constructions, such as defining a type-0 grammar for the language L in the proof of Theorem 9.6, where also the sequence E_i would have to be replaced by a sequence of type-0 grammars. The theorems that are established using Church's thesis are very few in number. For those readers who do not consider this as an adequate proof we always explicitly mention when we are dealing with a theorem whose proof either directly or indirectly depends on Church's thesis. Whenever possible, references to other proofs are given.

It is an immediate consequence of Church's thesis and Theorem 4.4 that every recursively enumerable language is of type 0 and hence by Theorem 9.3, the family of recursively enumerable languages equals the family of type-0 languages. (Note that we have here a proof of Proposition 4.3.) Therefore, the following theorem is an immediate corollary of Theorem 9.6.

Theorem 9.7. The family of type-0 languages is not closed under complementation.

We are now in the position to prove that the families of type-i languages, $i = 0, 1, 2, 3$, form a proper hierarchy.

Theorem 9.8. For $i = 1, 2, 3$ the family $\mathscr{L}_i$ is properly included in the family $\mathscr{L}_{i-1}$.

Proof. The inclusions $\mathscr{L}_3 \subseteq \mathscr{L}_2$ and $\mathscr{L}_1 \subseteq \mathscr{L}_0$ follow by the definition of type-i grammars. The inclusion $\mathscr{L}_2 \subseteq \mathscr{L}_1$ is due to Theorem 6.2. The family $\mathscr{L}_3$ is properly included in $\mathscr{L}_2$ since the context-free language $\{a^n b^n | n \geq 1\}$ is not of type 3. The length-increasing grammar G introduced at the beginning of Example 2.1 was shown to generate the language (2.10). By Theorem 9.2, (2.10) is of type 1. According to Example 6.2, it is not context-free. Consequently, $\mathscr{L}_2$ is properly included in $\mathscr{L}_1$. By Church's thesis and Theorems 9.4 and 9.5, $\mathscr{L}_1$ is properly included in $\mathscr{L}_0$. ∎

The following theorem illustrates the difference between type-0 and type-1 languages. It can be used as a lemma for establishing nonclosure of the family $\mathscr{L}_1$ under various operations.

Theorem 9.9. Let L be a type-0 language over the alphabet V_T and let $a, b \notin V_T$. Then there is a type-1 language L_1 such that (i) L_1 consists of words of the form $a^i b P$ where $i \geq 0$ and $P \in L$, and (ii) for every $P \in L$, there is an $i \geq 0$ such that $a^i b P \in L_1$.

Proof. Assume that L is generated by the grammar $G = (V_N, V_T, X_0, F)$. Introduce two new nonterminals X_0' and Y. Define

$$F_1 = \{P \to Q | P \to Q \text{ in } F \text{ and } lg(P) \leq lg(Q)\}$$

$$\cup \{P \to Y^{lg(P)-lg(Q)}Q | P \to Q \text{ in } F \text{ and } lg(P) > lg(Q)\}$$

$$F_2 = \{X_0' \to bX_0, Yb \to ab\} \cup \{\alpha Y \to Y\alpha | \alpha \in V_N \cup V_T \cup \{b\}\}.$$

Then the grammar

$$G_1 = (V_N \cup \{X_0', Y\}, V_T \cup \{a, b\}, X_0', F_1 \cup F_2)$$

is length-increasing and consequently, by Theorem 9.2, the language $L_1 = L(G_1)$ is of type 1. Since Y can be eliminated only in the position adjacent to the only occurrence of b, we conclude that L_1 satisfies condition (i). Furthermore, L_1 also satisfies condition (ii) because all derivations according to G are preserved by the productions in F_1. ∎

The exponent i in the word $a^i b P$ indicates roughly the amount of workspace needed in the derivation of P. The problem of workspace is dealt with in the next section as well as in Chapter IX.

Theorem 9.10. For every type-0 language L, there exist a type-1 language L_1, a homomorphism h, and a regular language R such that

$$L = h(L_1) = R \backslash L_1. \qquad (9.6)$$

Proof. Let L_1 be the language defined in the proof of Theorem 9.9. Let h be the homomorphism defined by

$$h(a) = h(b) = \lambda, \qquad h(c) = c \qquad \text{for} \quad c \in V_T.$$

Finally, let R be the language denoted by the regular expression $a^* b$. Then (9.6) is satisfied. ∎

Theorem 9.11. The family of context-sensitive languages is not closed under arbitrary homomorphisms. Consequently, it is not closed under substitution. It is also not closed under left (right) quotient with a regular language.

Proof. By Theorem 9.8, there is a type-0 language L which is not of type 1. Considering such a language L we conclude, by Theorem 9.10, that $\mathscr{L}_1$ is closed neither under arbitrary homomorphisms nor under left quotient with a regular language. The statement concerning right quotient follows similarly. The only difference is that the language L_1 of Theorem 9.9 consists now of words of the form $P b a^i$. ∎

Our proof of Theorem 9.11 uses Church's thesis in the argument showing the existence of the language L.

Note 9.1. Words over an alphabet V can be considered as nonnegative integers in many ways. A very convenient way is the following *m-adic* notation. Assume that $V = \{a_1, \ldots, a_m\}$, $m \geq 2$. Define $\varphi(\lambda) = 0$ and

$$\varphi(a_{i_k} a_{i_{k-1}} \cdots a_{i_0}) = \sum_{j=0}^{k} i_j \cdot m^j$$

where $k \geq 0$ and $1 \leq i_j \leq m$ for $j = 0, \ldots, k$. For instance, if $m = 3$, then $\varphi(a_3 a_1 a_2) = 2 \cdot 3^0 + 1 \cdot 3^1 + 3 \cdot 3^2 = 32$. It is easy to verify that φ is a bijection of the set $W(V)$ onto the set N of nonnegative integers. The bijection is easily decodable in both ways: Given a word, we may compute the corresponding number, and vice versa. This m-adic notation is different from the m-ary one considered in Section 5.

Consider now mappings f of the Cartesian power set N^n into N where $n \geq 1$. [By encoding according to the m-adic notation, mappings from

$W(A)^n$ into $W(B)$, where A and B are alphabets, can be reduced to mappings $f: N^n \to N$. If the alphabet consists of one letter a, then we let a^i correspond to i.] We consider also the case where f is defined in some subset of N^n only. Then f is referred to as a *partial* function. If the domain of f is N^n, then f is *total*. Examples of total functions (for different values of n) are

$$S_1(x) = x + 1, \; x + y, \; xy, \; U_i^n(x_1, ..., x_n) = x_i, \quad 1 \leq i \leq n.$$

The function $x - y$ is not total since it is defined only for values $x \geq y$. The function

$$x \div y = \begin{cases} x - y & \text{for} \quad x \geq y \\ 0 & \text{for} \quad x < y \end{cases}$$

is total.

A function f is *computable* iff there is a Turing machine TM_f which computes the values of f. More specifically, assume that f is a mapping of $W(A)^n$ into $W(B)$. Let

$$\text{TM}_f = (A \cup B \cup S \cup \{\#, o, b\}, F)$$

be such that (i) there is a halting computation from $\# s_0 x_1 b \cdots b x_n \#$, where $x_i \in W(A)$, iff $f(x_1, ..., x_n)$ is defined, and (ii) if there is a halting computation from $\# s_0 x_1 b \cdots b x_n \#$ and if the letters $s \in S$, $\#, o, b$ are erased from the last word of this computation, then the remaining word equals $f(x_1, ..., x_n)$. Under these assumptions, f is termed computable. Thus, computability can be defined both for partial and total functions. Note that b is a boundary marker needed in the input format for functions of several variables.

The class of computable functions can also be defined as the smallest class which contains certain basic functions and is closed under certain operations. To simplify notation, we write $f(x^{(n)})$ instead of $f(x_1, ..., x_n)$. The operation of *composition* associates with the functions $f(x^{(n)})$, $g_1(x^{(m)}), ..., g_n(x^{(m)})$ the function

$$h(x^{(m)}) = f(g_1(x^{(m)}), ..., g_n(x^{(m)}))$$

which is defined exactly for those arguments $x^{(m)}$ for which each of $g_i(x^{(m)})$, as well as the corresponding value of f, is defined. The operation of *minimalization* associates with a total function $f(x^{(n)}, y)$ the function

$$g(x^{(n)}) = (\mu y)(f(x^{(n)}, y) = 0)$$

whose value, for a given $x^{(n)}$, is the least value of y for which $f(x^{(n)}, y) = 0$, and which is undefined if no such y exists. The class of *recursive* functions is the smallest class which contains the basic functions $S_1, U_i^n, x + y, x \div y, xy$ and is closed under the operations of composition and minimalization. This definition of recursiveness seems quite artificial. However, one can prove that recursiveness thus defined is equivalent to computability. Hence, a language is recursive in the sense of Section 9 iff its characteristic function is recursive, provided Church's thesis is accepted. Similarly, a language is recursively enumerable in the sense of Section 9 iff its partial characteristic function is recursive. [For a language L over V, the *characteristic function* c of L is defined by

$$c(P) = \begin{cases} 1 & \text{for} \quad P \in L \\ 0 & \text{for} \quad P \in W(V) - L. \end{cases}$$

By m-adic encoding, c can be considered as a mapping of N into N. The *partial characteristic function* c_1 of L assumes the value 1 for arguments in L, and is undefined for arguments not in L.]

Several infinite sequences of subclasses of recursive functions have been introduced. Such *subrecursive hierarchies* induce, when characteristic functions are considered, infinite hierarchies of language classes and are therefore of interest for language theory. Two subrecursive hierarchies are described briefly below.

A class of functions is closed under the operation of *bounded recursion* iff the following condition is satisfied: Whenever $g(x^{(n)})$, $h(x^{(n+2)})$, and $j(x^{(n+1)})$ are in the class, and $f(x^{(n+1)})$ satisfies the conditions

(i) $f(x^{(n)}, 0) = g(x^{(n)})$,
(ii) $f(x^{(n)}, y+1) = h(x^{(n)}, y, f(x^{(n)}, y))$,
(iii) $f(x^{(n)}, y) \leqq j(x^{(n)}, y)$,

then also the function f belongs to the class. Let ε^i, $i = 0, 1, 2, \ldots$, be the smallest class of functions containing $x+1$, U_1^2, U_2^2, $f_i(x, y)$ and closed under composition and bounded recursion where

$$f_0(x, y) = y + 1, \qquad f_1(x, y) = x + y, \qquad f_2(x, y) = (x+1)(y+1),$$

$$\begin{aligned} f_{i+1}(0, y) &= f_i(y+1, y+1) \\ f_{i+1}(x+1, y) &= f_{i+1}(x, f_{i+1}(x, y)) \end{aligned} \qquad \text{for} \quad i \geqq 2.$$

The sequence of classes ε^i, $i = 0, 1, 2, \ldots$, is termed the *Grzegorczyk hierarchy*. Each of the classes ε^i is properly included in ε^{i+1}, as the function $f_{i+1}(x, x)$ increases faster than any function in the class ε^i. The union of all classes ε^i constitutes the class R of *primitive recursive* functions which, in turn, is properly included in the class of recursive (total) functions. The class R can also be defined as the smallest class containing the constant 0, S_1, U_i^n and closed under composition and primitive recursion. The operation of *primitive recursion* is defined as bounded recursion, with (iii) omitted. Although the class

ε^0 is lowest in the hierarchy, every nonempty recursively enumerable language equals the range of some function in ε^0. Here again we apply the m-adic encoding.

In the *Ritchie hierarchy* of function classes F^i, $i = 0, 1, 2, \ldots$, the complexity of a function is measured by the amount of tape required by a Turing machine in its computation. The class F^0 consists of gsm mappings. For $i \geqq 0$, F^{i+1} is the class of functions computed by Turing machines whose computations use a length of tape which is a function in F^i of the argument. The union of all classes F^i equals the class ε^3 in the Grzegorczyk hierarchy.

10. WORKSPACE

Derivations of nonempty words P according to context-sensitive grammars have the common property that word length increases monotonically. This implies that a derivation of P does not contain any words longer than P; that is, the "workspace" in the derivation does not exceed $lg(P)$. Suppose L is a type-0 language generated by a grammar G with the following property. There is a natural number p such that every $P \in L$ possesses a derivation according to G where the workspace does not exceed $p \cdot lg(P)$. Thus the ratio of the workspace to the size of the result has a common bound for all words in L. We are going to prove that under this assumption L is context-sensitive. This workspace theorem is a powerful tool for showing languages to be context-sensitive.

Definition. Assume that

$$D: X_0 = P_0 \Rightarrow P_1 \Rightarrow \cdots \Rightarrow P_n = P$$

is a derivation according to a grammar G. Then the *workspace of P by the derivation D* is defined by

$$WS_G(P, D) = \max\{lg(P_i) | 0 \leq i \leq n\}.$$

The *workspace* of $P \in L(G)$ is defined by

$$WS_G(P) = \min\{WS_G(P, D) | D \text{ is a derivation of } P\}.$$

Note that $WS_G(P) \geqq lg(P)$ for any G and P.

Theorem 10.1. If $G = (V_N, V_T, X_0, F)$ is a type-0 grammar and there is a natural number p such that

$$WS_G(P) \leqq plg(P), \tag{10.1}$$

for all nonempty words $P \in L(G)$, then $L(G)$ is of type 1.

Proof. Without loss of generality, we assume that $\lambda \notin L(G)$. For if this is not the case originally, we replace G by a λ-free grammar G^* generating the language $L(G) - \{\lambda\}$. (This construction was explained in the proof of Theorem 3.2 concerning closure of $\mathscr{L}_0$ under catenation closure.) If $L(G^*)$ is context-sensitive, then so is $L(G) = L(G^*) \cup \{\lambda\}$ by Theorem 3.2.

The proof is by induction on p. Consider first the basis of induction, $p = 1$. In this case

$$\mathrm{WS}_G(P) = lg(P), \tag{10.2}$$

for any P. Since G may contain productions $P \rightarrow Q$ with $lg(P) > lg(Q)$, we show how G can be replaced by an equivalent length-increasing grammar G'. We define

$$G' = (V_N \cup \{Y\}, V_T, X_0, F'),$$

where F' consists of productions indicated in (i)–(iii) below.

(i) If $P \rightarrow Q$ is in F and $lg(P) - lg(Q) = i > 0$, then $P \rightarrow Y^i Q$ is in F'.

(ii) If $P \rightarrow Q$ is in F and $lg(P) \leq lg(Q)$, then $Y^i P \rightarrow Q$ is in F' for $i = 0, \ldots, lg(Q) - lg(P)$.

(iii) $Y\alpha \rightarrow \alpha Y$ and $\alpha Y \rightarrow Y\alpha$ are in F' for all $\alpha \in V_N \cup V_T$.

Then G' is obviously length-increasing. (Letters Y are inserted to pad out the non-length-increasing productions.) It is also easy to verify that G' is equivalent to G. In fact, by (10.2), all inserted Y's can be absorbed. The productions of (iii) allow the Y's to migrate to where they can be absorbed. By Theorem 9.2, the language $L(G')$, and hence also $L(G)$, is context-sensitive.

We now make the inductive hypothesis that the theorem is true for the value $p - 1$ where $p \geq 2$. Let G be a grammar such that (10.1) is satisfied. We construct an equivalent grammar G' such that

$$\mathrm{WS}_{G'}(P) \leq (p-1)lg(P) \tag{10.3}$$

for all $P \in L(G') = L(G)$. This obviously will complete the inductive step. The idea in the construction of G' is to "pack" two letters of G into a single nonterminal letter of G'. This will reduce workspace so much that (10.3) will be satisfied. We will first construct an auxiliary grammar G_1 such that in all derivations according to G_1 every word except the first is of even length. Thus, G_1 will make it easy to pack two letters into one. We may assume that the only productions of G containing terminals are of the form $X \rightarrow x$ where X is a nonterminal and x is a terminal. For the construction in Theorem 3.1 does not alter workspace at all and hence the resulting grammar does not violate (10.1).

The auxiliary grammar G_1 is now defined:

$$G_1 = (V_N \cup \{Y_0, C\}, V_T \cup \{c\}, Y_0, F_1),$$

where F_1 consists of the productions listed as follows:

(i) The productions $Y_0 \rightarrow CX_0$, $\alpha C \rightarrow C\alpha$, $C\alpha \rightarrow \alpha C$, for each $\alpha \in V_N \cup V_T$, are in F_1. The productions $Ca \rightarrow ca$ are in F_1 for each $a \in V_T$.

(ii) If $P \rightarrow Q$ is in F and both $lg(P)$ and $lg(Q)$ are even, then $P \rightarrow Q$ is in F_1.

(iii) If $P \rightarrow Q$ is in F and both $lg(P)$ and $lg(Q)$ are odd, then $PX \rightarrow QX$, $XP \rightarrow XQ$ are in F_1 for each $X \in V_N \cup \{C\} \cup V_T$.

(iv) If $P \rightarrow Q$ is in F and $lg(P)$ is even, whereas $lg(Q)$ is odd, then $P \rightarrow CQ$, $CXP \rightarrow XQ$, $CPX \rightarrow QX$ are in F_1 for each $X \in V_N \cup V_T$.

(v) If $P \rightarrow Q$ is in F and $lg(P)$ is odd, whereas $lg(Q)$ is even, then $CP \rightarrow Q$, $PX \rightarrow CQX$, $XP \rightarrow CXQ$ are in F_1 for each $X \in V_N \cup V_T$.

We now establish some properties of G_1.

(a) Both sides of every production in G_1, except the production $Y_0 \rightarrow CX_0$, are words of even length. Consequently, if

$$Y_0 \Rightarrow P_1 \Rightarrow \cdots \Rightarrow P_n$$

is a derivation according to G_1, then $lg(P_i)$ is even for $i = 1, \ldots, n$.

(b) Let h be the homomorphism of $W(V_T \cup \{c\})$ into $W(V_T)$ defined by

$$h(c) = \lambda, \qquad h(a) = a \qquad \text{for} \quad a \in V_T.$$

Then $h(L(G_1)) \subseteq L(G)$. In fact, if a terminal word is derived according to G_1, then the same derivation, apart from introducing, eliminating, and moving C's and c's, can be performed according to G.

(c) For every $P \in L(G)$, there is a word $P^* \in L(G_1)$ such that $\mathrm{WS}_{G_1}(P^*) \le \mathrm{WS}_G(P) + 1$ and either $P^* = P$ or $P^* = cP$. [Consequently, by (b), $h(L(G_1)) = L(G)$.]

To prove (c), we establish the following stronger statement:

(d) For every derivation

$$D: X_0 \Rightarrow_G P_1 \Rightarrow_G \cdots \Rightarrow_G P_n, \qquad P_n \in W(V_N \cup V_T), \qquad (10.4)$$

there is a derivation

$$D_1: Y_0 \Rightarrow_{G_1}^* Q, \qquad Q = P_n \quad \text{or} \quad Q = CP_n, \qquad (10.5)$$

such that

$$\mathrm{WS}_{G_1}(Q, D_1) \le \mathrm{WS}_G(P_n, D) + 1. \qquad (10.6)$$

Using productions $Ca \rightarrow ca$ belonging to F_1, we see that the statement (d) implies (c). The statement (d) is clearly true for $n = 1$. [In this case, $X_0 \rightarrow P_1$ is in F. If $lg(P_1)$ is odd, then by (iii), $CX_0 \rightarrow CP_1$ is in F_1 and we obtain, using the initial production $Y_0 \rightarrow CX_0$, $Q = CP_1$ with (10.5) and (10.6) satisfied. If

$lg(P_1)$ is even, then by (v), $CX_0 \to P_1$ is in F_1 and we obtain $Q = P_1$.] Proceeding inductively, we assume that the statement (d) holds for a fixed value $n-1 \geqq 1$ in (10.4). Consider the derivation (10.4). By the inductive hypothesis, there is a derivation

$$D_1': Y_0 \Rightarrow^*_{G_1} Q_1, \qquad Q_1 = P_{n-1} \quad \text{or} \quad Q_1 = CP_{n-1}, \tag{10.7}$$

such that

$$\text{WS}_{G_1}(Q_1, D_1') \leqq \text{WS}_G(P_{n-1}, D_2) + 1, \tag{10.8}$$

where D_2 consists of the first $n-1$ steps of D. Let $R_1 \to R_2$ be the production applied in (10.4) at the last step. Several subcases arise, depending on the parity of $lg(R_1)$ and $lg(R_2)$ and also on which of the alternatives in (10.7) holds.

Assume first that $Q_1 = P_{n-1}$. If $lg(R_1)$ is even, then by (ii) and (iv), $R_1 \to R_2$ or $R_1 \to CR_2$ is in F_1. Using productions (i) to move C to the left we obtain, by (10.7) and (10.8), a word Q satisfying (10.5) and (10.6). If $lg(R_1)$ is odd, then Q_1 contains a subword XR_1 or R_1X for some $X \in V_N \cup V_T$. This follows because $lg(Q_1)$ is even, by (a). Suppose Q_1 contains a subword XR_1, the case of R_1X being treated similarly. By (iii) and (v), the production $XR_1 \to XR_2$ or $XR_1 \to CXR_2$ is in F_1. As before, we can now move C to the left.

Assume next that $Q_1 = CP_{n-1}$. In this case, no new C's will be introduced but rather the only C may be absorbed. Now $lg(P_{n-1})$ is odd. If both $lg(R_1)$ and $lg(R_2)$ are even, then $R_1 \to R_2$ is in F_1 by (ii), and we are through. If $lg(R_1)$ is even and $lg(R_2)$ odd, then P_{n-1} contains a subword XR_1 or R_1X for some $X \in V_N \cup V_T$. We now proceed using the production $CXR_1 \to XR_2$ or $CR_1X \to R_2X$ [cf. (iv)] which becomes applicable by moving, if necessary, C to the right according to (i). If both $lg(R_1)$ and $lg(R_2)$ are odd, we use the production $CR_1 \to CR_2$ [cf. (iii)] which can be made applicable by first moving C to the right. Finally, if $lg(R_1)$ is odd and $lg(R_2)$ is even, the production $CR_1 \to R_2$ is used.

We have now completed the induction and shown that (d) and consequently also (c) are satisfied. Having established properties (a)–(c) concerning the auxiliary grammar G_1, we return to the induction on p and the construction of the grammar G'.

Denote $V = V_N \cup V_\Gamma \cup \{c, C\}$. The grammar G' is defined by

$$G' = (\{[a,b] | a, b \in V\}, V_T, [C, X_0], F')$$

where F' consists of the productions

$$[a,b] \to ab, \qquad [c,a] \to a; \qquad a, b \in V_T,$$

and for every production $\alpha_1 \cdots \alpha_u \to \beta_1 \cdots \beta_v$ in F_1 with the α's and β's in V

(which excludes the production $Y_0 \to CX_0$ only), of the productions

$$[\alpha_1, \alpha_2] \cdots [\alpha_{u-1}, \alpha_u] \to [\beta_1, \beta_2] \cdots [\beta_{v-1}, \beta_v],$$

$$[\alpha, \alpha_1][\alpha_2, \alpha_3] \cdots [\alpha_u, \beta] \to [\alpha, \beta_1][\beta_2, \beta_3] \cdots [\beta_v, \beta],$$

for each $\alpha, \beta \in V$.

By (a) all productions in F_1, apart from $Y_0 \to CX_0$, are of the form $\alpha_1 \cdots \alpha_u \to \beta_1 \cdots \beta_v$ with u and v even, and hence the definition of F' is meaningful. By the choice of the initial letter of G' and by (c), it is immediately verified that $L(G') = L(G)$. Furthermore, for any $P \in L(G')$ there is a word $P^* \in L(G_1)$ such that

$$\mathrm{WS}_{G_1}(P^*) \leqq \mathrm{WS}_G(P) + 1 \qquad \text{and} \qquad P^* = P \quad \text{or} \quad P^* = cP. \tag{10.9}$$

This follows by (c). By the definition of G',

$$\mathrm{WS}_{G'}(P) \leqq \max\{lg(P), \tfrac{1}{2}\mathrm{WS}_{G_1}(P^*)\}.$$

If $\mathrm{WS}_{G'}(P) \leqq lg(P)$, (10.3) is satisfied. Otherwise, by (10.9) and (10.1),

$$\mathrm{WS}_{G'}(P) \leqq \tfrac{1}{2}\mathrm{WS}_{G_1}(P^*) \leqq \tfrac{1}{2}(\mathrm{WS}_G(P)+1) \leqq \tfrac{1}{2}(plg(P)+1).$$

For $p = 2$ we obtain, since $WS_{G'}(P)$ is an integer, $\mathrm{WS}_{G'}(P) \leqq lg(P)$. For $p \geqq 3$ we obtain

$$\mathrm{WS}_{G'}(P) \leqq \tfrac{1}{2}(plg(P)+1) = (p-1)lg(P) + \tfrac{1}{2} + (1-(p/2))\, lg(P)$$

$$\leqq (p-1)lg(P).$$

Hence, (10.3) is satisfied in all cases. ∎

The following theorem is an immediate corollary of Theorem 10.1.

Theorem 10.2. Assume that L is a type-0 language which is not of type 1. Then for every integer p and every grammar G generating L, there is a word $P \in L$ such that $\mathrm{WS}_G(P) > plg(P)$.

We are now in the position to settle also some problems concerning the closure of $\mathscr{L}_1$ which were left open in earlier sections.

Theorem 10.3. The family $\mathscr{L}_1$ is closed under intersection. It is closed also under λ-free substitution and consequently under λ-free homomorphisms.

Proof. To prove the first sentence, consider languages L and L' generated by type-1 grammars G and G'. We define the grammar G_1 exactly as in the proof of Theorem 3.6 and note that G_1 satisfies the hypothesis of Theorem 10.1 for $p = 5$. Hence, $L(G_1)$ is of type 1, which proves the first sentence.

To prove the second sentence, we return to the proof of Theorem 3.5 which, by the workspace theorem, becomes applicable to $\mathscr{L}_1$. Consider the grammar G_σ and assume that the given grammars G and G_i are context-sensitive. Since the substitution σ is λ-free, the grammar G_i does not contain the production $X_0^i \to \lambda$, $i = 1, \ldots, r$. (This is quite essential because otherwise we would have unlimited erasing possibilities in derivations according to G_σ.) Clearly, $Y \to \lambda$ is the only production in G_σ where the length of the left side exceeds that of the right side. Moreover, no word with two occurrences of Y can be derived according to G_σ. By these observations, it is obvious that G_σ satisfies the hypothesis of Theorem 10.1 for $p = 2$. ∎

The part of Theorem 10.3 concerning λ-free homomorphisms is now extended to concern such homomorphisms which do not erase "too much."

Definition. Assume that L is a language over an alphabet V. A homomorphism h of V is termed a *k-linear erasing* with respect to L iff, for each $P \in L$,

$$lg(P) \leqq klg(h(P)).$$

A family $\mathscr{L}$ of languages is said to be *closed under linear erasing* iff $h(L) \in \mathscr{L}$ whenever $L \in \mathscr{L}$, k is an integer, and h is a k-linear erasing with respect to L.

Theorem 10.4. The family $\mathscr{L}_1$ is closed under linear erasing.

Proof. Assume that L is context-sensitive, k is an integer, and h is a k-linear erasing with respect to L. By Theorem 3.1, L is generated by a type-1 grammar $G = (V_N, V_T, X_0, F)$ such that the only productions containing terminal letters are of the form $X \to x$ where X is a nonterminal and x is a terminal. We assume that $k \geqq 1$ since $L = \{\lambda\}$ or $L = \emptyset$ if $k = 0$. Let the range of h be included in $W(V_T')$. Then $h(L)$ is generated by the type-0 grammar

$$G' = (V_N, V_T', X_0, F')$$

where F' is obtained from F by replacing every production of the form $X \to x$ with the production $X \to h(x)$. Choose an arbitrary nonempty word $P' \in L(G')$. Let $P \in L$ be such that $h(P) = P'$. Since h is a k-linear erasing with respect to L, we obtain $lg(P) \leqq klg(P')$. Consequently,

$$WS_{G'}(P') = \max\{WS_G(P), lg(P')\}$$

$$= \max\{lg(P), lg(P')\} \leqq klg(P').$$

$L(G')$ is context-sensitive by Theorem 10.1. ∎

Table 1 summarizes the closure results we have so far established for each of the families $\mathscr{L}_0$–$\mathscr{L}_3$. For the documentation of these results, the reader is referred to Theorems 3.2–3.6, 4.2, 5.2, 6.6, 6.7, 9.7, 9.11, 10.3, and 10.4. The table is supplemented by a few more results in Part 2, Section 2.

TABLE 1

Closed under	$\mathscr{L}_3$	$\mathscr{L}_2$	$\mathscr{L}_1$	$\mathscr{L}_0$
Union	Yes	Yes	Yes	Yes
Catenation	Yes	Yes	Yes	Yes
Catenation closure	Yes	Yes	Yes	Yes
λ-free catenation closure	Yes	Yes	Yes	Yes
Complementation	Yes	No	?	No
Intersection	Yes	No	Yes	Yes
Intersection with regular language	Yes	Yes	Yes	Yes
Mirror image	Yes	Yes	Yes	Yes
Substitution	Yes	Yes	No	Yes
λ-free substitution	Yes	Yes	Yes	Yes
Homomorphism	Yes	Yes	No	Yes
λ-free homomorphism	Yes	Yes	Yes	Yes
Linear erasing	Yes	Yes	Yes	Yes

Sometimes it is convenient to use *end markers* in connection with context-sensitive grammars. As another application of the workspace theorem, we show that this use does not increase the generative capacity.

Definition. A *grammar* with the *end marker* $\#$ is a grammar $G_\# = (V_N, V_T \cup \{\#\}, X_0, F)$ such that every production is of one of the forms

$$P \to Q, \qquad \#P \to \#Q, \qquad P\# \to Q\#, \qquad P, Q \in W(V_N \cup V_T).$$

The language *generated* by $G_\#$ *within end markers* is defined by

$$L(G, \#) = \{P \in W(V_T) | \#X_0\# \Rightarrow^* \#P\#\}.$$

Clearly, for every context-sensitive language L, there is a type-1 grammar $G_\#$ (which is also length-increasing) with the end marker $\#$ such that $L = L(G, \#)$. The following theorem shows that the converse is also true.

Theorem 10.5. For any length-increasing grammar $G_\#$ with the end marker $\#$, the language $L(G, \#)$ is context-sensitive.

Proof. If the given grammar $G_\# = (V_N, V_T \cup \{\#\}, X_0, F)$ contains the production $X_0 \to \lambda$, we remove it and make the corresponding change in the final grammar. Thus we assume that $G_\#$ does not contain the production $X_0 \to \lambda$. We define

$$G = (V_N \cup \{Y_0\}, V_T \cup \{\#\}, Y_0, F \cup \{Y_0 \to \#X_0\#\})$$

and the homomorphism h by

$$h(\#) = \lambda, \qquad h(a) = a \qquad \text{for} \quad a \in V_T.$$

Then $L(G, \#) = h(L(G))$. Furthermore, G is length-increasing and h is a 3-linear erasing with respect to $L(G)$. The assertion now follows by Theorems 9.2 and 10.4. ∎

We now establish certain sufficient conditions for a language to be context-sensitive. The proofs are straightforward applications of the workspace theorem. Note that the "only if" part of Proposition 4.2 can easily be established in this manner.

Definition. Let

$$D: P_1 \Rightarrow \cdots \Rightarrow P_n \tag{10.10}$$

be a derivation according to a grammar G. Then the *erase number* $E(D)$ of D is the number of integers in the set $\{i \,|\, lg(P_{i+1}) < lg(P_i)\}$. Denote by D_{uv} the subderivation $P_u \Rightarrow \cdots \Rightarrow P_{u+v}$ of (10.10) where $1 \leq u \leq n-1$ and $u < u+v \leq n$. Assume, furthermore, that no terminals appear on the left side of any production of G. The *deposit number* $E_1(D)$ of D is the largest integer in the set $\{i \,|\, \text{for some } u \text{ and } v, E(D_{uv}) = i \text{ and } P_{u+v} \text{ contains the same terminals as } P_u\}$.

Thus, the erase number equals the number of applications of length-decreasing rules in the derivation. The deposit number is the maximum number of applications of length-decreasing rules before a new terminal letter is "deposited." For $k \geq 0$, we denote

$$L(G, k) = \{P \in L(G) \,|\, E(D) \leq klg(P) \text{ for some } D: X_0 \Rightarrow \cdots \Rightarrow P\},$$

$$L_1(G, k) = \{P \in L(G) \,|\, E_1(D) \leq k \text{ for some } D: X_0 \Rightarrow \cdots \Rightarrow P\}.$$

Theorem 10.6. For every grammar G and integer $k \geq 0$, the languages $L(G, k)$ and $L_1(G, k)$ are context-sensitive. Hence, $L(G)$ is context-sensitive if $L(G) = L(G, k)$ or $L(G) = L_1(G, k)$ for some k.

Proof. Given $G = (V_N, V_T, X_0, F)$ and k, we construct first a grammar G_1 generating the language $L(G, k)$. By Theorem 3.1, we assume in this construction that the only productions in F containing terminals are of the form $X \to x$ where X is a nonterminal and x is a terminal. The language $L(G, k)$ is not affected if a change corresponding to Theorem 3.1 is made in G.

We define

$$G_1 = (V_N \cup \{Y\}, V_T, X_0, F_1)$$

where

$$F_1 = \{P \to Q | P \to Q \text{ in } F, lg(P) \leq lg(Q)\}$$
$$\cup \{P \to YQ | P \to Q \text{ in } F, lg(P) > lg(Q)\}$$
$$\cup \{XY \to YX, YX \to XY | X \in V_N \cup V_T\}$$
$$\cup \{Y^i X \to x | X \to x \text{ in } F, X \in V_N, x \in V_T, 0 \leq i \leq k\}.$$

It is easy to verify that $L(G_1) = L(G, k)$. Indeed, an application of a length-decreasing production in G introduces one occurrence of Y in G_1 and, for each terminal x, any number of Y's less than or equal to k can be eliminated. Denote

$$u = \max\{lg(P) - lg(Q) | P \to Q \text{ in } F\}. \qquad (10.11)$$

Then we obtain, for every nonempty word $P \in L(G_1)$,

$$\mathrm{WS}_{G_1}(P) \leq (uk + 1) lg(P).$$

By Theorem 10.1, $L(G, k)$ is context-sensitive.

To prove that $L_1(G, k)$ is context-sensitive, we consider the number u defined by (10.11). If $u \leq 0$, the assertion follows by Theorem 9.2. Assume that $u \geq 1$. Consider the grammar

$$G_2 = (V_N \cup \{Y_0, Y_1, Y_2\}, V_T, Y_0, F_2),$$

where F_2 consists of the following productions:

(i) $\quad Y_0 \to Y_1 X_0 Y_1$;
(ii) $\quad P \to Q$, if $P \to Q$ is in F, $lg(P) \leq lg(Q)$, and Q contains no terminals;
(iii) $\quad P \to Y_2 Q$, if $P \to Q$ is in F, $lg(P) > lg(Q)$, and Q contains no terminals;
(iv) $\quad XY \to YX$ and $YX \to XY$ where $X \in \{Y_1, Y_2\}$ and $Y \in V_N \cup V_T$;
(v) $\quad Y_1 Y_2^i P Y_1 \to Y_1 Q Y_1$, $Y_1 Y_2^i P Y_1 \to Q$, if $P \to Q$ is in F, $0 \leq i \leq k$, and Q contains at least one terminal.

Since G_2 is a modification of G_1, it is again easy to verify that $L(G_2) = L_1(G, k)$. The role of Y_2 is to prevent the use of more than k length-decreasing productions before depositing a terminal. Note here that Y_2's located between two Y_1's cannot be removed outside this interval since Y_1 and Y_2 cannot be permuted. For a nonempty word $P \in L(G_2)$, we obtain

$$\mathrm{WS}_{G_2}(P) \leq (uk + u + k + 3) lg(P).$$

In fact, before depositing a terminal at most uk letters are erased, and at the step when a terminal is deposited at most $u + k + 2$ letters are erased. By Theorem 10.1, $L_1(G, k)$ is context-sensitive. ∎

It is left to the reader to formulate a corollary of Theorem 10.6 analogous to Theorem 10.2. As another corollary of Theorem 10.6, we obtain the following theorem which is strengthened in Chapter VI, Section 10.

Theorem 10.7. Assume that terminals do not occur on the left sides of the productions of a grammar G. If in every production $P \to Q$, where $lg(P) > lg(Q)$, the word Q contains a terminal letter, then the language generated by the grammar is context-sensitive. Hence, if in every production of G the right side contains at least one terminal letter, then $L(G)$ is context-sensitive.

Note 10.1 Left context-sensitive languages are a special case of context-sensitive languages. By definition, a grammar $G = (V_N, V_T, X_0, F)$ is *left context-sensitive* iff each production in F is of the form $QX \to QP$ where $X \in V_N$ and $P, Q \in W(V_N \cup V_T)$, $P \neq \lambda$, with the possible exception of the production $X_0 \to \lambda$ whose occurrence in F implies, however, that X_0 does not occur on the right side of any production. A language is *left context-sensitive* iff it is generated by a left context-sensitive grammar. The notions of a *right context-sensitive* grammar and language are defined analogously.

It is an immediate consequence of these definitions that every context-free language is left (right) context-sensitive. It is also clear that the mirror image of a left context-sensitive language is right context-sensitive, and vice versa. The language $\{a^n b^n c^m | n > m \geq 1\}$ is generated by the left context-sensitive grammar G with the following productions (where capital letters are nonterminals and X_0 is the initial letter):

$$X_0 \to aaBBC, \quad aB \to aaBB_1, \quad B_1 BC \to B_1 BC_1 C, \quad B_1 B \to B_1 B_1,$$

$$B_1 C_1 \to B_1 C, \quad BB_1 \to BB, \quad B \to b, \quad C \to c.$$

The verification of this is left to the reader. Hence, the family of left (right) context-sensitive languages properly includes the family of context-free languages.

By definition, every left (right) context-sensitive language is context-sensitive. It is not known whether or not every context-sensitive language is left context-sensitive. One can prove that every context-sensitive language is generated by a grammar where the productions are either left context-sensitive or "permuting," that is, of the form $XY \to YX$, X and Y being nonterminals.

Note 10.2. Of the various characterizations of the family of context-sensitive languages, we mention the recently introduced *bug automaton*. It is a read-only recognition device which possesses finitely many internal states and operates on a two-dimensional rectangular array of letters called a *scene*. In a single move, the bug may change its state and its position one square in any direction. The move depends only on the current state and on the letter under scan. However, the bug automaton is nondeterministic, and so there may be several choices for a move. If the bug falls off the scene, it can never come back. The bug has a special initial state and a designated set of final states. A scene is accepted iff there exists a sequence of moves, beginning with the bug being in the upper left-hand corner in the initial state, and ending by the bug falling off the scene in a final state. The language accepted by the bug consists of the top rows of the scenes accepted by the bug. It can be shown that a language is context-sensitive iff it is accepted by some bug automaton. One can consider also bugs operating on scenes of dimension $n > 2$. Then the family of acceptable languages equals $\mathscr{L}_0$.

11. HOMOMORPHIC CHARACTERIZATION OF TYPE-0 LANGUAGES

We now continue the reduction process begun in Section 7, trying to express complex languages in terms of simpler ones. We prove that every type-0 language equals a homomorphic image of the intersection of two context-free languages. In fact, we establish three theorems of growing strength to this effect.

Theorem 11.1. Every type-0 language L can be expressed in the form

$$L = h(L_1 \cap L_2) \tag{11.1}$$

where h is a homomorphism and L_1 and L_2 are context-free languages.

Proof. Assume that L is generated by a type-0 grammar $G = (V_N, V_T, X_0, F)$ where

$$F = \{P_i \to Q_i | 1 \leqq i \leqq k\}.$$

Denote $V = V_N \cup V_T$, and consider the auxiliary alphabets

$$V_T' = \{a' | a \in V_T\}, \qquad V_{cd} = \{c, d_1, ..., d_k\}.$$

For a word $P \in W(V_T)$, we denote by P' the word obtained from P by replacing every letter a with a'. (By definition, $\lambda' = \lambda$.) Finally, denote

$$V_1 = V_N \cup V_T \cup V_T' \cup V_{cd}.$$

Let h be the homomorphism of $W(V_1)$ into $W(V_T)$, defined by

$$h(b) = \begin{cases} a & \text{for} \quad b = a' \in V_T' \\ \lambda & \text{for} \quad b \in V_N \cup V_T \cup V_{cd}. \end{cases}$$

In order to establish (11.1), we consider two languages L_1 and L_2 obtained from derivations according to G. More specifically, we define two languages L_1 and L_2 over V_1 as follows.

$$L_1 = \{R_1\, P_i d_i\, R_2\, c\, \mathrm{mi}(R_2)\, \mathrm{mi}(Q_i)\, \mathrm{mi}(R_1) c | R_1,\, R_2 \in W(V),\, 1 \leq i \leq k\}^+ (V_T')^*,$$

$$L_2 = \{X_0 d_i c | 1 \leq i \leq k\} \{\mathrm{mi}(R_1\, R_2) c R_1\, d_j\, R_2\, c | R_1,\, R_2 \in W(V),$$

$$1 \leq j \leq k\}^* \{Pc\, \mathrm{mi}(P') | P \in W(V_T)\}.$$

(The number k and the words P_i and Q_i have been defined above in connection with G.)

To prove that L_1 is context-free, we note that L_1 is of the form $L_1 = L_3^+ (V_T')^*$. By Theorems 3.2 and 3.3 it suffices to prove that L_3 is context-free. This again follows because L_3 is generated by the context-free grammar with the productions

$$Y_0 \to Y_1\, c, \quad Y_1 \to x Y_1\, x, \quad Y_1 \to P_i d_i\, Y_2\, \mathrm{mi}(Q_i), \quad Y_2 \to x Y_2\, x, \quad Y_2 \to c,$$

where the Y's are nonterminals, Y_0 is the initial letter, x ranges over V, and i ranges over the numbers $1, \ldots, k$. The proof of L_2 being context-free is similar, and is left to the reader.

For h, L_1, and L_2 thus defined, we now prove that (11.1) holds. Basically, this follows from the fact that words in $h(L_1 \cap L_2)$ are the last words in derivations according to G. We prove first that the left side of (11.1) is included in the right side.

Assume that $P \in L$. Since G generates L, there is an integer m, words $R_{j1}, R_{j2} \in W(V)$, and indices $g(j)$ with $1 \leq g(j) \leq k$ defined for all $j = 0, \ldots, m$ such that the following conditions are satisfied. For every $j = 0, \ldots, m-1$,

$$R_{j1}\, Q_{g(j)}\, R_{j2} = R_{(j+1)1}\, P_{g(j+1)}\, R_{(j+1)2}. \tag{11.2}$$

Furthermore,

$$R_{01} = R_{02} = \lambda, \quad P_{g(0)} = X_0, \quad R_{m1}\, Q_{g(m)}\, R_{m2} = P. \tag{11.3}$$

In other words, we consider the following derivation according to G:

$$X_0 = R_{01}\, P_{g(0)}\, R_{02} \Rightarrow R_{01}\, Q_{g(0)}\, R_{02} = R_{11}\, P_{g(1)}\, R_{12} \Rightarrow R_{11}\, Q_{g(1)}\, R_{12}$$

$$= R_{21}\, P_{g(2)}\, R_{22} \Rightarrow \cdots \Rightarrow R_{(m-1)1}\, Q_{g(m-1)}\, R_{(m-1)2}$$

$$= R_{m1}\, P_{g(m)}\, R_{m2} \Rightarrow R_{m(1)}\, Q_{g(m)}\, R_{m2} = P.$$

We now define, for any $R_1, R_2 \in W(V)$ and $1 \leq i \leq k$,

$$t(R_1, i, R_2) = R_1\, P_i d_i\, R_2\, c\, \mathrm{mi}(R_2)\, \mathrm{mi}(Q_i)\, \mathrm{mi}(R_1) c$$

and consider the word

$$R = t(R_{01}, g(0), R_{02}) t(R_{11}, g(1), R_{12}) \cdots t(R_{m1}, g(m), R_{m2}) P'. \tag{11.4}$$

By the definition of L_1, we have $R \in L_1$. Using the notation

$$s(R_1, i, R_2) = \mathrm{mi}(R_1\, R_2) c R_1\, d_i\, R_2\, c,$$

we may also write [using (11.2) and (11.3)]

$$R = X_0 d_{g(0)} c \, \text{mi}(R_{01} Q_{g(0)} R_{02}) c R_{11} P_{g(1)}^{\cdot} d_{g(1)} R_{12} c$$

$$\cdots \text{mi}(R_{(m-1)1} Q_{g(m-1)} R_{(m-1)2}) c R_{m1} P_{g(m)} d_{g(m)} R_{m2} c \, \text{mi}(R_{m1} Q_{g(m)} R_{m2}) c P'$$

$$= X_0 d_{g(0)} c \, \text{mi}(R_{11} P_{g(1)} R_{12}) c R_{11} P_{g(1)} d_{g(1)} R_{12} c$$

$$\cdots \text{mi}(R_{m1} P_{g(m)} R_{m2}) c R_{m1} P_{g(m)} d_{g(m)} R_{m2} c \, \text{mi}(R_{m1} Q_{g(m)} R_{m2}) c P'$$

$$= X_0 d_{g(0)} cs(R_{11} P_{g(1)}, g(1), R_{12}) \cdots s(R_{m1} P_{g(m)}, g(m), R_{m2}) \text{mi}(P) c P'.$$

From the last expression we see that $R \in L_2$ and hence $R \in L_1 \cap L_2$. On the other hand, $h(R) = P$. This implies that $P \in h(L_1 \cap L_2)$.

Having established that the left side of (11.1) is included in the right side, we now prove the reverse inclusion. Assume that $P \in h(L_1 \cap L_2)$. Consequently, there is a word $R \in L_1 \cap L_2$ such that $P = h(R)$. Since $R \in L_1$, it can be expressed in the form (11.4) for some numbers m, $g(i)$, and words R_{ij}. Since $R \in L_2$, it can be expressed in the form

$$R = X_0 d_{f(0)} cs(\bar{R}_{11}, f(1), \bar{R}_{12}) \cdots s(\bar{R}_{n1}, f(n), \bar{R}_{n2}) \text{mi}(P) c P', \quad (11.5)$$

for some numbers n, $f(i)$, and words $\bar{R}_{ij}$. Comparing the number of occurrences of the boundary marker c in (11.4) and (11.5), we see that $m = n$. It is also clear that $g(i) = f(i)$ for $i = 0, \ldots, m$. A further comparison between (11.4) and (11.5) gives the equations

$$R_{01} = R_{02} = \lambda, \qquad P_{g(0)} = X_0, \qquad R_{i1} P_{g(i)} = \bar{R}_{i1}, \qquad R_{i2} = \bar{R}_{i2},$$

$$R_{(i-1)1} Q_{g(i-1)} R_{(i-1)2} = \bar{R}_{i1} \bar{R}_{i2} = R_{i1} P_{g(i)} R_{i2},$$

for $1 \leq i \leq m$, and also the equation

$$P = R_{m1} Q_{g(m)} R_{m2}.$$

Thus we obtain the following derivation according to G:

$$X_0 = R_{01} P_{g(0)} R_{02} \Rightarrow R_{01} Q_{g(0)} R_{02}$$

$$= R_{11} P_{g(1)} R_{12} \Rightarrow \cdots \Rightarrow R_{(m-1)1} Q_{g(m-1)} R_{(m-1)2}$$

$$= R_{m1} P_{g(m)} R_{m2} \Rightarrow R_{m1} Q_{g(m)} R_{m2} = P.$$

Therefore, $P \in L$. ∎

It is easy to see that the languages L_1 and L_2 in the previous proof are, in fact, *deterministic* context-free languages.

In the construction above, the alphabet of L_1 and L_2 and the homomorphism h depend on the grammar generating the given language L. We now strengthen the result so that the dependence will be on the alphabet of L alone.

Theorem 11.2. Consider an alphabet V_T and denote

$$V_T' = \{a' | a \in V_T\}, \qquad V_1' = V_T' \cup \{0, 1\}. \tag{11.6}$$

There is a homomorphism h of $W(V_1')$ onto $W(V_T)$ with the following property. For any type-0 language L over V_T, there exist context-free languages L_1 and L_2 over V_1' such that

$$L = h(L_1 \cap L_2). \tag{11.7}$$

Proof. The proof of Theorem 11.2 is a modification of the preceding proof. Letters of the alphabet $V_2 = V_N \cup V_T \cup V_{cd}$ are now encoded using the letters 0 and 1.

Our assumptions are now the same as in the preceding proof. (See, the proof of Theorem 11.1 up to the definition of h.) Assume that V_2 consists of the letters a_i, $i = 1, \ldots, r$. We define a homomorphism h_1 of $W(V_2)$ into $W\{0, 1\}$ by

$$h_1(a_i) = 10^i 1 \qquad \text{for} \quad 1 \leq i \leq r.$$

The definition of the homomorphism h will now be

$$h(b) = \begin{cases} a & \text{for} \quad b = a' \in V_T' \\ \lambda & \text{for} \quad b = 0 \quad \text{and} \quad b = 1. \end{cases}$$

In our previous definition of the languages L_1 and L_2, every word is replaced by its homomorphic image under h_1. Thus, assuming that $c = a_r$ and $d_i = a_{r-k-1+i}$, we have

$$L_1 = \{R_1 h_1(P_i) 10^{r-k-1+i} 1 R_2 10^r 1 \, mi(R_2) h_1(mi(Q_i))$$

$$mi(R_1) 10^r 1 | 1 \leq i \leq k; \, R_1, R_2 \in (h_1(V))^*\}^+ (V_T')^*$$

and

$$L_2 = \{h_1(X_0) 10^{r-k-1+i} 1 10^r 1 | 1 \leq i \leq k\}$$

$$\{mi(R_1 R_2) 10^r 1 R_1 10^{r-k-1+j} 1 R_2 10^r 1 | R_1, R_2 \in (h_1(V))^*, \, 1 \leq j \leq k\}^*$$

$$\{\bar{R}_1 10^r 1 \bar{R}_2 | \bar{R}_2 \in W(V_T'), \, \bar{R}_1 = h_1 h(mi(\bar{R}_2))\}.$$

Note that, for any word P, $h_1(mi(P)) = mi(h_1(P))$.

The equation (11.7), with these new meanings for h, L_1, and L_2, now follows similarly as (11.1). The proof for the inclusion of the left side in the right side is unaltered. In the proof for the reverse inclusion, one has to note that the word $R \in L_1 \cap L_2$ [with $P = h(R)$] has been encoded correctly, that is,

$$R \in (h_1(V_2))^+ (V_T')^*.$$

Finally, L_1 and L_2 are shown to be context-free similarly as in the proof of Theorem 11.1. ∎

Our next theorem is an immediate corollary of Theorems 7.5 and 11.2.

Theorem 11.3. Let V_T be an alphabet with r letters. There exist alphabets V_1 and V_2 with $r+2$ and $2r+8$ letters, respectively, homomorphisms

$$h_1 : W(V_1) \to W(V_T), \qquad h_2 : W(V_2) \to W(V_1),$$

and a Dyck language D over V_2 satisfying the following condition. For every type-0 language L over V_T, there are regular languages R_1 and R_2 over V_2 such that

$$L = h_1\big(h_2(D \cap R_1) \cap h_2(D \cap R_2)\big).$$

We conclude this section with a still stronger version of Theorem 11.2. Now only a regular language is determined by the given type-0 language L, everything else depends on the alphabet of L alone.

Theorem 11.4. Consider an alphabet V_T and the notations (11.6). There exist context-free languages L_1' and L_2' over V_1' and a homomorphism h of $W(V_1')$ onto $W(V_T)$ with the following property. For every type-0 language L over V_T, there is a regular language K over V_1' such that

$$L = h(L_1' \cap L_2' \cap K). \tag{11.8}$$

Proof. Assume that $V_T = \{a_1, \ldots, a_{u-4}\}$, $u \geqq 5$. We introduce first four boundary markers a_i, $u-3 \leqq i \leqq u$. (The role of a_u is the same as that of c in previous proofs.) Any type-0 language over V_T is generated by a grammar whose nonterminals form an initial segment of the sequence

$$a_{u+1}, a_{u+3}, a_{u+5}, \ldots, \tag{11.9}$$

a_{u+1} being the initial letter. The letters in the sequence

$$a_{u+2}, a_{u+4}, a_{u+6}, \ldots$$

will play the role of production indicators, similarly as the letters d_i in previous proofs.

We now define

$$V_T' = \{a' | a \in V_T\}, \qquad V_1' = V_T' \cup \{0, 1\}.$$

All letters a_i, $i \geqq 1$, are now encoded in the alphabet $\{0, 1\}$ by defining

$$h_1(a_i) = 10^i 1, \qquad i \geqq 1.$$

To make the following definitions more readable, we also use the following abbreviations:

$$h_1(a_u) = c, \qquad h_1(a_{u-i}) = c_i \qquad \text{for} \quad 1 \leqq i \leqq 3,$$

$$h_1(a_{u+1}) = X_0, \qquad h_1(a_{u+2i}) = d_i \qquad \text{for} \quad i \geqq 1.$$

Furthermore, we denote

$$U_T = \left(h_1(a_1) \cup \cdots \cup h_1(a_{u-4})\right)^*.$$

By U we denote the language consisting of λ and of all words of the form $h_1(a_{i_1}) \cdots h_1(a_{i_v})$ where $v \geqq 1$ and, for each $j = 1, \ldots, v$, either $1 \leqq i_j \leqq u-4$ or else $i_j = u+2t+1$ for some $t \geqq 0$. (Intuitively, U_T consists of encoded words over the terminal alphabet and U of encoded words in terminal and non-terminal letters.)

The homomorphism h is defined exactly as in the proof of Theorem 11.2. We now define two languages over V_1' which we denote by L_1' and L_2' to indicate their relationship with the previously considered languages L_1 and L_2. By definition,

$$L_1' = \{R_1 c_1 P d_i R_2 c \, \text{mi}(R_2) c_2 \, \text{mi}(Q) c_3 \, \text{mi}(R_1) c|$$

$$R_1, R_2, P, Q \in U, \, i \geqq 1\}^+ (V_T')^*$$

and

$$L_2' = \{c_1 X_0 d_i c | i \geqq 1\} \{R_1 c_2 R_2 c_3 R_3 c R_4 c_1 R_5 d_j R_6 c|$$

$$R_1, R_2, R_3, R_4, R_5, R_6 \in U, j \geqq 1, \, R_1 R_2 R_3 = \text{mi}(R_4 R_5 R_6)\}^*$$

$$\{P_1 c_2 P_2 c_3 P_3 c P_4 | P_4 \in W(V_T'); P_1, P_2, P_3 \in U_T,$$

$$P_1 P_2 P_3 = h_1 h(\text{mi}(P_4))\}.$$

So far our definitions are based on the alphabet V_T alone. We now consider a type-0 language L over V_T generated by $G = (V_N, V_T, a_{u+1}, F)$. Denote $V = V_N \cup V_T$. We assume that V_N consists of an initial segment of (11.9) and

$$F = \{P_i \rightarrow Q_i | 1 \leqq i \leqq k\}.$$

We now define $K = K_1 \cap K_2$ where

$$K_1 = \{R_1 c_1 h_1(P_i) d_i R_2 c R_3 c_2 h_1(\text{mi}(Q_i)) c_3 R_4 c|$$

$$R_1, R_2, R_3, R_4 \in (h_1(V))^*, \, 1 \leqq i \leqq k\}^+ (V_T')^*$$

and

$$K_2 = \{c_1 X_0 d_i c | 1 \leqq i \leqq k\} \{R_1 c_2 R_2 c_3 R_3 c R_4 c_1 R_5 d_j R_6 c|$$

$$R_1, R_2, R_3, R_4, R_5, R_6 \in (h_1(V))^*, \, 1 \leqq j \leqq k\}^*$$

$$\{\bar{R}_1 c_2 \bar{R}_2 c_3 \bar{R}_3 c \bar{R}_4 | \bar{R}_4 \in W(V_T'); \bar{R}_1, \bar{R}_2, \bar{R}_3 \in U_T\}.$$

Clearly, K_1 and K_2 are regular languages and consequently K is also a regular language. For a language L', let $\rho(L')$ be the language obtained from L' by erasing all occurrences of c_1, c_2, and c_3 from all words. [Note that ρ is not a homomorphism since c_i is a sequence of 0's and 1's. Note also that for any language L', $h(L') = h(\rho(L'))$.]

Let L_1 and L_2 be the languages considered in the proof of Theorem 11.2, modified in such a way that the definition of $h_1(b)$ is the same as in the present proof for all letters b involved. Comparing the positions of the boundary markers c_i and the production indicators d_j, we obtain the equations

$$\rho(L_1' \cap K_1) = L_1, \qquad \rho(L_2' \cap K_2) = L_2. \tag{11.10}$$

The inclusion

$$L_1 \cap L_2 \subseteq \rho(L_1' \cap L_2' \cap K_1 \cap K_2) \tag{11.11}$$

is established by (i) considering an arbitrary word P belonging to the left side, (ii) inserting the markers c_1, c_2, and c_3 in P at proper places, and (iii) noting that the resulting word belongs to all four languages in the intersection on the right side. By (11.10) and (11.11),

$$\rho(L_1' \cap L_2' \cap K_1 \cap K_2) = L_1 \cap L_2.$$

Hence,

$$h(L_1' \cap L_2' \cap K) = h(\rho(L_1' \cap L_2' \cap K))$$
$$= h(\rho(L_1' \cap L_2' \cap K_1 \cap K_2))$$
$$= h(L_1 \cap L_2) = L. \quad \blacksquare$$

The languages L_1' and L_2' (as well as the languages L_1 and L_2 in Theorem 11.2) are deterministic context-free languages. It can be shown that the language K can always be chosen as a noncounting language.

12. RUDIMENTARY PREDICATES

Apart from regular expressions, we have been considering only generation and recognition devices. However, it was pointed out in Chapter I that property specification is another device for defining languages. We now introduce a class of predicates, so-called *rudimentary predicates*, which constitutes a basis for characterizing type-1 and type-0 languages. In this characterization, a language is denoted by a formula which specifies a property to be satisfied by the words of the language. Rudimentary predicates are very convenient in the sense that they make the translation between intuitive and formal descriptions of a language, and sometimes also the construction of new languages from given ones, easy and natural.

Consider the Cartesian power $W(V)^n$ where V is an alphabet and $n \geqq 1$. By definition, $W(V)^n$ consists of all ordered n-tuples $(P_1, \ldots, P_n)$ where each P_i is a word over V. Any subset T_n of $W(V)^n$ is called an *n-ary predicate* over V. Instead of $(P_1, \ldots, P_n) \in T_n$, we write $T_n(P_1, \ldots, P_n)$ or use one of the expressions "$T_n(P_1, \ldots, P_n)$ is true" or "T_n is true for the argument $(P_1, \ldots, P_n)$." Thus a unary predicate over V is a subset of $W(V)$, that is, a *language* over V. One can also consider n-ary predicates as functions in n variables ranging over $W(V)$ and with values in the set {true, false}. In this interpretation, we may also allow the case $n = 0$.

We now introduce operations for constructing new predicates from given ones. We can then define a class of predicates by specifying certain basic predicates for the class and requiring that the class be closed under certain operations. We consider Boolean operations and the operations of explicit transformation and (bounded and unbounded) quantification. The predicates considered are over the alphabet V. As in Note 9.1, we use the abbreviation $x^{(n)}$ for $x_1, \ldots, x_n$.

Conjunction. $T_n(x^{(n)}) \wedge U_n(x^{(n)})$ is the n-ary predicate which is true iff both $T_n(x^{(n)})$ and $U_n(x^{(n)})$ are true. We read "$T_n(x^{(n)})$ *and* $U_n(x^{(n)})$."

Disjunction. $T_n(x^{(n)}) \vee U_n(x^{(n)})$ is the n-ary predicate which is true iff at least one of $T_n(x^{(n)})$ and $U_n(x^{(n)})$ is true. We read "$T_n(x^{(n)})$ *or* $U_n(x^{(n)})$."

Negation. $\sim T_n(x^{(n)})$ is the n-ary predicate which is true iff $T_n(x^{(n)})$ is not true. We read "*not* $T_n(x^{(n)})$."

Clearly, the corresponding subsets of $W(V)^n$ are $T_n \cap U_n$, $T_n \cup U_n$, and $\sim T_n$, respectively.

Explicit Transformation. The n-ary predicate $T_n(x^{(n)})$ is an *explicit transform* of the m-ary predicate $U_m(y^{(m)})$ iff there are words $z_1, \ldots, z_m$ over the alphabet $V \cup \{x_1, \ldots, x_n\}$ such that $T_n(x^{(n)})$ is true iff $U_m(z^{(m)})$ is true.

Explicit transformations allow, for instance, variables to be permuted, identified, or replaced by constants (words over V). For a binary predicate $T(x_1, x_2)$ over $\{0, 1\}$, each of the predicates

$$T(x_1, x_1), \qquad T(x_2, x_1), \qquad T(x_2, 01), \qquad T(x_1 0 x_2 11, x_2 00)$$

is an explicit transform of T.

Unbounded Existential Quantification. $(\exists x_1) T_n(x^{(n)})$ is the $(n-1)$-ary predicate which is true for the argument $(x_2, \ldots, x_n)$ iff there exists a word x_1 over V such that $T_n(x^{(n)})$ is true.

Unbounded Universal Quantification. $(\forall x_1) T_n(x^{(n)})$ is the $(n-1)$-ary predicate which is true for the argument $(x_2, \ldots, x_n)$ iff, for all words x_1 over V, $T_n(x^{(n)})$ is true.

Bounded Existential Quantification. $(\exists x_1)_{S_y} T_n(x^{(n)})$ is the n-ary predicate which is true for the argument $(x_2, ..., x_n, y)$ iff there is a *subword* x_1 of y such that $T_n(x^{(n)})$ is true.

Bounded Universal Quantification. $(\forall x_1)_{S_y} T_n(x^{(n)})$ is the n-ary predicate which is true for the argument $(x_2, ..., x_n, y)$ iff, for all subwords x_1 of y, $T_n(x^{(n)})$ is true.

There are many interdependencies between the operations introduced. For instance, $(\forall x_1) T_n(x^{(n)})$ and $\sim (\exists x_1)(\sim T_n(x^{(n)}))$ define the same predicate, and so do $(\exists x_1) T_n(x^{(n)})$ and $\sim (\forall x_1)(\sim T_n(x^{(n)}))$. These interrelationships hold for bounded quantifiers as well.

Example 12.1. Let $T(x, y, z)$ be the ternary predicate over the alphabet $\{0, 1\}$ which is true for the argument (x, y, z) iff $x + y = z$ when x, y, and z are considered as binary integers. Thus, $T(01, 11, 100)$ is true but $T(1, 1, 1)$ is not true. The binary predicate $(\exists x) T(x, y, z)$ is true iff $y \leq z$ (in binary notation). The unary predicate $(\exists x) T(x, x, z)$ is true iff z is even. The unary predicate $(\forall z)(\exists y) T(x, y, z)$ is true iff x equals 0 in binary notation. (According to our original definition, only the first variable should be quantified. However, explicit transformations make the order of variables immaterial.) The unary predicate $(\exists y)(\forall z) T(x, y, z)$ is never true. The unary predicate $(\exists x)(\exists y) T(x, y, z)$ is true for all $z \neq \lambda$. Each of these unary predicates defines a language over $\{0, 1\}$. These languages are also denoted by the regular expressions $(0 \cup 1)^*0$, 0^*0, $\varnothing$, and $(0 \cup 1)^*(0 \cup 1)$, respectively. The unary predicate

$$(\exists x)_{S_u}(\exists y)_{S_u}(\exists z)_{S_u} T(x, y, z)$$

is true iff u contains at least one occurrence of 0. The language defined by this predicate is denoted by the regular expression $(0 \cup 1)^*0(0 \cup 1)^*$.

The notions of *recursiveness* and *recursive enumerability* are readily extended to concern predicates also. These notions were defined for languages in Section 9. However, we have already pointed out that a unary predicate over V is nothing but a language over V. Also an n-ary predicate whose elements are of the form $(P_1, ..., P_n)$ can be regarded as a language if the alphabet V is extended to include comma and parentheses. Thus to say that a predicate T_n is *recursive* means that there is an algorithm which, given any ordered n-tuple $(P_1, ..., P_n)$ of words over V, decides whether or not $T_n(P_1, ..., P_n)$ is true. It is obvious that all predicates considered in Example 12.1 are recursive. A predicate T_n is *recursively enumerable* iff there is an effective procedure of listing all ordered n-tuples $(P_1, ..., P_n)$ for which $T_n(P_1, ..., P_n)$ is true.

The catenation relation

$$xy = z \qquad (12.1)$$

defines a ternary predicate $C(x, y, z)$ (over some given alphabet V) which is true for exactly those triples (x, y, z) which satisfy (12.1). Its negation $\sim C(x, y, z)$ is true for exactly those triples (x, y, z) for which $xy \neq z$. In the following definition, these two predicates C and $\sim C$ are referred to as *basic* predicates. The operations of conjunction, disjunction, explicit transformation, and bounded (existential and universal) quantification are referred to as *rudimentary* operations.

Definition. A predicate is *rudimentary* iff it can be constructed from the basic predicates by a finite number of applications of rudimentary operations. A predicate is *existentially definable* iff it is rudimentary or can be constructed from a rudimentary predicate by one application of unbounded existential quantification.

Whenever a predicate is rudimentary or existentially definable, it is denoted by a formula which shows how the predicate is constructed from the basic predicates. This formula is quite analogous to a regular expression which shows how a regular language is constructed from the basic languages. Such a formula may have different interpretations for different alphabets. Thus the basic alphabet has to be indicated whenever ambiguities may arise. Since languages are unary predicates, we may use the terms "rudimentary" and "existentially definable" about languages also.

Example 12.2. For $m, n \geq 1$, the $(m+n)$-ary predicate $T_{m+n}(x_1, \ldots, x_m, y_1, \ldots, y_n)$ defined by the equation

$$x_1 \cdots x_m = y_1 \cdots y_n$$

is rudimentary as an explicit transform of the catenation relation. The binary predicate $B(x, y)$, meaning that x begins y (i.e., x is an initial subword of y), is rudimentary because it can be defined by

$$(\exists z)_{Sy}(xz = y).$$

Similarly, the binary predicate $E(x, y)$, meaning that x ends y, is rudimentary. The binary predicate $S(x, y)$, meaning that x is a subword of y, is also rudimentary, as seen from its definition:

$$(\exists z)_{Sy}(z = x).$$

It is easy to prove (cf. Exercises 7 and 8) that the class of rudimentary predicates is closed under negation and that the class of existentially definable predicates is closed under existential quantification. In fact, there are various equivalent ways of defining these classes. We could include negation among the rudimentary operations and consider the catenation relation as the only basic predicate. We could also assume in the definition of explicit transformation that each of the words $z_1, ..., z_m$ consists of one letter only.

We now establish an interconnection with our hierarchy of language families by proving that a language is existentially definable iff it is of type 0. First some closure properties of recursive predicates are considered.

Theorem 12.1. Both of the basic predicates are recursive, and the class of recursive predicates is closed under each of the rudimentary operations. Hence, every rudimentary predicate is recursive.

Proof. The second sentence follows from the first sentence by the definition of rudimentary predicates. It is obvious that the basic predicates are recursive. An explicit transform T' of a recursive predicate T is recursive because an algorithm for deciding T' is obtained from an algorithm for T by a suitable modification of the input format. Assume next that $T_n(x^{(n)})$ and $U_n(x^{(n)})$ are recursive, E_T and E_U being the corresponding algorithms. To decide whether or not $T_n(x^{(n)}) \wedge U_n(x^{(n)})$ is true, for a given argument $x^{(n)}$, we first form two copies of $x^{(n)}$. The procedure E_T is applied to the first copy. If the answer is "yes" [i.e., $T_n(x^{(n)})$ is true], then E_U is applied to the second copy. If now the answer is also "yes," we conclude that $T_n(x^{(n)}) \wedge U_n(x^{(n)})$ is true. Otherwise (i.e., if in either case we have obtained an answer "no"), it is not true. Disjunction is handled similarly. To take care of bounded quantifications, we denote by E_N an algorithm which, given a word y, produces all of the (finitely many) subwords of y. (Such an E_N clearly exists. It can produce the subwords, for instance, in the length-increasing and alphabetic order.) To decide whether or not $(\exists x_1)_{Sy} T_n(x^{(n)})$ is true, we first call E_N to produce a subword y_1 of y. Then E_T is applied to the argument $(y_1, x_2, ..., x_n)$. If the answer is "yes," we conclude that $(\exists x_1)_{Sy} T_n(x^{(n)})$ is true. Otherwise, E_N is called to produce the next subword y_2 or y. Then E_T is applied to $(y_2, x_2, ..., x_n)$, and so on. Whenever a "yes" answer is obtained, we conclude that $(\exists x_1)_{Sy} T_n(x^{(n)})$ is true. It is not true if E_N halts, that is, is not able to produce any more subwords of y. The proof for bounded universal quantification is similar. ∎

Theorem 12.2. An unbounded existential quantification of a recursive predicate is recursively enumerable.

Proof. Assume that $T_n(x^{(n)})$ is recursive. We are going to show that $(\exists x_1) T_n(x^{(n)})$ is recursively enumerable by giving an effective procedure for listing the arguments $(x_2, ..., x_n)$ such that $(\exists x_1) T_n(x^{(n)})$ is true. Since there is an algorithm E for deciding T_n, we may test different values of x_1 for any given $(x_2, ..., x_n)$ until we eventually find one satisfying T_n. The only problem is to organize the testing in such a way that we never continue to test one argument forever. This is accomplished as in the proof of Theorem 9.6.

All ordered n-tuples $(x^{(n)})$ are enumerated using numbers $0, 1, 2, \ldots$. We denote by E_j the procedure E with the jth n-tuple as its input, $j \geq 0$. By the (i, j)th step we mean the ith step in E_j. We perform these steps in such an order that if the (i, j)th step is kth in this order, then k satisfies (9.5). Whenever E_j terminates with an answer "yes," we list the $(n-1)$ last components of the jth n-tuple as an argument for which the predicate $(\exists x_1)\, T_n(x^{(n)})$ is true.   ∎

Theorems 12.1 and 12.2 remain valid if the intuitive notion of an effective procedure is replaced by the formal notion of a Turing machine. Although not difficult in principle, the constructions become somewhat lengthy (cf. Exercise 10).

It is an immediate consequence of Theorems 12.1 and 12.2 that every existentially definable language is recursively enumerable. Hence, by Church's thesis and Theorem 4.4, we obtain the following.

Theorem 12.3. Every existentially definable language is of type 0.

Our next theorem establishes the converse.

Theorem 12.4. Every type 0 language is existentially definable.

Proof. Assume that L is generated by the grammar

$$G = (\{X_0, X_1, \ldots, X_m\}, V_T, X_0, \{P_1 \to Q_1, \ldots, P_n \to Q_n\}).$$

We denote $V = \{X_0, \ldots, X_m, \#\} \cup V_T$, and define some predicates over V. PRODUCTION(x, y) is a binary predicate which is true iff $x \to y$ is a production of G. DERIVATION(x) is a unary predicate which is true iff x is of the form

$$\# X_0 \# P_1 \# \cdots \# P_k \#, \qquad k \geq 1, \tag{12.2}$$

where

$$X_0 \Rightarrow P_1 \Rightarrow \cdots \Rightarrow P_k \tag{12.3}$$

is a derivation according to G. DERIVATION(x, y) is a binary predicate which is true iff x is of the form (12.2), $y = P_k$, and (12.3) is a derivation according to G. We shall prove that these three predicates are rudimentary. Predicates introduced and shown rudimentary in Example 12.2 and their explicit transforms are used. Note especially that the binary predicate $x = y$ is rudimentary as a special case of T_{m+n}.

PRODUCTION(x, y) is defined by the formula

$$((x = P_1) \wedge (y = Q_1)) \vee \cdots \vee ((x = P_n) \wedge (y = Q_n))$$

and, hence, it is rudimentary. (In fact, any finite predicate can be shown rudimentary in a similar way.)

DERIVATION(x) is defined by the formula

$$B(\#X_0\#,x) \wedge (\sim(x = \#X_0\#)) \wedge E(\#,x)$$

$$\wedge (\forall y)_{Sx}(\forall z)_{Sx}[(\sim S(\#y\#z\#,x)) \vee S(\#,y) \vee S(\#,z)$$

$$\vee (\exists y_1)_{Sy}(\exists y_2)_{Sy}(\exists y_3)_{Sy}(\exists z_2)_{Sz}((y = y_1 y_2 y_3) \wedge (z = y_1 z_2 y_3)$$

$$\wedge \text{PRODUCTION}(y_2, z_2))].$$

(Note that the expression within the brackets says that whenever we choose two consecutive words y and z between the boundary markers $\#$, then z is obtained from y by applying some production.) This implies that DERIVATION(x) is rudimentary.

Finally, DERIVATION(x, y) is defined by the formula

$$\text{DERIVATION}(x) \wedge E(\#y\#,x) \wedge (\sim S(\#,y))$$

and, hence, it is rudimentary.

The unary predicate $y \in L$ is existentially definable since it can be expressed in the form

$$(\exists x)[\text{DERIVATION}(x, y) \wedge (\sim S(X_0, y)) \wedge \cdots \wedge (\sim S(X_m, y))],$$

where the binary predicate within the brackets is rudimentary. ∎

The proof of Theorem 12.4 shows that a type-0 language L over V_{T} is existentially definable over an extended alphabet V. By a suitable encoding, one can prove a stronger result that L is existentially definable over V_{T} (provided V_{T} contains at least two letters).

Combining Theorems 12.3 and 12.4, we obtain the following.

Theorem 12.5. The family of existentially definable languages equals $\mathscr{L}_0$.

In view of Theorems 9.6 and 12.5, it is clear that the class of recursive predicates is not closed under existential quantification, that is, Theorem 12.2 cannot be strengthened in this respect. A consequence of Theorems 9.7 and 12.5 is that the class of existentially definable predicates is not closed under negation.

Note 12.1. Basic notions about Turing machines are expressed very conveniently in terms of rudimentary predicates. A Turing machine is defined by its rewriting rules. These in turn can be written in a sequence, separated by markers, and thus the whole definition consists of a single word P. The unary predicate $\text{TM}(x)$, which is true iff x equals such a word P, is rudimentary.

Also a computation of a Turing machine can be expressed as a single word. For $n \geq 1$, the $(n+2)$-ary predicate $T_{n+2}(y, x_1, ..., x_n, z)$, which is true iff (i) $\mathrm{TM}(y)$ is true, (ii) z is a halting computation of the Turing machine denoted by y, and (iii) the computation z begins with the word $x_1 b \cdots b x_n$, is rudimentary. (Here b acts as a boundary marker.) Assume that $U_n(x^{(n)})$ is a recursively enumerable n-ary predicate. By Church's thesis, there is a Turing machine, say y_U in encoded form, which halts with exactly those inputs $x_1 b \cdots b x_n$ for which $U_n(x^{(n)})$ is true. Hence, $U_n(x^{(n)})$ is true iff

$$(\exists z) T_{n+2}(y_U, x_1, ..., x_n, z) \tag{12.4}$$

is true. Consequently, every recursively enumerable n-ary predicate is existentially definable from a single rudimentary predicate T_{n+2}; (12.4) is referred to as the *Kleene normal form* for predicates.

Note 12.2. Consider functions $f(x^{(n)})$ of n variables [ranging over $W(V)$ or some subsets of $W(V)$ for some alphabet V]. Such a function is termed *rudimentary* iff (i) the $(n+1)$-ary predicate $f(x^{(n)}) = y$ is rudimentary and (ii) there is an integer j, $1 \leq j \leq n$, and a finite set A such that, for all $x^{(n)}$, $f(x^{(n)})$ either belongs to A or is a subword of x_j. [Note that partial functions are allowed. Condition (ii) restricts the range of f.]

It was pointed out in Note 12.1 that a computation of a Turing machine can be expressed as a single word. Such a word is of the form

$$P_1 B \cdots B P_k \tag{12.5}$$

where B is a boundary marker and the P's denote consecutive steps of the computation. Thus each P is of the form $P'sP''$ where s is a letter of the state alphabet, and P' and P'' are words over the remaining alphabet. In particular, $P_k = P_k' s P_k''$. We assume that Q_k is the longest initial subword of P_k'' which contains neither the letter $\#$ nor the letter o. (See the definition of Turing machines in Section 4.) Let U now be a unary function whose value for words of the form (12.5) equals Q_k. The function U is undefined for words not of the form (12.5). Then it is easy to prove that U is a rudimentary function.

Let $f(x^{(n)})$ be any (partial) computable function. Then f can be expressed, for some y_f, in the form

$$f(x^{(n)}) = U((\mu z) T_{n+2}(y_f, x_1, ..., x_n, z)) \tag{12.6}$$

where T_{n+2} is as in Note 12.1 and the μ-operator defines the least z such that the predicate is true. If no such z exists for some argument, then μ is undefined. (See Note 9.1 where μ was defined in exactly the same way for a particular predicate.)

To prove that (12.6) holds true, we note that f is computed by some Turing machine, say, y_f in encoded form. Hence, for each input $x^{(n)}$, y_f possesses a terminating computation z iff $f(x^{(n)})$ is defined. Consequently, both sides of

(12.6) are defined for the same arguments $x^{(n)}$. Furthermore, if both sides are defined, then their values are equal. This follows by the definition of U and the fact that y_f can be assumed to halt in such a configuration that Q_k equals $f(x^{(n)})$ (cf. Exercise 12).

Conversely, every function of the form (12.6) is computable. Since U and T_{n+2} are rudimentary, there is an effective procedure to compute f. By Church's thesis, this is accomplished by a Turing machine TM which computes the function $U((\mu z) T_{n+2}(y, x_1, ..., x_n, z))$ of $n+1$ variables $y, x_1, ..., x_n$. TM has the remarkable property of being capable to simulate any Turing machine: When we choose $y = y_f$, then TM simulates the machine computing f. Therefore, TM is called the *universal Turing machine*. The representation (12.6) is called the *Kleene normal form* for functions.

We can still establish the rather surprising result that *every nonempty recursively enumerable language L equals the range of some total rudimentary function*. Since L is nonempty, there is a word $Q \in L$. Since L is recursively enumerable, it is accepted by some Turing machine, say, y_L in encoded form. Without loss of generality (cf. Exercise 13) we assume that y_L halts only for words in L. A binary (total) function g is now defined as follows: $g(x, z) = P$ iff

$$\left(P = x \wedge T_3(y_L, x, z)\right) \vee \left(P = Q \wedge \left(\sim T_3(y_L, x, z)\right)\right)$$

is true. Since T_3 is a rudimentary predicate and $g(x, z)$ always equals either x or Q, we conclude that g is a rudimentary function. If $x \in L$, then y_L has a terminating computation z from the input x. For this z, $T_3(y_L, x, z)$ is true and $g(x, z) = x$. Conversely, if $g(x, z) = P$ for some x and z, then either $P = Q$ and so P belongs to L or $T_3(y_L, x, z)$ is true which implies that y_L accepts x, and so $x = P$ is again in L. Consequently, L is the range of $g(x, z)$; $g(x, z)$ can be replaced by a unary function.

Note 12.3. It was shown in this section how rudimentary predicates are used in a characterization of type-0 languages. They are also useful in a characterization of type-1 languages. (Both of these characterizations are of the property-specifying type.) For type-1 languages, it is convenient to modify slightly the definition of bounded quantifiers: $(\exists x_1)_{\leq y} T_n(x^{(n)})$ is the n-ary predicate which is true for the argument $(x_2, ..., x_n, y)$ iff there is a word x_1 such that $lg(x_1) \leq lg(y)$ and $T_n(x^{(n)})$ is true. Bounded universal quantification is defined similarly. In this note, we assume that rudimentary predicates have been introduced using bounded quantifiers thus defined.

For a binary predicate T, the operation of *transitive closure* on T yields the following binary predicate $U = tc(T)$: $U(x, y)$ is true iff there is an integer $m > 1$ and words $x = x_1, x_2, ..., x_m = y$ such that, for each $i = 1, ..., m-1$, $T(x_i, x_{i+1})$ is true. A binary predicate T is *increasing* iff, for all P and Q, $T(P, Q)$ being true implies $lg(P) \leq lg(Q)$. A binary predicate T is *functional* iff, for all P, Q_1, and Q_2, $T(P, Q_1)$ and $T(P, Q_2)$ are both true only if $Q_1 = Q_2$. The operation of *increasing transitive closure* (itc) takes any increasing binary predicate into its transitive closure, and is undefined for other predicates. The operation of *deterministic itc* takes any functional increasing binary predicate into its transitive closure, and is undefined for other predicates.

Let $\mathscr{T}\mathscr{C}$, $\mathscr{I}\mathscr{T}\mathscr{C}$, and $\mathscr{D}\mathscr{I}\mathscr{T}\mathscr{C}$ be the classes of predicates obtained from the basic predicates by finitely many applications of rudimentary operations and, in addition, transitive closure, itc, or deterministic itc, respectively. Then it can be shown that the languages (i.e., unary predicates) in these three classes coincide with type-0 languages, type-1 languages, and languages acceptable by deterministic linear bounded automata, respectively. By definition, the class of rudimentary predicates is contained in $\mathscr{D}\mathscr{I}\mathscr{T}\mathscr{C}$. Consequently, every rudimentary language is acceptable by a deterministic linear bounded automaton. It is not known whether or not the converse holds true. It can be shown that the family of rudimentary languages properly includes the family of context-free languages.

EXERCISES

1. In the proof of Theorem 9.2, replace the last lines in the definition of F' by

$$Z_1 Z_2 \cdots Z_m Y_{m+1} \cdots Y_n \rightarrow Z_1 \cdots Z_{m-1} Y_m Y_{m+1} \cdots Y_n,$$
$$\vdots$$
$$Z_1 Y_2 \cdots Y_m \cdots Y_n \rightarrow Y_1 Y_2 \cdots Y_m \cdots Y_n.$$

Show by counterexample that the proof becomes invalid. (This invalid construction has been frequently presented in the literature, which shows that one has to be careful when dealing with context-sensitive grammars in order to avoid contexts which are not wanted.)

2. Change the definition of type-1 grammars (given in Section 2) in such a way that the portion beginning with the words "with the possible exception" reads "with the possible exception of productions $X \rightarrow \lambda$ where $X \in V_N$." Prove that every type-0 language is of type 1 in this new sense.

3. Establish the second sentence of Theorem 10.3 without using the work-space theorem. (Introduce Y as an index attached to nonterminals rather than as a separate nonterminal.)

4. Consider a type-0 grammar $G = (V_N, V_T, X_0, F)$, $V = V_N \cup V_T$. Let g be a mapping of V into the set of positive real numbers. Define, furthermore,

$$g(\lambda) = 0, \qquad g(PQ) = g(P) + g(Q),$$

for all words P and Q. Prove that $L(G)$ is of type 1 if $g(P) \leqq g(Q)$ for every production $P \rightarrow Q$ in F.

5. Assume that a grammar G satisfies the following conditions: (i) No terminals appear on the left side of any production, and (ii) for each production $P \to Q$ with $lg(P) < lg(Q)$, the word Q contains at least one terminal. Prove that $L(G)$ is of type 1.

6. Does Theorem 11.4 remain true if the words "a regular language K" are replaced by the words "a locally testable language K"?

7. Show that if a predicate is rudimentary, then so is its negation. (Using induction on the number of rudimentary operations defining the predicate, the problem is reduced to the two basic predicates, each of which is the negation of the other.)

8. Show that if a predicate T is existentially definable, then so is any predicate constructed from T by an application of unbounded existential quantification.

9. Prove that the class of rudimentary predicates is not altered if in the definition of explicit transformation the further assumption is made that each of the words $z_1, \ldots, z_m$ consists of one letter.

10. Formulate and prove for Turing machines results corresponding to Theorems 12.1 and 12.2. [A basic auxiliary machine will duplicate a given input. For each machine M, there is a machine M_1 which (i) operates between boundary markers L and R, (ii) leaves everything to the left of L untouched, and (iii) behaves otherwise exactly as M.]

11. Prove that U in Note 12.2 is rudimentary.

12. Prove that every computable function $f(x^{(n)})$ is computed by a Turing machine such that all final words are of the form $P_1 s Q P_2$ where Q equals the value of the function.

13. Prove that every language L acceptable by a Turing machine is accepted by a machine where only words $\# s_0 P \#$, $P \in L$, yield final words.

BIBLIOGRAPHICAL REMARKS

For a general discussion on recursive and recursively enumerable sets, as well as matters related to Note 9.1, the reader is referred to Rogers (1967). Some of the results of Section 9 dealing directly with languages are due to Chomsky (1959), notably Theorems 9.2 and 9.8. More information about subrecursive hierarchies can be obtained from Grzegorczyk (1953) and Kozmidiadi and Muchnik (1970). (The Ritchie hierarchy described above is due to R. Ritchie. Another hierarchy belongs to D. Ritchie.) The workspace theorem is due to Jones (1966). Similar results are contained in Kuroda (1964) and Ginsburg and Greibach (1966). The latter paper also introduces the notions of an erase number and a deposit number. Theorem 10.5 is due to Landweber

(1963). Bug automata were introduced by Fischer (1969). For left context-sensitive grammars, see Havel (1970). Theorem 11.1 is from Ginsburg *et al.* (1967). Theorem 11.4 has been established (in an entirely different way) by Fisher and Raney (1969). Rudimentary predicates are due to Smullyan (1961) and the approach of Section 12 to Jones (1967, 1968, 1969). The latter references also contain more information about matters discussed in Note 12.3.

BIBLIOGRAPHY

N. **Chomsky.** On certain formal properties of grammars. *Information Control* **2** (1959) 137–167.

G. **Fisher** and G. **Raney.** On the representation of formal languages using automata on networks. *IEEE Conf. Record 10th Ann. Symp. Switching Automata Theory* (1969) 157–165.

M. **Fischer.** Two characterizations of context-sensitive languages. *IEEE Conf. Record 10th Ann. Symp. Switching Automata Theory* (1969) 149–156.

S. **Ginsburg** and S. **Greibach.** Mappings which preserve context-sensitive languages. *Information Control* **9** (1966) 563–582.

S. **Ginsburg,** S. **Greibach,** and M. **Harrison.** One-way stack automata. *J. Assoc. Comput. Mach.* **14** (1967) 389–418.

A. **Grzegorczyk.** Some classes of recursive functions. *Rozprawy Mat.* **4** (1953) 1–45.

I. **Havel.** On one-sided context-sensitive grammars. *In* J. Dörr and G. Hotz (eds.), *Automatentheorie und formale Sprachen.* Bibliographisches Inst., Mannheim, 1970, pp. 221–225.

N. D. **Jones.** A survey of formal language theory. Univ. of Western Ontario, *Comp. Sci. Dept. Tech. Rep.* No 3 (1966).

N. D. **Jones.** Formal Languages and Rudimentary Attributes. Dissertation, Univ. of Western Ontario (1967).

N. D. **Jones.** Notes on the Theory of Computability. Pennsylvania State Univ. (1968).

N. D. **Jones.** Context-free languages and rudimentary attributes. *Math. Systems Theory* **3** (1969) 102–109.

V. A. **Kozmidiadi** and A. A. **Muchnik** (eds.). "Problemy matematicheskoi logiki. Sloznost algoritmov i klassy vychislimykh funktsii." Izd. "Mir," 1970.

S-Y. **Kuroda.** Classes of languages and linear bounded automata. *Information Control* **7** (1964) 207–223.

P. S. **Landweber.** Three theorems on phrase structure grammars of type 1. *Information Control* **6** (1963) 131–136.

H. **Rogers, Jr.** "Theory of Recursive Functions and Effective Computability." McGraw-Hill, New York, 1967.

R. M. **Smullyan.** "Theory of Formal Systems." Princeton Univ. Press, Princeton, New Jersey, 1961.

PART TWO

Chapter IV

Abstract Families of Languages

In Part 1 of this book we introduced certain specific language families and studied them from various angles. When we showed that these families possess some particular properties, we usually needed only a few of their defining properties. Thus, those particular properties are shared by any language family that possesses the properties we needed. This gives rise to the following abstraction: We do not consider any specific language family but rather a collection of language families, each of which possesses certain basic properties. Using these basic properties, we then establish other properties which, thus, are shared by all families in the collection. The basic properties are shared by all four families $\mathscr{L}_i$, $i = 0, 1, 2, 3$, in our basic hierarchy. Consequently, the results obtained are valid also for the families $\mathscr{L}_i$. Members of the aforementioned collection of language families are referred to as *abstract families of languages*. This notion enables us to unify some parts of the theory, since it becomes unnecessary to repeat proofs for different families, each of which possesses the basic properties and is thus an abstract family of languages.

1. INTERDEPENDENCE OF OPERATIONS

In Part 1, we often used the term "a family of languages" to mean a set or a collection of languages. We did not assume that all languages in the collection are over some fixed alphabet V_T. In infinite collections, the size of the alphabet of the individual languages may increase beyond all bounds. On the other hand, for every language L in the collection, there must exist an alphabet V_T such that L is a language over V_T. (This follows from our definition of a language.) Thus we may view a family of languages as a pair $(V, \mathscr{L})$ where V is an infinite set of letters and $\mathscr{L}$ is a set of languages such that each $L \in \mathscr{L}$ is a language over an alphabet $V_T \subset V$.

To say that a family of languages is *closed* under an operation defined for languages means that whenever the operation is applied to languages in the family, the resulting language is also in the family. To avoid the ambiguity inherent in complementation, we make the convention that a family $\mathscr{L}$ of languages is *closed under complementation* iff, for every language L in $\mathscr{L}$ and every alphabet V_T such that L is over V_T, the complement of L with respect to V_T is in $\mathscr{L}$. It is obvious that the closure results obtained in Part 1 about complementation are valid if the closure is thus defined.

A language is *λ-free* iff it does not contain the empty word λ. A family of languages is *λ-free* iff every language in the family is λ-free. For λ-free language families, we often consider the operation of *λ-free catenation closure* + introduced in Section 3 of Part 1.

We now introduce a special case of a k-linear erasing. Assume that L is a language over the alphabet $V_T \cup \{c\}$. (Recall the convention that whenever new letters are introduced, they do not belong to alphabets previously considered. Thus, $c \notin V_T$.) Assume, furthermore, that $L \subseteq (V_T\{\lambda, c, ..., c^{k-1}\})^*$ for some $k \geq 1$. Define a homomorhpism h of $V_T \cup \{c\}$ by

$$h(c) = \lambda, \qquad h(a) = a \quad \text{for} \quad a \in V_T.$$

Then we say that h is *k-restricted* on L. Since by our assumption no word in L contains more than $k - 1$ consecutive occurrences of the letter c, we conclude that

$$lg(P) \leq k\,lg(h(P)) \qquad \text{for all} \quad P \in L.$$

Hence, every homomorphism which is k-restricted on L is also a k-linear erasing with respect to L. The converse is not true because one can easily construct k-linear erasings which map more than one letter into λ. A family of languages is *closed under restricted homomorphism* iff whenever $k \geq 1$, L is in the family and h is a homomorphism k-restricted on L; then $h(L)$ is also in the family. If a family of languages is closed under linear erasing, it is closed under restricted homomorphism, since the latter is a special case of the former.

For two alphabets V_1 and V_2, a mapping g of $W(V_2)$ into the set of subsets of $W(V_1)$ is termed an *inverse homomorphism* iff there exists a homomorphism h of $W(V_1)$ into $W(V_2)$ such that

$$g(P) = \{Q | h(Q) = P\}$$

for all $P \in W(V_2)$. We denote $g = h^{-1}$. For a language L over V_2, we define

$$g(L) = h^{-1}(L) = \{Q|Q \in g(P) \text{ for some } P \in L\}$$

$$= \{Q|h(Q) \in L\}.$$

We now establish two results about the interdependence of various operations. These results are basic lemmas in our subsequent discussions.

Theorem 1.1. If a family $\mathscr{L}$ of languages is closed under union, λ-free catenation closure, λ-free homomorphism, inverse homomorphism, and intersection with regular languages, then $\mathscr{L}$ is closed under catenation.

Proof. We will show that the catenation $L_1 L_2$ of two arbitrary languages L_1 and L_2 from $\mathscr{L}$ also belongs to $\mathscr{L}$. There exists an alphabet V_T such that L_1 and L_2 are both languages over V_T. We define

$$V_T' = \{a'|a \in V_T\}, \qquad V_T'' = \{a''|a \in V_T\},$$

and denote $V = V_T \cup V_T' \cup V_T''$. Let h be the following λ-free homomorphism of $W(V)$ onto $W(V_T)$:

$$h(a) = h(a') = h(a'') = a, \qquad a \in V_T.$$

Let L_1' (resp. L_2') be the language obtained by replacing in each word of the language $L_1 - \{\lambda\}$ (resp. $L_2 - \{\lambda\}$) its first letter a with the letter a' (resp. a''). Consequently,

$$L_1' = h^{-1}(L_1) \cap \{a'P|a \in V_T, P \in W(V_T)\},$$

$$L_2' = h^{-1}(L_2) \cap \{a''P|a \in V_T, P \in W(V_T)\}.$$

Since the second languages in the intersections obviously are regular, we conclude that L_1' and L_2' are in the family $\mathscr{L}$. Consider the language

$$L_3 = (L_1' \cup L_2')^+ \cap \{a'Pb''Q|a,b \in V_T \text{ and } P,Q \in W(V_T)\}$$

$$= \{a'Pb''Q|a,b \in V_T, aP \in L_1 \text{ and } bQ \in L_2\}.$$

Since again the latter language in the intersection is regular, we conclude that L_3 is in the family $\mathscr{L}$. Hence, $h(L_3)$ is also in the family $\mathscr{L}$. But $L_1 L_2$ equals one of the four languages

$$h(L_3), \qquad h(L_3) \cup L_1, \qquad h(L_3) \cup L_2, \qquad h(L_3) \cup L_1 \cup L_2,$$

depending on which of the following four cases occurs: (i) λ is neither in L_1 nor in L_2; (ii) λ is in L_2 but not in L_1; (iii) λ is in L_1 but not in L_2; (iv) λ is both in L_1 and in L_2. In each case, $L_1 L_2$ is in $\mathscr{L}$. ∎

Theorem 1.2. If a family $\mathscr{L}$ of languages is closed under λ-free regular substitution, restricted homomorphism, union with regular languages, and intersection with regular languages, then $\mathscr{L}$ is closed under inverse homomorphism. The same conclusion can be made for λ-free families $\mathscr{L}$ even without assuming closure under union with regular languages.

Proof. Let L be an arbitrary language in the family $\mathscr{L}$. Assume that L is a language over an alphabet V_T. Let h be a homomorphism of $W(V)$ into $W(V_T)$ where $V = \{a_1, ..., a_r\}$, defined by

$$h(a_i) = P_i, \quad 1 \leq i \leq r, \quad P_i \in W(V_T).$$

We will prove that $h^{-1}(L)$ is in $\mathscr{L}$. We consider first the case where L is λ-free.

Choose $k = \max\{lg(P_i)|1 \leq i \leq r\} + 1$. We introduce a new alphabet $V' = \{a_1', ..., a_r'\}$ and a λ-free regular substitution σ by

$$\sigma(a) = W(V')aW(V') \quad \text{for} \quad a \in V_T.$$

Let L_1 be the finite language $\{a_i'P_i|1 \leq i \leq r\}$ and

$$L_2 = \sigma(L) \cap L_1^*.$$

By the hypothesis, L_2 is in $\mathscr{L}$. So is $h_1(L_2)$ also where h_1 is the λ-free homomorphism defined by

$$h_1(a_i') = a_i, \quad 1 \leq i \leq r; \quad h_1(a) = c, \quad a \in V_T.$$

(Since $\mathscr{L}$ is closed under λ-free regular substitution, it is closed under λ-free homomorphism.) Clearly, $h_1(L_2)$ is a language over the alphabet $V \cup \{c\}$. Define another homomorphism h_2 by

$$h_2(c) = \lambda, \quad h_2(a_i) = a_i \quad \text{for} \quad a_i \in V.$$

By the definition of L_2 and the choice of k, h_2 is k-restricted on $h_1(L_2)$. Furthermore,

$$h_2(h_1(L_2)) = h^{-1}(L). \tag{1.1}$$

This is seen as follows. Since L was assumed to be λ-free, both sides of (1.1) contain only nonempty words. Consider an arbitrary nonempty word

$$Q = a_{i_1} \cdots a_{i_n}, \quad n \geq 1, \quad a_{i_j} \in V.$$

Then $Q \in h^{-1}(L)$ iff

$$h(Q) = P_{i_1} \cdots P_{i_n} \in L. \tag{1.2}$$

(1.2) is satisfied iff

$$a_{i_1}' P_{i_1} \cdots a_{i_n}' P_{i_n} \in L_2$$

which, in turn, holds true iff

$$Q = a_{i_1} \cdots a_{i_n} \in h_2(h_1(L_2)).$$

Therefore, (1.1) is valid and thus $h^{-1}(L)$ is in $\mathscr{L}$.

Assume, finally, that $\lambda \in L$. This implies that $\mathscr{L}$ is not λ-free, and hence it is assumed to be closed under union with regular languages. Since

$$L - \{\lambda\} = L \cap (V_T W(V_T))$$

is in $\mathscr{L}$ by the hypothesis, we conclude that $h^{-1}(L - \{\lambda\})$ is in $\mathscr{L}$ by the first part of the proof. If h is λ-free, $h^{-1}(\lambda) = \{\lambda\}$. Otherwise, $h^{-1}(\lambda) = W(V_1)$ where $V_1 \subseteq V$ consists of letters a_i such that $h(a_i) = \lambda$. Consequently, the language $h^{-1}(\lambda)$ is regular. This implies that

$$h^{-1}(L) = h^{-1}(L - \{\lambda\}) \cup h^{-1}(\lambda) \tag{1.3}$$

is in the family $\mathscr{L}$ also in this case. ∎

We now study language families which are closed under certain operations. The choice of the basic operations is of course arbitrary, but is motivated by the fact that, for instance, all of the four families $\mathscr{L}_i$ in our basic hierarchy are closed under these operations.

Definition. A family of languages is termed an *abstract family of languages* or, in short, an *AFL* iff it contains a nonempty language and is closed under each of the following operations: union, λ-free catenation closure, λ-free homomorphism, inverse homomorphism, and intersection with regular languages. An AFL is termed *full* iff it is closed under arbitrary homomorphism.

Theorem 1.3. Every AFL is closed under catenation. Every AFL contains all λ-free regular languages. If an AFL is not λ-free, then it contains all regular languages and is closed under catenation closure.

Proof. The first sentence is an immediate consequence of Theorem 1.1. To prove the second sentence, we consider an arbitrary AFL $\mathscr{L}$. By definition, $\mathscr{L}$ contains a nonempty language. Moreover, $\mathscr{L}$ contains a language L containing a word $P \neq \lambda$. For if $\{\lambda\}$ were the only nonempty language in $\mathscr{L}$, we could choose a letter a and a homomorphism h of $W\{a\}$ defined by $h(a) = \lambda$. Since the language $h^{-1}\{\lambda\}$ is in $\mathscr{L}$, we would have a contradiction.

Let R be an arbitrary λ-free regular language over an alphabet $\{a_1, ..., a_r\}$. Since

$$R = \{a_1, ..., a_r\}^+ \cap R$$

and $\mathscr{L}$ is closed under intersection with regular languages, it suffices to prove that

$$\{a_1, ..., a_r\}^+ \tag{1.4}$$

is in $\mathscr{L}$ in order to be able to conclude that R is in $\mathscr{L}$. We choose a new letter c and define two λ-free homomorphisms h_1 and h_2 by

$$h_1(c) = P \quad \text{and} \quad h_2(a_i) = c, \quad 1 \leqq i \leqq r.$$

Since $L \cap \{P\} = \{P\}$ is regular, we conclude that $\{P\}$ is in $\mathscr{L}$. Since $P \neq \lambda$, we obtain

$$h_1^{-1}\{P\} = \{c\}$$

and consequently $\{c\}$ is in $\mathscr{L}$. Thus, $\{c\}^+$ is also in $\mathscr{L}$. Since the language (1.4) obviously equals the language $h_2^{-1}(\{c\}^+)$, we conclude that the language (1.4) is in $\mathscr{L}$ and, therefore, R is also in $\mathscr{L}$. This proves the second sentence.

Assume that $\mathscr{L}$ contains a language L_1 such that $\lambda \in L_1$. Then $\{\lambda\} = L_1 \cap \{\lambda\}$ is also in $\mathscr{L}$. Choose an arbitrary regular language R_1. If R_1 is λ-free, then it is in $\mathscr{L}$ by the proof above. Otherwise, $R_1 - \{\lambda\}$ is a regular language which is in $\mathscr{L}$ by the proof above. Consequently, also

$$R_1 = (R_1 - \{\lambda\}) \cup \{\lambda\}$$

is in $\mathscr{L}$. Since, for any language L, L^* equals one of the languages L^+ or $L^+ \cup \{\lambda\}$, we conclude that $\mathscr{L}$ is closed under catenation closure. ∎

AFL's can be characterized in many different ways. As regards specific language families, it is usually difficult to establish closure under inverse homomorphism. We now present some criteria where closure under inverse homomorphism is not needed.

Theorem 1.4. If a family $\mathscr{L}$ of languages includes a language containing a nonempty word and is closed under union, λ-free catenation closure, λ-free regular substitution, intersection with regular languages, and restricted homomorphism, then $\mathscr{L}$ is an AFL. If $\mathscr{L}$ includes a language containing a nonempty word and is closed under union, λ-free catenation closure, λ-free regular substitution, intersection with regular languages, and (arbitrary) homomorphism, then $\mathscr{L}$ is a full AFL.

Proof. If $\mathscr{L}$ is λ-free, then it is closed under inverse homomorphism, by the second sentence of Theorem 1.2. This implies that $\mathscr{L}$ possesses all of the defining properties of an AFL. (Closure under λ-free homomorphism follows from closure under λ-free regular substitution.)

The proof for the case where $\mathscr{L}$ is not λ-free is accomplished by a slight modification of the proof of Theorem 1.2. For any language L in $\mathscr{L}$ and any homomorphism h, the language $h^{-1}(L - \{\lambda\})$ is in $\mathscr{L}$. This is seen exactly as in Theorem 1.2. (Note that $L - \{\lambda\} = L \cap V_T^+$ is in $\mathscr{L}$ where V_T is the alphabet of L.) Equation (1.3) holds true also now. Thus, to prove that $h^{-1}(L)$ is in $\mathscr{L}$, it suffices to show that the regular language $h^{-1}(\lambda)$ is in $\mathscr{L}$. Since $\mathscr{L}$ is not

λ-free, it contains a language L_1 such that $\lambda \in L_1$. Consequently, $L_1 \cap \{\lambda\} = \{\lambda\}$ is in $\mathscr{L}$. Since $\mathscr{L}$ contains a language L_2 such that $P \in L_2$ and $P \neq \lambda$, we conclude that $L_2 \cap \{P\} = \{P\}$ is in $\mathscr{L}$. For a letter a, let h_1 be the homomorphism defined by $h_1(a) = P$. Since $\{P\}$ is λ-free, we apply once more the argument of Theorem 1.2 to show that $h_1^{-1}(P) = \{a\}$ is in $\mathscr{L}$. Therefore, since $\mathscr{L}$ is closed under λ-free regular substitution and contains the language $\{\lambda\}$, it contains all regular languages and consequently the language $h^{-1}(\lambda)$. This implies that $\mathscr{L}$ is an AFL also in this case.

The second sentence of the theorem is an immediate consequence of the first sentence and the definition of a full AFL. ∎

It is not sufficient to assume in Theorem 1.4 that $\mathscr{L}$ contains at least one nonempty language. Then the family consisting of the language $\{\lambda\}$ would satisfy the hypothesis without being an AFL.

By our closure results (cf. Table 1, Section 10 of Part 1), the following theorem is an immediate corollary of Theorem 1.4. Note that closure under restricted homomorphism follows from closure under linear erasing.

Theorem 1.5. Each of the families $\mathscr{L}_i$, $0 \leq i \leq 3$, is an AFL. The families $\mathscr{L}_0, \mathscr{L}_2, \mathscr{L}_3$ are full AFL's. The family $\mathscr{L}_1$ is not a full AFL.

Examples of language families which are not AFL's are the family of k-linear languages (for any k) and the family of metalinear languages. (See Theorem 8.4 in Part 1.) In Section 13 we exhibit some *anti-AFL's*, that is, families which are closed under none of the AFL operations.

Closure under substitution usually implies many other closure properties. Consequently, if it has been established that a family $\mathscr{L}$ is closed under substitution, very little is needed to conclude that $\mathscr{L}$ is an AFL. This is illustrated by the following two theorems.

Theorem 1.6. If a family of languages contains all regular languages and is closed under intersection with regular languages and substitution, then the family is a full AFL.

Proof. Closure under substitution implies closure under homomorphism. Since our family $\mathscr{L}$ contains all regular languages, it contains the languages $\{a\}^+$ and $\{a, b\}$ for some letters a and b. Let L_1 and L_2 be arbitrary languages in $\mathscr{L}$. The language $L_1{}^+$ is obtained from the language $\{a\}^+$ by the substitution $\sigma(a) = L_1$. The language $L_1 \cup L_2$ is obtained from the language $\{a, b\}$ by the substitution $\sigma_1(a) = L_1$, $\sigma_1(b) = L_2$. Hence, $\mathscr{L}$ is closed under union and λ-free catenation closure. Since $\mathscr{L}$ contains all regular languages and is closed under substitution, it is closed under regular substitution.

Consequently, the assumptions in the second sentence of Theorem 1.4 are satisfied. ∎

Theorem 1.7. If a λ-free family of languages contains all λ-free regular languages and is closed under λ-free substitution, intersection with regular languages, and restricted homomorphism, then the family is an AFL.

Proof. Closure under union and λ-free catenation closure is shown exactly as in the proof of Theorem 1.6. (Note that here the assumption of the family being λ-free is needed because otherwise closure under λ-free substitution would not be sufficient.) Since the family contains all λ-free regular languages and is closed under λ-free substitution, it is closed under λ-free regular substitution. Consequently, the assumptions in the first sentence of Theorem 1.4 are satisfied. ∎

It can be shown that none of the five defining closure properties of an AFL is redundant: They are all independent in the sense that none of them follows from the others.

2. AFL'S AND RELATED SYSTEMS

In this section we establish some further properties of AFL's, as well as study some related concepts. Closure under gsm and inverse gsm mappings is considered first.

When dealing with generalized sequential machines, we use in this section the terminology and notations introduced in Section 4 of Part 1. We say that a GSM is λ-*free* iff all words P appearing in its defining productions (4.11) are nonempty. A gsm mapping is λ-*free* iff it is realized by a λ-free GSM [i.e., its defining GSM in (4.12) is λ-free].

The next theorem is actually a lemma about regular languages. It is needed in the proofs below, as well as in Chapter V.

Theorem 2.1. Let T be a binary relation defined on an alphabet V. Then the language

$$\{b_1 \cdots b_n | n \geq 1, \text{ each } b_j \text{ in } V, \text{ and } T(b_i, b_{i+1}) \text{ holds for } i = 1, \ldots, n-1\} \quad (2.1)$$

is regular.

Proof. Assume that $V = \{a_1, \ldots, a_r\}$. It is easy to verify that the right-linear grammar

$$G = (\{X_0, X_1, \ldots, X_r\}, V, X_0, F),$$

where

$$F = \{X_0 \to a_i X_i | 1 \leq i \leq r\} \cup \{X_i \to a_j X_j | 1 \leq i, j \leq r,$$

$$\text{and } T(a_i, a_j)\} \cup \{X_i \to \lambda | 1 \leq i \leq r\}$$

generates the language (2.1). Hence, Theorem 2.1 follows by Theorem 5.6 in Part 1. ∎

Theorem 2.2. Every AFL is closed under λ-free gsm mapping. Every full AFL is closed under gsm mapping.

Proof. Let GSM be a λ-free generalized sequential machine with the input alphabet V_1, output alphabet V_0, state alphabet S, initial state s_0, final state set S_1, and the set F of productions of the form

$$s_i a \to P s_j, \quad a \in V_1, \quad s_i, s_j \in S, \quad P \in V_0 W(V_0). \tag{2.2}$$

Let $\mathscr{L}$ be an AFL. To prove the first sentence of the theorem, we choose an arbitrary language L over the alphabet V_1 from $\mathscr{L}$ and show that $\text{GSM}(L)$ is in $\mathscr{L}$. [It is no loss of generality to assume that L is over V_1 because, for any L,

$$\text{GSM}(L) = \text{GSM}(L \cap W(V_1))$$

and the language $L \cap W(V_1)$ is in $\mathscr{L}$ whenever L is.]

We introduce the auxiliary alphabet

$$V_1 = \{[s_i, a, P, s_j] | (2.2) \text{ is in } F\}. \tag{2.3}$$

(Since F is finite, V_1 is indeed an alphabet.) A binary relation T on V_1 is defined as follows:

$$T([s_i, a, P, s_j], [s_i', a', P', s_j'])$$

holds true iff $s_j = s_i'$. By Theorem 2.1, the language

$$R = \{\alpha_1 \cdots \alpha_n | n \geq 1, \text{ each } \alpha_j \text{ in } V_1, T(\alpha_i, \alpha_{i+1}) \text{ for } i = 1, \ldots, n-1\}$$

is regular. Let R_1 be the subset of R consisting of words $\alpha_1 \cdots \alpha_n$ such that (i) the first state symbol of α_1 is s_0, and (ii) the second state symbol of α_n belongs to S_1. [In (2.3), s_i (resp. s_j) is referred to as the first (resp. second) state symbol of $[s_i, a, P, s_j]$.] Clearly,

$$R_1 = (R_2 W(V_1) R_3 \cup R_4) \cap R,$$

where R_2 is the finite language consisting of the letters α_1 of V_1 which satisfy (i), R_3 consists of the letters which satisfy (ii), and R_4 consists of the letters which satisfy both (i) and (ii). Consequently R_1 is regular. Finally, we denote by R_5 the regular language $R_1 \cup \{\lambda\}$ or R_1, depending on whether or not $s_0 \in S_1$.

We now introduce two λ-free homomorphisms h_1 and h_2 of $W(V_1)$ into $W(V_1)$ and $W(V_0)$, respectively, as follows:

$$h_1([s_i, a, P, s_j]) = a, \qquad h_2([s_i, a, P, s_j]) = P.$$

(The homomorphism h_2 is λ-free because GSM was assumed to be λ-free.) It is an immediate consequence of the definition of h_1 and h_2 that

$$\text{GSM}(L) = h_2(h_1^{-1}(L) \cap R_5). \tag{2.4}$$

By the definition of an AFL, we conclude that $\text{GSM}(L)$ is in $\mathscr{L}$. This proves the first sentence of the theorem. (In fact, we needed here only closure under λ-free homomorphism, inverse homomorphism, and intersection with regular languages. Thus, any language family possessing these closure properties is closed under λ-free gsm mapping.)

The proof of the second sentence of the theorem is quite similar. The only difference is that now the homomorphism h_2 is not necessarily λ-free. But since we are dealing with a full AFL, (2.4) implies also now that $\text{GSM}(L)$ is in $\mathscr{L}$. ∎

Theorem 2.3. Every AFL is closed under inverse gsm mapping.

Proof. We need a slight modification of the previous proof. Let $\mathscr{L}$ be an AFL, let GSM be a generalized sequential machine with the defining productions (2.2), and let L be a language in $\mathscr{L}$. Without loss of generality, we assume that L is over V_0. Consider the rewriting system RW obtained from GSM by reversing all productions: The production set of RW consists of all productions

$$Ps_j \rightarrow s_i a \tag{2.5}$$

such that (2.2) is a production of GSM. Hence

$$\text{GSM}^{-1}(L) = \{Q | Q's_1 \Rightarrow_{\text{RW}}^* s_0 Q \text{ for some } Q' \in L, s_1 \in S_1\}. \tag{2.6}$$

To show that this language is in $\mathscr{L}$, we introduce the auxiliary alphabet

$$V_1 = \{[P, s_j, s_i, a] | (2.5) \text{ is a production of RW}\}.$$

The relation

$$T([P, s_j, s_i, a], [P', s_j', s_i', a']),$$

defined on V_1 holds true iff $s_i = s_j'$. The language R is defined exactly as in the previous proof, and R_1 is the subset of R consisting of words $\alpha_1 \cdots \alpha_n$ such that (i) the first state symbol of α_1 belongs to S_1, and (ii) the second state symbol of α_n is s_0. It is again seen by Theorem 2.1 that R_1 is regular; R_5 is defined from R_1 exactly as in the previous proof. The homomorphisms h_1 and h_2 are defined by

$$h_1([P, s_j, s_i, a]) = P, \qquad h_2([P, s_j, s_i, a]) = a.$$

Homomorphism h_2 is λ-free. By (2.6) we obtain

$$\text{GSM}^{-1}(L) = h_2(h_1^{-1}(L) \cap R_5),$$

which completes the proof. ∎

Closure under gsm mapping implies other closure properties. This is seen in the next three theorems. It was pointed out in the proof of Theorem 2.2 that all closure properties of an AFL were actually not needed to establish closure under gsm mapping. The same holds true also below. For instance, Theorem 2.4 remains valid if the full AFL is replaced by any language family which is closed under homomorphism, inverse homomorphism, and intersection with regular languages. (Such a family is usually termed a cone.) On the other hand, Theorem 2.4 is not true for AFL's, as seen by Theorem 9.11 in Part 1.

Theorem 2.4. Every full AFL is closed under left and right quotient by regular languages.

Proof. Let L be a language in a full AFL $\mathscr{L}$, and let R be a regular language. We may assume that both L and R are languages over the alphabet V_T. We prove first that the left quotient of L by R,

$$R\backslash L = \{Q | PQ \in L \text{ for some } P \in R\},$$

is in $\mathscr{L}$.

We define a generalized sequential machine GSM as follows. The input alphabet is $V_T \cup \{c\}$, the output alphabet being V_T. The state alphabet is $S = \{s_0, s_1\}$, s_0 is the initial state, and the final state set is S. The production set is

$$\{s_0 a \to s_0 | a \in V_T\} \cup \{s_0 c \to s_1\} \cup \{s_1 a \to a s_1 | a \in V_T\}.$$

Let h be the homomorphism defined by

$$h(c) = \lambda, \qquad h(a) = a \quad \text{for} \quad a \in V_T.$$

Then we obtain

$$R\backslash L = \text{GSM}(h^{-1}(L) \cap RcW(V_T)).$$

Since the language $RcW(V_T)$ is regular, we conclude by Theorem 2.2 that $R\backslash L$ is in $\mathscr{L}$.

The proof for the right quotient L/R is quite similar. We intersect now with the language $W(V_T)cR$, and the GSM erases everything beyond and including c. ∎

Theorem 2.5. Every AFL is closed under restricted homomorphism.

Proof. Assume that $\mathscr{L}$ is an AFL, $k \geqq 1$, and

$$L \subseteq (V_T\{\lambda, c, ..., c^{k-1}\})^*$$

is a language in $\mathscr{L}$. Hence, the homomorphism h defined by

$$h(c) = \lambda, \qquad h(a) = a \quad \text{for} \quad a \in V_T,$$

is k-restricted on L. We prove that $h(L)$ is in $\mathscr{L}$.

Consider the λ-free GSM with the input alphabet

$$V_I = \{[a, c^i] | a \in V_T, 0 \leqq i \leqq k-1\},$$

output alphabet V_T, state alphabet and final state set $\{s_0\}$, and productions

$$s_0[a, c^i] \to as_0 \quad \text{for each} \quad [a, c^i] \in V_I.$$

Let h_1 be the homomorphism on $W(V_I)$, defined by

$$h_1([a, c^i]) = ac^i.$$

Then

$$h(L) = \text{GSM}(h_1^{-1}(L)),$$

which shows, by Theorem 2.2, that $h(L)$ is in $\mathscr{L}$. ∎

Theorem 2.5 cannot be used as a shortcut to prove that the family $\mathscr{L}_1$ of context-sensitive languages is closed under restricted homomorphism, to avoid the application of the workspace theorem, since closure under restricted homomorphism was needed in establishing that $\mathscr{L}_1$ is an AFL.

Theorem 2.6. Every AFL is closed under λ-free regular substitution. Every full AFL is closed under regular substitution.

Proof. Let $\mathscr{L}$ be an AFL, and L a language in $\mathscr{L}$, over the alphabet

$$V = \{a_1, ..., a_r\}.$$

Let σ be the λ-free regular substitution defined by

$$\sigma(a_i) = R_i, \qquad i = 1, ..., r,$$

where R_i is a λ-free regular language over the alphabet V_i. We will show that $\sigma(L)$ is in $\mathscr{L}$.

Consider the auxiliary alphabet $V' = \{a_i' | a_i \in V\}$. Denote

$$R = \left(\bigcup_{i=1}^{r} R_i a_i' \right)^*.$$

Thus R is regular.

Let h_1 and h_2 be the homomorphisms on $W(V' \cup V_1 \cup \cdots \cup V_r)$, defined by

$$h_1(a_i') = a_i, \qquad h_1(a) = \lambda, \qquad h_2(a_i') = c, \qquad h_2(a) = a$$

1ere

$$a \in V_1 \cup \cdots \cup V_r \qquad \text{and} \qquad 1 \leqq i \leqq r.$$

ι h_3 be the homomorphism on $W(\{c\} \cup V_1 \cup \cdots \cup V_r)$, defined by

$$h_3(c) = \lambda, \qquad h_3(a) = a \qquad \text{for} \quad a \in V_1 \cup \cdots \cup V_r.$$

follows from these definitions that

$$\sigma(L) = h_3(h_2(h_1^{-1}(L) \cap R)). \tag{2.7}$$

ιrthermore, h_2 is λ-free and h_3 is 2-restricted on the language $h_2(h_1^{-1}(L) \cap R)$ ιce the languages R_i are λ-free. By Theorem 2.5, $\sigma(L)$ is in $\mathscr{L}$.
To prove the second sentence of the theorem, we assume that $\mathscr{L}$ is a full
^{F}L. The regular languages R_i are now not necessarily λ-free. Consequently,
is not necessarily 2-restricted. However, (2.7) remains valid, and $\mathscr{L}$ is
Jsed under arbitrary homomorphism. This implies that $\sigma(L)$ is in $\mathscr{L}$. ∎

Combining Theorems 1.4, 2.5, and 2.6, we obtain the following criterion
r AFL's and full AFL's.

Theorem 2.7. Let $\mathscr{L}$ be a family of languages which includes a language
$\mathsf{r}$ntaining a nonempty word. Then $\mathscr{L}$ is an AFL iff it is closed under union,
$\mathsf{f}$ree catenation closure, λ-free regular substitution, intersection with regular
$\mathsf{r}$guages, and restricted homomorphism. The family $\mathscr{L}$ is a full AFL iff it
closed under union, catenation closure, regular substitution, intersection
th regular languages, and homomorphism.

We are now in the position to continue Table 1 given in Section 10 of Part 1.
ιe results in Table 2 have been established in Theorems 9.11 (in Part 1), 1.5,
$\mathsf{2}$–2.4, and 2.6.

TABLE 2

Closed under	$\mathscr{L}_3$	$\mathscr{L}_2$	$\mathscr{L}_1$	$\mathscr{L}_0$
λ-free gsm mapping	Yes	Yes	Yes	Yes
gsm mapping	Yes	Yes	No	Yes
Inverse gsm mapping	Yes	Yes	Yes	Yes
Left quotient by regular language	Yes	Yes	No	Yes
Right quotient by regular language	Yes	Yes	No	Yes
λ-free regular substitution	Yes	Yes	Yes	Yes
Regular substitution	Yes	Yes	No	Yes

We now consider the operation of *complementation*. Given an AFL we denote by $\sim\mathscr{L}$ the family consisting of the complements of the languag in $\mathscr{L}$, that is,

$$\sim\mathscr{L} = \{W(V_T) - L \,|\, L \text{ in } \mathscr{L} \text{ and } L \subseteq W(V_T)\}.$$

By our previous definition, $\mathscr{L}$ is closed under complementation iff $\sim\mathscr{L} \subseteq$ Neither closure nor nonclosure under complementation follows from t definition of a full AFL, as seen by considering the full AFL's $\mathscr{L}_3$ and $\mathscr{L}$ However, we can prove that the complement $\sim\mathscr{L}$ of an AFL $\mathscr{L}$ is a weak structure, a so-called *pre-AFL*. We now define the latter notion.

Assume that $L_1 \subseteq W(V_1)$ and c is a letter not in V_1. Then $(L_1 c)^+$ is term a *marked λ-free catenation closure* of L_1. Assume, furthermore, th $L_2 \subseteq W(V_2)$ and c_1 is a letter not in $V_1 \cup V_2$. Then $L_1 c_1 L_2$ is termed a *mark catenation* of L_1 and L_2. A family of languages is termed a *pre-AFL* iff it closed under marked catenation, marked λ-free catenation closure, inver homomorphism, intersection with regular languages, and union with t language $\{\lambda\}$.

The notion of a pre-AFL is motivated by its close relation to AFL, whi is seen from the following proposition. In general, if $\mathscr{L}$ is a family of languag and O is a set of operations, then by the *closure* of $\mathscr{L}$ under O, in symbol

$$Cl(\mathscr{L}, O),$$

we mean the smallest family of languages which (i) includes $\mathscr{L}$ and (ii) closed under each operation in O. In particular, if O consists of the operatic of union and complementation, then $Cl(\mathscr{L}, O)$ is referred to as the *Boole closure* of $\mathscr{L}$. If O consists of a single operation, then $Cl(\mathscr{L}, O)$ is referr to as the closure of $\mathscr{L}$ under that particular operation.

Proposition 2.1. The closure of a pre-AFL under λ-free homomorphism an AFL. The Boolean closure of an AFL is a pre-AFL.

Theorem 2.8. If $\mathscr{L}$ is an AFL which is not λ-free, then $\sim\mathscr{L}$ is a pre-AFI

Proof. By Theorem 1.3, $\mathscr{L}$ contains all regular languages. We prove t $\sim\mathscr{L}$ is closed under each of the five pre-AFL operations. We assume that

$$L_1 \subseteq W(V_1), \qquad L_2 \subseteq W(V_2)$$

are arbitrary languages in $\mathscr{L}$.

Marked Catenation. We have to show that the language

$$(W(V_1) - L_1) c (W(V_2) - L_2) \tag{2}$$

is in $\sim\mathscr{L}$. Language (2.8) can be expressed in the form

$$W(V_3) - [(W(V_3) - W(V_1) c W(V_2)) \cup L_1 c W(V_2) \cup W(V_1) c L_2],$$

where $V_3 = V_1 \cup V_2 \cup \{c\}$. Since $\mathscr{L}$ contains all regular languages and is closed under union and catenation, the language within the brackets is in $\mathscr{L}$. Hence, (2.8) is in $\sim\mathscr{L}$.

Marked λ-Free Catenation Closure. The equation

$$((W(V_1)-L_1)c)^+ = W(V_1 \cup \{c\})$$
$$- [(W(V_1 \cup \{c\})-(W(V_1)c)^+) \cup (W(V_1)c)^*L_1c(W(V_1)c)^*]$$

shows that the language on the left side is in $\sim\mathscr{L}$.

Inverse Homomorphism. Let h be a homomorphism of $W(V)$ into $W(V_1)$. Since

$$h^{-1}(W(V_1)-L_1) = W(V) - h^{-1}(L_1)$$

and $\mathscr{L}$ is closed under inverse homomorphism, we conclude that the language on the left side is in $\sim\mathscr{L}$.

Intersection with Regular Languages. Let R be an arbitrary regular language. The equation

$$(W(V_1)-L_1) \cap R = W(V_1) - (L_1 \cup (W(V_1)-R))$$

shows that $\sim\mathscr{L}$ is closed under intersection with regular languages.

Union with the Language $\{\lambda\}$. Closure of $\sim\mathscr{L}$ is seen from the equation

$$(W(V_1)-L_1) \cup \{\lambda\} = W(V_1) - (L_1 \cap V_1 W(V_1)). \quad \blacksquare$$

If $\mathscr{L}$ is a λ-free AFL, then $\sim\mathscr{L}$ is not a pre-AFL. This follows because every language in $\sim\mathscr{L}$ contains the empty word and consequently $\sim\mathscr{L}$ is not closed under intersection with regular languages.

Denote by O_5 the set consisting of the operations in the definition of an AFL. Let O_5' be the set obtained from O_5 by replacing λ-free homomorphism with arbitrary homomorphism. Let $\mathscr{L}$ be a family of languages. Then

$$Cl(\mathscr{L}, O_5) \quad [\text{resp. } Cl(\mathscr{L}, O_5')] \quad (2.9)$$

is the smallest AFL (resp. full AFL) containing the family $\mathscr{L}$. If an AFL (resp. a full AFL) $\mathscr{K}_1$ is of the form (2.9), where $\mathscr{L}$ consists of one language, then $\mathscr{K}_1$ is termed *principal* (resp. *full principal*). Since

$$\mathscr{L}_3 = Cl(\{\{a\}\}, O_5'),$$

where a is a letter, we conclude that the family of regular languages is a full principal AFL. Similarly, we see that the family of λ-free regular languages is a principal AFL.

It is an immediate consequence of Theorem 7.4 in Part 1 that

$$\mathscr{L}_2 = Cl(\{D_1\}, O_5'),$$

where D_1 is the Dyck language over the alphabet $\{a_1, a_1'\}$. (In fact, this result remains valid if O_5' is replaced by the set of operations defining a cone.) Therefore, the family of context-free languages is a full principal AFL. It can be shown that the family of context-sensitive languages is a principal AFL. This implies, by Theorem 9.9 in Part 1, that $\mathscr{L}_0$ is full principal.

Note 2.1. We have seen that to each of the families $\mathscr{L}_i$, $i = 0, 1, 2, 3$, in our basic hierarchy there corresponds a class of recognition devices or *automata*. This correspondence can be extended to concern arbitrary full AFL's. One can introduce the notion of an *abstract family of acceptors* (automata), AFA, such that (i) for each AFA $\mathscr{F}$, the family of languages acceptable by the devices in $\mathscr{F}$ is a full AFL, and (ii) for each full AFL $\mathscr{L}$, there is an AFA $\mathscr{F}$ such that $\mathscr{L}$ equals the family of languages acceptable by the devices in $\mathscr{F}$.

An AFL need not be closed under mirror image. For instance, the principal AFL generated by the language

$$L = \{a^n b^m | 0 \leqq m < n\}$$

does not contain the language mi(L) and consequently is not closed under mirror image. For a language family $\mathscr{L}$, we denote by mi($\mathscr{L}$) the family consisting of the mirror images of the languages in $\mathscr{L}$. If $\mathscr{L}$ is an AFL, then

$$\mathscr{L} \cap \text{mi}(\mathscr{L}) \tag{2.10}$$

is an AFL closed under mirror image. Furthermore, (2.10) is the maximal AFL closed under mirror image which is contained in $\mathscr{L}$.

Apart from the types of substitution we have considered so far, one can still introduce other types of substitution. In general, let sub($\mathscr{K}_1, \mathscr{K}_2$) be the family obtained by substituting languages of the family $\mathscr{K}_1$ into languages of the family $\mathscr{K}_2$, that is, the family of all languages of the form $\sigma(L_2)$ where L_2 is in $\mathscr{K}_2$ and $\sigma(a)$ is always in $\mathscr{K}_1$; sub($\mathscr{K}_1, \mathscr{K}_2$) need not equal sub($\mathscr{K}_2, \mathscr{K}_1$). A family $\mathscr{L}$ is closed under substitution iff sub($\mathscr{L}, \mathscr{L}$) $\subseteq \mathscr{L}$. It can be shown that if $\mathscr{K}_1$ and $\mathscr{K}_2$ are (full) AFL's, then sub($\mathscr{K}_1, \mathscr{K}_2$) is also a (full) AFL. Moreover, if a full AFL $\mathscr{L}$ is not closed under substitution, then sub($\mathscr{L}, \mathscr{L}$) is also not closed under substitution. This gives rise to an infinite hierarchy of full AFL's.

Let $\mathscr{L}$ be a full AFL which is not closed under substitution. Let $S_0(\mathscr{L})$ be the family of regular languages, $S_1(\mathscr{L}) = \mathscr{L}$, and

$$S_{n+1}(\mathscr{L}) = \text{sub}(\mathscr{L}, S_n(\mathscr{L})), \qquad n \geqq 1.$$

Then, for each $i \geqq 0$, $S_i(\mathscr{L})$ is properly included in $S_{i+1}(\mathscr{L})$. Furthermore, the smallest full AFL which contains $\mathscr{L}$ and is closed under substitution is not full principal. Since the family of context-free languages $\mathscr{L}_2$ is a full principal AFL which is closed under substitution, the smallest full AFL which contains $\mathscr{L}$ and is closed under substitution is properly contained in $\mathscr{L}_2$ provided the family $\mathscr{L}$ above is a subfamily of $\mathscr{L}_2$. Furthermore, we obtain an infinite ascending chain of full AFL's properly containing $\mathscr{L}$ and properly contained in $\mathscr{L}_2$.

It is not known whether or not there exists a full AFL $\mathscr{L}$ "adjacent" to $\mathscr{L}_3$; that is, $\mathscr{L}$ properly contains $\mathscr{L}_3$ but contains properly no full AFL properly containing $\mathscr{L}_3$.

It can be shown that if a full AFL $\mathscr{L}$ is of the form

$$\mathscr{L} = Cl(\mathscr{K}_1, O_5'), \tag{2.11}$$

for some finite family $\mathscr{K}_1$, then $\mathscr{L}$ is full principal. Thus any finitely generated full AFL possesses a single generator. For full AFL's $\mathscr{L}$ which are not of the form (2.11), there are the following two possibilities: (i) $\mathscr{L}$ possesses an infinite independent generating family, or (ii) no generating family of $\mathscr{L}$ is indedendent. Here independence is defined as follows. Assume that (2.11) holds, where $\mathscr{K}_1$ is not necessarily finite. Then $\mathscr{K}_1$ is termed an *independent* generating family for $\mathscr{L}$ iff no proper subfamily $\mathscr{K}_2$ of $\mathscr{K}_1$ satisfies

$$\mathscr{L} = Cl(\mathscr{K}_2, O_5').$$

Let $\mathscr{L}$ be a full principal AFL containing $\mathscr{L}_2$. Then $\mathscr{L}$ possesses a *maximal* nonprincipal full sub-AFL $\mathscr{K}_1$: $\mathscr{K}_1$ is not full principal (and hence not finitely generated) but if $\mathscr{K}_2$ is a full AFL satisfying

$$\mathscr{K}_1 \subset \mathscr{K}_2 \subseteq \mathscr{L},$$

then $\mathscr{K}_2$ is full principal.

EXERCISES

1. Prove that if a family of languages is closed under catenation, catenation closure, λ-free homomorphism, inverse homomorphism, and intersection with regular languages, then it is closed under union.

2. Prove that if a λ-free family of languages is closed under catenation, λ-free homomorphism, and inverse homomorphism, then it is closed under intersection with regular languages.

3. Using the previous exercises, prove that a λ-free nonempty family of languages is an AFL iff it is closed under the following operations: catenation, λ-free catenation closure, λ-free homomorphism, and inverse homomorphism.

4. Prove that the family of recursive languages is an AFL which is not full.

5. Assume that a family of languages contains all languages $\{a\}^*$, where a is a letter, and is closed under intersection with regular languages and substitution. Prove that the family is not necessarily an AFL.

6. Prove that if L is in an AFL $\mathscr{L}$, and R is regular, then $L - R$ is in $\mathscr{L}$.

7. The *initial extension* ie(L) of a language L consists of all initial subwords of the words in L. The *final extension* fe(L) is defined similarly. The *subword extension* se(L) of L consists of all subwords of the words in L. Prove that a full AFL is closed under the three operations ie, fe, and se. Is the family of context-sensitive languages closed under these operations?

8. Prove that every AFL is closed under linear erasing.

9. Prove that every pre-AFL contains all regular languages.

10. Prove that the Boolean closure of the family of context free languages is properly included in the family of context-sensitive languages. (Consider languages over one letter to show that the inclusion is proper.)

11. Assume that $\mathscr{L}$ is a family of languages which includes a language containing a nonempty word. Prove the following theorems where $\mathscr{R}$ denotes the family of regular languages and $\mathscr{R}_\lambda$ the family of λ-free regular languages: (i) $\mathscr{L}$ is an AFL iff $\mathscr{L}$ is closed under intersection with regular languages and restricted homomorphism, and sub$(\mathscr{R}_\lambda, \mathscr{L}) \subseteq \mathscr{L}$, sub$(\mathscr{L}, \mathscr{R}_\lambda) \subseteq \mathscr{L}$. (ii) $\mathscr{L}$ is a full AFL iff $\mathscr{L}$ is closed under intersection with regular languages, and sub$(\mathscr{R}, \mathscr{L}) \subseteq \mathscr{L}$, sub$(\mathscr{L}, \mathscr{R}_\lambda) \subseteq \mathscr{L}$.

BIBLIOGRAPHICAL REMARKS

The basic results concerning AFL's are in Ginsburg *et al.* (1969), which is a collection of three papers, the first of them being by Ginsburg and Greibach. For principal AFL's and the questions discussed in Note 2.1, the reader is referred to Ginsburg and Greibach (1970), Ginsburg and Spanier (1970), Ginsburg and Harrison (1970), and Greibach (1969). Of the more recent work we mention Ginsburg and Spanier (1971), dealing with Parikh mappings. Essentially, an AFL is a family of languages closed under regular operations and gsm mappings. For an approach along these lines, the reader is referred to Nivat (1968) and Boasson (1971). For example, problems concerning generators and principal AFL's are discussed from this point of view by Boasson (1971).

BIBLIOGRAPHY

L. **Boasson**. Cônes Rationnels et Familles Agréables de Langages--Application au Langage à Compteur. Thesis, Univ. of Paris (1971).

S. **Ginsburg** and S. **Greibach**. Principal AFL. *J. Comput. System Sci.* **4** (1970) 308–338.

S. **Ginsburg**, S. **Greibach**, and J. **Hopcroft**. Studies in Abstract Families of Languages. Memoirs of the American Mathematical Society, No. 87 (1969).

S. Ginsburg and M. Harrison. On the closure of AFL under reversal. *Information Control* **17** (1970) 395–409.

S. Ginsburg and E. Spanier. Substitution in families of languages. *Information Sci.* **2** (1970) 83–110.

S. Ginsburg and E. Spanier. AFL with the semilinear property. *J. Comput. System Sci.* **5** (1971) 365–396.

S. Greibach. An infinite hierarchy of context-free languages. *J. Assoc. Comput. Mach.* **16** (1969) 91–106.

M. Nivat. Transduction des langages de Chomsky. *Ann. Inst. Fourier, Grenoble* **18** (1968) 339–455.

Chapter V

Regulated Rewriting

The basic hierarchy of four language families $\mathscr{L}_i$ was obtained by imposing restrictions on the *form* of the productions. A natural generalization is to restrict also the manner in which a grammar is allowed to generate words, that is, to impose restrictions also on the *use* of productions. Thus, not every derivation of a terminal word from the initial letter is acceptable. There is a control device which lets through acceptable derivations only. In this chapter we study various such control devices. For instance, an application of a production may determine which productions are applicable at the next step (this is called a programmed grammar), or some productions cannot be applied if some others are applicable (an ordered grammar), or one has to apply only certain previously specified strings of productions (a matrix grammar, a grammar with a control language), or at the ith step of the derivation only a subset F_i of the whole set F of productions is applicable (a time-varying grammar). Such control devices may be considered in connection with any rewriting system, leading into regulated rewriting. We are concerned mostly with context-free grammars added with a control device. The resulting system is simple in principle and easy to deal with. However, by the control device the generative capacity is remarkably increased.

3. MATRIX GRAMMARS

Assume that, instead of single productions, one is given a finite set of finite sequences of productions. Productions cannot be applied separately: A whole sequence always has to be applied. In applying such a sequence, one first rewrites according to the first production, then according to the second production, and so on, until one has rewritten according to the last production. The sequences are referred to as *matrices*. The resulting grammar is now formally defined.

Definition. A *matrix grammar* is an ordered quadruple $G = (V_N, V_T, X_0, M)$, where V_N, V_T, and X_0 are exactly as in the definition of a generative grammar but M is a finite set of finite nonempty sequences whose elements are ordered pairs

$$(P, Q), \qquad P \in W(V) V_N W(V), \quad Q \in W(V), \quad V = V_N \cup V_T.$$

The pairs are referred to as *productions* and written $P \to Q$. The sequences are referred to as *matrices* and written

$$m = [P_1 \to Q_1, ..., P_r \to Q_r], \qquad r \geq 1. \tag{3.1}$$

Let F be the collection of all productions appearing in the matrices m of a matrix grammar G. Then the matrix grammar G is of *type i*, $i = 0, 1, 2, 3$, *length-increasing*, *linear*, *λ-free*, *context-free*, *context-sensitive* iff the grammar $G_1 = (V_N, V_T, X_0, F)$ has the corresponding property.

For a matrix grammar G, we define a binary relation $\Rightarrow_G$ or, in short, $\Rightarrow$ on the set $W(V)$ as follows. For any $P, Q \in W(V)$, $P \Rightarrow Q$ holds iff there exist an integer $r \geq 1$ and words

$$\alpha_1, ..., \alpha_{r+1}, \qquad P_1, ..., P_r, \qquad Q_1, ..., Q_r, \qquad R_1, ..., R_r, \qquad R^1, ..., R^r \tag{3.2}$$

over V such that (i) $\alpha_1 = P$ and $\alpha_{r+1} = Q$, (ii) the matrix (3.1) is one of the matrices of G, and (iii) $\alpha_i = R_i P_i R^i$ and $\alpha_{i+1} = R_i Q_i R^i$ for every $i = 1, ..., r$. If (i)–(iii) are satisfied, we also say that $P \Rightarrow Q$ holds with *specifications* (m, R_1).

Let $\Rightarrow^*$ be the reflexive transitive closure of the relation $\Rightarrow$. The terminology introduced in connection with the relation $\Rightarrow$ for ordinary grammars is extended to concern matrix grammars. Thus we may speak of *derivations*. The language *generated* by the matrix grammar G is defined by

$$L(G) = \{P \in W(V_T) | X_0 \Rightarrow^* P\}.$$

We are concerned mostly with context-free matrix grammars. The reason for this is that the generative capacity of type-i matrix grammars is the same as that of type-i grammars for $i \neq 2$, whereas the generative capacity of context-free matrix grammars is remarkably larger than that of context-free grammars. The family of languages generated by context-free λ-free matrix grammars is denoted by $\mathcal{M}$, and the family of languages generated by context-free matrix grammars is denoted by $\mathcal{M}^{\lambda}$. (Thus the upper index indicates that productions $X \to \lambda$ are allowed.)

Example 3.1. The matrix grammar

$$G = (\{X_0, X_1\}, \{a, b, c\}, X_0,$$

$$\{[X_0 \to X_0 X_1], [X_0 \to aX_0 b, X_1 \to cX_1], [X_0 \to ab, X_1 \to c]\})$$

generates the language $\{a^n b^n c^n | n \geq 1\}$. (Note that in each derivation the first matrix has to be applied exactly once. Otherwise, nonterminals cannot be eliminated.) The matrix grammar

$$G_1 = (\{X_0, X_1\}, \{a, b\}, X_0, \{[X_0 \to X_0 X_1], [X_0 \to aX_0, X_1 \to aX_1],$$

$$[X_0 \to bX_0, X_1 \to bX_1], [X_0 \to a, X_1 \to a], [X_0 \to b, X_1 \to b]\})$$

generates the language $\{PP | P \in W(\{a, b\}), P \neq \lambda\}$. Hence, both of these languages belong to the family $\mathcal{M}$. They are not context-free. On the other hand, every grammar can be regarded as a matrix grammar whose matrices consist of one production. Thus, the family $\mathcal{M}^{\lambda}$ properly includes the family $\mathcal{L}_2$, and the family $\mathcal{M}$ properly includes the family of λ-free context-free languages.

Given a matrix grammar G, it is possible to consider also languages other than $L(G)$: The generation process involved may be defined differently. Suppose that we want to apply the matrix

$$m = [X_1 \to abX_1, X_2 \to b, X_1 \to bX_2]$$

to the word $P = abX_1 b$. By the definitions given above, m is not applicable to P; that is, there are no words Q and R_1 such that $P \Rightarrow Q$ holds with specifications (m, R_1). However, we might understand the "application" of the matrix m in the following broader sense. We first rewrite P according to the first production, yielding $ababX_1 b$. Then we notice that the second production cannot be used since X_2 does not appear in the word under scan. This is considered as an application of the second production, and so we finally rewrite according to the third production, yielding $ababbX_2 b$.

In general, we may define the application of a matrix in the following *appearance checking* sense: If the left side of a production is not a subword of the word under scan, then we may move on to the next production. In the subsequent formal definition, a subset F_1 of the set F of productions is specified such that the appearance checking is possible only for productions in F_1; for productions in $F - F_1$, application always means actual rewriting. Moreover, F is understood as the set of *occurrences* of the productions in the matrices of M. Thus it is possible that an occurrence of a production $P_1 \to P_2$ in matrix m belongs to F_1, whereas an occurrence of $P_1 \to P_2$ in matrix m' does not belong to F_1.

Definition. Let $G = (V_N, V_T, X_0, M)$ be a matrix grammar. Let F be the totality of occurrences of productions in the matrices of M, and F_1 a subset of F. A binary relation $\Rightarrow_{ac}$ (which depends on G and F_1) on the set $W(V)$ is defined as follows. For any P, $Q \in W(V)$, $P \Rightarrow_{ac} Q$ holds iff there exist an integer $r \geq 1$ and words (3.2) over V such that (i) $\alpha_1 = P$ and $\alpha_{r+1} = Q$, (ii) the matrix (3.1) is one of the matrices of G, and (iii) for every $i = 1, ..., r$, either $\alpha_i = R_i P_i R^i$ and $\alpha_{i+1} = R_i Q_i R^i$ or else the (occurrence of the) production $P_i \to Q_i$ belongs to F_1, P_i is not a subword of α_i, and $\alpha_i = \alpha_{i+1}$. Let $\Rightarrow_{ac}^*$ be the reflexive transitive closure of the relation $\Rightarrow_{ac}$. The language *generated* by G with *appearance checking* for productions in F_1 is defined by

$$L_{ac}(G, F_1) = \{P \in W(V_T) | X_0 \Rightarrow_{ac}^* P\}. \tag{3.3}$$

Thus, apart from the condition "or else" in point (iii), the relation $\Rightarrow_{ac}$ is defined exactly as the relation $\Rightarrow$. Consequently, for any matrix grammar G,

$$L(G) = L_{ac}(G, \varnothing), \tag{3.4}$$

because if $F_1 = \varnothing$, then the condition "or else" is never satisfied.

We denote by $\mathcal{M}_{ac}^\lambda$ the family of languages of the form (3.3) where G is a context-free matrix grammar. Similarly, we denote by $\mathcal{M}_{ac}$ the family of languages of the form (3.3) where G is a context-free λ-free matrix grammar. The inclusions

$$\mathcal{M} \subseteq \mathcal{M}^\lambda \subseteq \mathcal{M}_{ac}^\lambda, \qquad \mathcal{M} \subseteq \mathcal{M}_{ac} \subseteq \mathcal{M}_{ac}^\lambda \tag{3.5}$$

follow immediately by the definitions and by (3.4). (Thus, in our notation, the presence of the index λ indicates that productions $X \to \lambda$ are allowed, whereas the presence of the index ac indicates that the appearance checking interpretation in the application of production is allowed.)

It is not seen by the definitions how the families $\mathcal{M}^\lambda$ and $\mathcal{M}_{ac}$ are interrelated and this is, indeed, an open problem. The productions $X \to \lambda$ can be eliminated from an ordinary context-free grammar, as was seen in Theorem 6.2 in Part 1. The situation is not the same as regards matrix grammars: It makes a big difference whether or not we include productions of the form $X \to \lambda$. In the following sections, we are going to show that all of the four $\mathcal{M}$-families can also be obtained using restrictive devices other than matrices.

Example 3.2. Consider the context-free λ-free matrix grammar $G = (\{X, Y, Z, U, A\}, \{a\}, X, M)$ where M consists of the matrices

$$[Y \to U, A \to U, X \to ZZ], \qquad [X \to U, Z \to Y], \qquad [Z \to U, Y \to X],$$

$$[Y \to U, Z \to U, X \to A], \qquad [X \to U, A \to a].$$

Define $F_1 = \{X \to U, Y \to U, Z \to U, A \to U\}$. Then

$$L_{ac}(G, F_1) = \{a^{2^n} | n \geq 0\}. \tag{3.6}$$

The nonterminal U does not appear on the left side of any production, so it can never be eliminated if it has been introduced. The "essential" production in each of the matrices is the last one. The other productions only serve the purpose of checking that certain nonterminals are not present in the word under scan. Thus, for any $n \geq 0$, the word X^{2^n} yields (in the sense of the relation $\Rightarrow_{ac}$) either the word A^{2^n} or the words $Z^{2^{n+1}}$, $Y^{2^{n+1}}$, and $X^{2^{n+1}}$ (in this order). All other words which X^{2^n} yields contain at least one occurrence of U and hence do not yield any terminal word. Consequently, the language (3.6) belongs to the family $\mathcal{M}_{ac}$ (and thus also to the family $\mathcal{M}_{ac}^{\lambda}$). The reader may try to find a context-free λ-free (or simply a context-free) matrix grammar G_1 such that $L(G_1)$ equals the language (3.6). Some deliberation will show that appearance checking is indeed a very convenient tool. In fact, we do not know whether or not such a G_1 exists; that is, whether or not the language (3.6) belongs to the family $\mathcal{M}^{\lambda}$.

We now consider another modification in the definition of the yield-relation for matrix grammars: At each step of the derivation, one has to use a matrix whose application begins as far to the left as possible. This "leftmost" restriction concerns only the first productions in the matrices. Otherwise, the application of the matrices is understood in the original sense of the relation $\Rightarrow$: Appearance checking is not considered.

Definition. Let G be a matrix grammar. A binary relation $\Rightarrow_{left}$ on the set $W(V)$ is defined as follows. For any $P, Q \in W(V)$, $P \Rightarrow_{left} Q$ holds iff (i) for some m and R_1, $P \Rightarrow Q$ holds with specifications (m, R_1), and (ii) for no m', Q', and R_1' such that $lg(R_1') < lg(R_1)$, $P \Rightarrow Q'$ holds with specifications (m', R_1'). Denote by $\Rightarrow_{left}^{*}$ the reflexive transitive closure of the relation $\Rightarrow_{left}$. The language *generated* by the matrix grammar G under *leftmost restriction* on derivations is defined by

$$L_{left}(G) = \{P \in W(V_T) | X_0 \Rightarrow_{left}^{*} P\}. \tag{3.7}$$

We denote by $\mathcal{M}_{left}^{\lambda}$ ($\mathcal{M}_{left}$) the family of languages of the form (3.7) where G is a context-free (context-free λ-free) matrix grammar.

Example 3.3. For the matrix grammars G and G_1 in Example 3.1, we have

$$L(G) = L_{\text{left}}(G), \qquad L(G_1) = L_{\text{left}}(G_1),$$

whereas for the matrix grammar G in Example 3.2, $L_{\text{left}}(G)$ is empty. Consider now the matrix grammar

$$G = (\{X_0, X, X', Z, Z', A, B, C\}, \{a\}, X_0, M),$$

where M consists of the matrices

$$[X_0 \to a], \qquad [X_0 \to X'A], \qquad [X \to ZZ, A \to A],$$

$$[X' \to ZZ', A \to B], \qquad [Z \to X, B \to B], \qquad [Z' \to X', B \to A],$$

$$[Z' \to X', B \to C], \qquad [X \to a, C \to C], \qquad [X' \to a, C \to \lambda].$$

For this G, the language $L_{\text{left}}(G)$ equals the language (3.6). Each derivation consists of successive loops: (i) Change X's into Z's and duplicate their number, (ii) change Z's into X's, (iii) change X's into a's. The letters A, B, and C indicate which of the three loops is active. By the definition of the relation $\Rightarrow_{\text{left}}$, the fourth matrix (resp. the sixth or seventh matrix) cannot be applied if the third matrix (resp. the fifth matrix) is still applicable. Consequently, the language (3.6) belongs to the family $\mathscr{M}^{\lambda}_{\text{left}}$. It is not difficult to prove that the language (3.6) belongs also to the family $\mathscr{M}_{\text{left}}$. This is done by replacing the nonterminals A, B, and C with indices attached to other nonterminals, or by Theorem 3.2 below.

The inclusions

$$\mathscr{M} \subseteq \mathscr{M}_{\text{left}}, \qquad \mathscr{M}^{\lambda} \subseteq \mathscr{M}^{\lambda}_{\text{left}}$$

would be easy to establish already at this stage. (Given a matrix grammar, one introduces auxiliary nonterminals such that all derivations will satisfy the leftmost restriction.) However, we will not do so since we are going to prove later the more general results

$$\mathscr{M}_{\text{ac}} \subseteq \mathscr{M}_{\text{left}}, \qquad \mathscr{M}^{\lambda}_{\text{ac}} = \mathscr{M}^{\lambda}_{\text{left}} = \mathscr{L}_0.$$

We are going to show now that

$$\mathscr{M}_{\text{left}} = \mathscr{L}_1', \tag{3.8}$$

where $\mathscr{L}_1'$ is the family of context-sensitive λ-free languages. (It is, of course, easy to modify the definition of the family $\mathscr{M}_{\text{left}}$ in such a way that $\mathscr{L}_1$ is obtained instead of $\mathscr{L}_1'$.) We need first a lemma concerning context-sensitive languages.

Theorem 3.1. Every context-sensitive λ-free language L is generated by a grammar whose productions are of the forms $X \to YZ$, $XU \to YZ$, $X \to a$ where a is a terminal and X, Y, Z, and U are nonterminals.

Proof. For an integer $n \geq 1$ and a grammar G, we say that G is of *degree* n iff terminals occur only in productions of the form $X \to a$ where X is a nonterminal and a is a terminal, and every production $P \to Q$ satisfies the condition $lg(P) \leq lg(Q) \leq n$. By Theorem 3.1 in Part 1, we may assume that there exists an n such that L is generated by a grammar of degree n. We will prove first that L is generated by a grammar of degree 2. To do this, it suffices to show how one can construct, for any grammar G of degree $n \geq 3$, an equivalent grammar G' of degree $n - 1$.

Let $P \to Q$ be a production of G. If $lg(Q) \leq 2$, then we let $P \to Q$ be a production of G'. Otherwise, there exist nonterminals X_1, X_2, X_3, and X_4 such that $P = X_1 P'$ and $Q = X_2 X_3 X_4 Q'$ for some (possibly empty) words P' and Q'. If $P' = \lambda$, then we introduce a new nonterminal Y_1, and let

$$X_1 \to X_2 Y_1, \qquad Y_1 \to X_3 X_4 Q'$$

be productions of G'. If $P = X_1 X_5 P''$ for some nonterminal X_5 and a word P'', then we introduce a new nonterminal Y_2, and let

$$X_5 P'' \to Y_2 X_4 Q', \qquad X_1 Y_2 \to X_2 X_3$$

be productions of G'. This procedure is repeated for each production $P \to Q$ of G. Clearly, the resulting grammar G' is of degree $n - 1$ and equivalent to G.

Consequently, L is generated by a grammar $G = (V_N, V_T, X_0, F)$ of degree 2. We will construct an equivalent grammar $G' = (V_N \cup \{X_0'\}, V_T, X_0', F')$ which satisfies the condition required in Theorem 3.1. (This means that productions of the form $X \to Y$, where X and Y are nonterminals, are eliminated from G.) Define

$$K = \{P \mid X_0 \Rightarrow^* P \text{ and either } P \in V_T, \text{ or else } P \in W(V_N) \text{ and } lg(P) = 2\}.$$

(The finite set K can be determined, for instance, using the method of Theorem 9.1 in Part 1.) The set F' consists of (i) all productions $X_0' \to P$ such that $P \in K$, (ii) all productions $ZX \to ZY$, $XZ \to YZ$ such that $Z \in V_N$ and $X \to Y$ is in F where $X, Y \in V_N$, (iii) all productions $X \to YZ$, $XU \to YZ$, $X \to a$ in F where $X, Y, Z, U \in V_N$ and $a \in V_T$. Then G' satisfies the required condition. It is also clear that G' is equivalent to G. ∎

Theorem 3.2. A λ-free language is context-sensitive iff it is generated by a λ-free context-free matrix grammar under leftmost restriction, that is, Eq. (3.8) is valid.

Proof. We show first that the left-hand side of (3.8) is included in the right-hand side. Assume that L is generated by the context-free λ-free matrix grammar $G = (V_N, V_T, X_0, M)$ under leftmost restriction. We will construct a grammar G_1 which simulates the grammar G. The grammar G_1 is not length-increasing. However, it follows by the workspace theorem that $L(G_1)$ is context-sensitive.

Assume that the matrices in M are m_i, $i = 1, \ldots, k$, where

$$m_i = [X_1^{\ i} \to P_1^{\ i}, \ldots, X_{u(i)}^i \to P_{u(i)}^i], \qquad u(i) \geq 1, \quad X_j^{\ i} \in V_N, \quad P_j^{\ i} \neq \lambda.$$

For each m_i we let Q_i be a word of minimum length such that, for some R and R_1, $Q_i \Rightarrow R$ holds with specifications (m_i, R_1). (Clearly, Q_i can be determined by inspecting the matrix m_i. The word Q_i consists of nonterminals, one of which is $X_1^{\ i}$. It is unique up to the order of letters. For instance, for the matrix

$$m_i = [X_1 \to X_2 X_3, X_1 \to a, X_2 \to b],$$

we have $Q_i = X_1 X_1$. Thus Q_i gives the information as to which nonterminals have to be present in order that m_i be applicable.)

Consider Parikh mappings ψ introduced in Part 1, Section 7. For words P over $V_N = \{U_1, \ldots, U_n\}$, $\psi(P)$ is an ordered n-tuple of nonnegative integers. For two such n-tuples v_1 and v_2, we write $v_1 \leq v_2$ iff the ith component of v_1 is less than or equal to the ith component of v_2 for every $i = 1, \ldots, n$.

The grammar G_1 is now defined. The nonterminal alphabet of G_1 is

$$V_N \cup \{\#, X_0', Y_0, Y_{k+1}, Z, Z_1\} \cup \{Y_i, Y_i^1, Y_i^2 | 1 \leq i \leq k\}$$

$$\cup \{Y(v, i) | 1 \leq i \leq k; v \leq \psi(Q_i)\} \cup \{Z(i, j) | 1 \leq i \leq k; 2 \leq j \leq u(i)\}.$$

[Thus, $Y(v, i)$ is a single nonterminal for each i and for each n-tuple v satisfying $v \leq \psi(Q_i)$. The nonterminal $Z(i, j)$ is defined for those values of i only for which $u(i) \geq 2$.] The initial letter is X_0' and the terminal alphabet V_T. The productions are listed below. Together with the productions, we give in parentheses intuitive explanations.

(i) $X_0' \to \# Y_0 X_0 \#$. (Begin the derivation by including the initial letter X_0 within boundary markers $\#$ and introducing the scanner Y_0.)

(ii) $Y_0 \alpha \to \alpha Y_0$, $\alpha Y_0 \to Y_0 \alpha$ for all $\alpha \in V = V_N \cup V_T$. (The scanner moves freely within the space between the boundary markers $\#$.)

(iii) $Y_0 X \to Y_1 Z X$ for all $X \in V_N$. (The scanner Y_0 has found a nonterminal, where the derivation will be continued. The position marker Z is introduced, as well as the first of the messengers Y_i for the matrices m_i.)

(iv) $\alpha Y_i \to Y_i \alpha$ for $1 \leq i \leq k+1$ and $\alpha \in V \cup \{Z\}$. (The messenger Y_i goes to the left boundary marker.)

(v) $\# Y_i \to \# Y_i^1$ for $1 \leq i \leq k$. (Begin to check whether it is possible to begin an application of m_i at a position to the left of Z.)

(vi) $Y_i^1 \alpha \to \alpha Y_i^1$ for $1 \leq i \leq k$ and all $\alpha \in V - \{X_1^i\}$, $Y_i^1 Z \to Y_{i+1} Z$. (Such an application is not possible, and the next messenger Y_{i+1} is introduced.)

(vii) $Y_i^1 X_1^i \to Y_i^2 X_1^i$ for $1 \leq i \leq k$. (Such an application is possible.)

(viii) $\alpha Y_i^2 \to Y_i^2 \alpha$, $\# Y_i^2 \to \# Y(\psi(Q_i), i)$ for $1 \leq i \leq k$ and $\alpha \in V$. (Begin to check whether the entire m_i can be applied. It has been found out that it is possible to begin an application of m_i at a position to the left of Z.)

(ix) $Y(v, i) \alpha \to \alpha Y(v, i)$, $Y(v_1, i) X \to X Y(v_1', i)$, $Y(v_2, i) \# \to Y_{i+1} \#$ where $1 \leq i \leq k$, and v, v_1, v_2 are arbitrary such that the Y's are defined, and v_2 possesses at least one component greater than 0; $\alpha \in V_T \cup \{Z\}$, or $\alpha = U_j \in V_N$, and the jth component in v equals 0; $X = U_j \in V_N$, the jth component in v_1 equals $t > 0$, and v_1' is obtained from v_1 by replacing this component with $t - 1$. [$Y(v, i)$ travels to the right, counting whether or not all letters in Q_i are present. If the answer is "no," the next messenger Y_{i+1} is introduced. Otherwise, the entire m_i is applicable, beginning at a position to the left of Z. This means that Z was placed incorrectly: The leftmost restriction will not be satisfied. Then $Y((0, ..., 0), i)$ cannot be eliminated, and the derivation terminates without producing a terminal word.]

(x) $Y_{k+1} Z \to Z_1$. (It has been found out that none of the matrices $m_1, ..., m_k$ can be applied beginning at a position to the left of Z. The leftmost restriction is thus satisfied and the actual application of a matrix may begin.)

(xi) $Z_1 X_1^i \to Y_0 P_1^i$ for $u(i) = 1$, $Z_1 X_1^i \to Z(i, 2) P_1^i$ for $u(i) \geq 2$, where $1 \leq i \leq k$. (Rewrite according to the first production in the ith matrix. If it is the only production in the matrix, introduce again the scanner Y_0. Otherwise, introduce $Z(i, j)$ which indicates that the jth production in the ith matrix is active.)

(xii) $Z(i, j) \alpha \to \alpha Z(i, j)$, $\alpha Z(i, j) \to Z(i, j) \alpha$ for all $\alpha \in V$ and i, j such that $Z(i, j)$ is defined. (Hunt for a nonterminal X_j^i.)

(xiii) $Z(i, u(i)) X_{u(i)}^i \to Y_0 P_{u(i)}^i$, $Z(i, j) X_j^i \to Z(i, j+1) P_j^i$ for $1 \leq i \leq k$ and $2 \leq j < u(i)$. (Rewrite according to the jth production in the ith matrix. If it was the last production in the matrix, introduce the scanner Y_0.)

(xiv) $\# \to \lambda$, $Y_0 \to \lambda$. (Eliminate the scanner and the boundary markers.)

Using the intuitive explanations given, it is easy to verify that $L(G) = L(G_1)$. Moreover, for any $P \in L(G_1)$, we have $WS_{G_1}(P) \leq lg(P) + 4$. It follows, by Theorem 10.1 in Part 1, that L is context-sensitive.

We show now that the right side of (3.8) is included in the left side. Assume that L is a context-sensitive λ-free language. By Theorem 3.1, we assume that L is generated by a grammar $G = (V_N, V_T, X_0, F)$ where all productions in F

are of the three forms

$$X \to YZ, \qquad X, Y, Z \in V_N, \tag{3.9}$$

$$f: XU \to YZ, \qquad X, U, Y, Z \in V_N, \tag{3.10}$$

$$X \to a, \qquad X \in V_N, \quad a \in V_T. \tag{3.11}$$

[A distinct label f is attached to each of the productions of the form (3.10).] Define

$$V_N' = \{X'|X \in V_N\}, \qquad V_N'' = \{X''|X \in V_N\}.$$

Let V_1 consist of the nonterminals $A_0, A_1, A_2, A_3, A_4, A_f$ where f ranges over the productions (3.10) in F. Let b be a fixed letter of V_T. We introduce a matrix grammar G_1 which simulates G if derivations according to G_1 satisfying leftmost restriction are considered. However, the language $L_{\text{left}}(G_1)$ equals Lb rather than L. By definition,

$$G_1 = (V_N \cup V_N' \cup V_N'' \cup V_1, V_T, A_0, M),$$

where M consists of the following matrices.

(i) $[A_0 \to X_0 A_1]$. (Begin the derivation by creating the phase indicator A_1 of the prime-introducing phase.)

(ii) $[Y \to Y', A_1 \to A_1]$ for each $Y \in V_N$. [Mark nonterminals with primes, beginning from the left and continuing up to the indended position of application of (3.9) or (3.10).]

(iii) $[X \to Y'Z'', A_1 \to A_2]$ for each production (3.9) in F. [Apply (3.9). Introduce the indicator A_2 of the prime-eliminating phase.]

(iv) $[X \to Y', A_1 \to A_f]$, $[U \to Z'', A_f \to A_2]$, $[B \to A_4, A_f \to A_4]$ for each production (3.10) in F and each $B \in V_N$ such that $B \neq U$. [Apply (3.10). First rewrite X and introduce the indicator A_f. If the letter following X is not U, the leftmost restriction causes A_4 to be introduced, and the derivation terminates without producing a terminal word. Otherwise, U is rewritten and the indicator A_2 of the prime-eliminating phase is introduced.]

(v) $[Y' \to Y, A_2 \to A_2]$, $[Y'' \to Y, A_2 \to A_1]$ for each $Y \in V_N$. (Eliminate primes. The letter marked with the double prime is the rightmost of the primed letters. When the double prime is eliminated, all primes have been eliminated, and the indicator A_1 is introduced.)

(vi) $[X \to a, A_1 \to A_3]$, $[X \to a, A_3 \to A_3]$, $[X \to a, A_3 \to b]$, $[X \to a, A_1 \to b]$ for each production (3.11) in F. (Replace nonterminals by terminals. Introduce the indicator A_3 of the terminal phase. Finally, rewrite the indicator as b. If only one letter of V_N is present, then A_1 can also be rewritten as b.)

It is now easy to verify that $L_{\text{left}}(G_1) = L(G)b$. In fact, G_1 simulates such derivations of G where productions $X \to a$ are applied last: No other productions are applied after an application of one of the productions $X \to a$. But clearly every word in $L(G)$ possesses such a derivation.

We, thus, have obtained the following result: For every context-sensitive λ-free language L over an alphabet V_T and every $b \in V_T$, the language Lb belongs to the family $\mathcal{M}_{\text{left}}$. On the other hand, for any λ-free language L_1 over V_T,

$$L_1 = \bigcup_{b \in V_T} (\partial_b^r L_1) b, \qquad (3.12)$$

where ∂^r denotes the right derivative.

Assume now that L_1 is an arbitrary context-sensitive λ-free language over V_T. For any $b \in V_T$, the language $\partial_b^r L_1$ is also context-sensitive. [This is seen as follows. Assume that L_1 is generated by a context-sensitive grammar whose initial letter is X_0. We add to this grammar nonterminals $\#$ and X_0' (which is the new initial letter) and productions $X_0' \to X_0 \#$ and $b\# \to \lambda$. The resulting grammar generates the language $\partial_b^r L_1$. By Theorem 10.1 in Part 1, this language is context-sensitive.] If $\lambda \notin \partial_b^r L_1$ (i.e., $b \notin L_1$), we use our result concerning the language L and conclude that

$$(\partial_b^r L_1) b \in \mathcal{M}_{\text{left}}. \qquad (3.13)$$

If $\lambda \in \partial_b^r L_1$, we denote $L_2 = \partial_b^r L_1 - \{\lambda\}$ and conclude that $L_2 b$ belongs to $\mathcal{M}_{\text{left}}$; (3.13) holds true also in this case because

$$(\partial_b^r L_1) b = L_2 b \cup \{b\}$$

and $\mathcal{M}_{\text{left}}$ is obviously closed under union. By (3.12) and (3.13), we conclude that L_1 belongs to $\mathcal{M}_{\text{left}}$, which implies that the right side of (3.8) is included in the left side. ∎

Since none of the matrices of the matrix grammar G_1 presented in the previous proof contains more than two productions, we obtain the following corollary.

Theorem 3.3. For any language L in the family $\mathcal{M}_{\text{left}}$, there is a context-free λ-free matrix grammar G such that $L = L_{\text{left}}(G)$ and none of the matrices of G contains more than two productions.

We are going to see that the result corresponding to Theorem 3.3 holds true for all of the $\mathcal{M}$-families introduced in this section. Thus, there is no loss of generality in assuming that the matrices contain at most two productions.

4. TIME-VARYING GRAMMARS

Another device restricting the use of productions is considered in this section. Given a grammar G with the set F of productions, we assume that the entire F is not available at each step of a derivation by specifying an infinite sequence

$$F^1, F^2, \ldots, F^i \subseteq F, \qquad (4.1)$$

such that, for each i, only productions in F^i can be used at the ith step of a derivation. Thus, it depends on the time elapsed, that is, on the length of the derivation performed, whether or not a particular production can be applied. In the general definition, we impose no restrictions whatsoever on how the sequence (4.1) is defined. However, we then restrict the attention to the case where (4.1) is periodic.

Definition. A *time-varying grammar* of type i, $0 \leq i \leq 3$, is an ordered pair (G, φ) where $G = (V_N, V_T, X_0, F)$ is a type-i grammar and φ is a mapping of the set of natural numbers into the set of subsets of F. (For $i = 3$, G may be either right-linear or left-linear.) A binary relation $\Rightarrow$ on the set of all pairs (P, j), where P is a word over the alphabet $V = V_N \cup V_T$ and j is a natural number, is defined as follows: $(P, j_1) \Rightarrow (Q, j_2)$ holds iff (i) $j_2 = j_1 + 1$, and (ii) there are words R_1, R_2, P', and Q' over V such that $P = R_1 P' R_2$, $Q = R_1 Q' R_2$, and $P' \to Q'$ is a production in the set $\varphi(j_1)$. Let $\Rightarrow^*$ be the reflexive transitive closure of the relation $\Rightarrow$. The language *generated* by the time-varying grammar (G, φ) is defined by

$$L(G, \varphi) = \{P \in W(V_T) | (X_0, 1) \Rightarrow^* (P, j) \text{ for some } j\}.$$

A language L is *time-varying* of type i iff $L = L(G, \varphi)$ for some time-varying grammar (G, φ) of type i.

Thus, a time-varying language is not necessarily recursively enumerable since there may not exist any effective procedure for determining the values of φ. We therefore make additional assumptions concerning the function φ. In order to give an idea of the generative capacity of time-varying grammars with an arbitrary φ, we first show that any language whatsoever (not necessarily recursively enumerable) belongs to the "smallest" among the families of time-varying languages.

Theorem 4.1. Any language is time-varying of type 3.

Proof. Let L be a language over the alphabet $V_T = \{a_1, \ldots, a_n\}$. If L is empty, it is obviously time-varying of type 3. Otherwise, assume that the sequence

$$P_1, P_2, \ldots, P_i = b_1 \cdots b_{u(i)}, \qquad u(i) \geq 0, \quad b_j \in V_T, \qquad (4.2)$$

contains exactly all the words in L. Repetitions are allowed in the sequence

(4.2) and hence we may assume the sequence to be infinite. It is understood that, for $u(i) = 0$, $P_i = \lambda$.

Consider the type-3 grammar $G = (\{X_0, X\}, V_T, X_0, F)$ where

$$F = \{X_0 \to X_0, X_0 \to X, X \to \lambda\} \cup \{X \to a_i X | 1 \leq i \leq n\}.$$

A mapping φ of the set of natural numbers into the set of subsets of F is defined as follows. For all i, $\varphi(i)$ consists of two productions, one of which is $X_0 \to X_0$. The other is defined recursively. Assume that

$$P_1 = c_1 \cdots c_{u(1)}, \qquad u(1) \geq 0, \quad c_j \in V_T.$$

Then the production $X_0 \to X$ is in $\varphi(1)$ and, for $1 \leq j \leq u(1)$, the production $X \to c_j X$ is in $\varphi(1+j)$, and the production $X \to \lambda$ is in $\varphi(2+u(1))$. Assume that, for some $i \geq 1$, the second production in $\varphi(j)$ has been defined for all values of j satisfying

$$j \leq lg(P_1 \cdots P_i) + 2i = j_0. \tag{4.3}$$

Consider the word $P_{i+1} = b_1 \cdots b_{u(i+1)}$, $u(i+1) \geq 0$, where the b's belong to V_T. Then the production $X_0 \to X$ is in $\varphi(j_0+1)$ and, for $1 \leq j \leq u(i+1)$, the production $X \to b_j X$ is in $\varphi(j_0+1+j)$, and the production $X \to \lambda$ is in $\varphi(j_0+2+u(i+1))$. This completes the definition of φ.

It is an immediate consequence of the definition that $L = L(G, \varphi)$. Indeed, the production $X_0 \to X_0$ is applied until, for some j_0, the production $X_0 \to X$ is applied at the (j_0+1)th step of the derivation. [Here j_0 either equals 0 or is of the form (4.3).] This causes the derivation to terminate, the derived word being P_{i+1}. ∎

The grammar G in the previous proof depends on the alphabet V_T alone. In general, there is no algorithm for computing the values of φ. [Clearly, the existence of an algorithm depends on how the sequence (4.2) is given.] To follow our general requirement of the effectiveness of constructions we could, for instance, assume that φ is computable by a Turing machine. However, because of reasons which become apparent in the next two sections, we make the much stronger assumption that φ is *periodic*.

Definition. A time-varying grammar (G, φ) is *periodically time-varying* iff the function φ is periodic; that is, there is an integer $k \geq 1$ such that $\varphi(j+k) = \varphi(j)$ for all j.

Thus, to specify a periodically time-varying grammar, it suffices to specify G, k, and the values $\varphi(j)$ for $1 \leq j \leq k$. The family of languages of the form $L(G, \varphi)$, where G is a context-free (resp. context-free λ-free) grammar and φ is periodic, is denoted by $\mathcal{T}^\lambda$ (resp. $\mathcal{T}$). Languages in $\mathcal{T}^\lambda$ are referred to as periodically time-varying context-free or, in short, *ptvcf* languages. Similarly, languages in $\mathscr{T}$ are referred to as *ptvcf* λ-*free* languages. These abbreviations are used for grammars, too.

Example 4.1. Consider the ptvcf λ-free grammar (G, φ), where the period k equals 3, defined as follows:

$$\varphi(1) = \{X_0 \to XYZ, Z \to cZ, Z \to c\},$$

$$\varphi(2) = \{X \to aX, X \to a, U \to b\},$$

$$\varphi(3) = \{Y \to bY, Y \to U\}.$$

Capital (lowercase) letters are nonterminals (terminals) and X_0 is the initial letter. Then

$$L(G, \varphi) = \{a^n b^n c^n \,|\, n \geqq 1\}. \tag{4.4}$$

Note that the exceptional pattern and the nonterminal U are introduced in order to prevent the derivation of additional words, for instance, $a^{n+1} b^n c^n$.

As another illustration, consider the ptvcf grammar (G, φ) with period 4, defined as follows:

$$\varphi(1) = \{X_0 \to X_1 Y_1, X_1 \to X_1, Y_2 \to Y_2\},$$

$$\varphi(2) = \{X_1 \to aX_1, X_1 \to bX_2, X_1 \to \lambda, X_2 \to aX_1, X_2 \to bX_2, X_2 \to \lambda\},$$

$$\varphi(3) = \{Y_1 \to aY_1, Y_1 \to bY_2, Y_1 \to \lambda, Y_2 \to aY_1, Y_2 \to bY_2, Y_2 \to \lambda\},$$

$$\varphi(4) = \{X_2 \to X_2, Y_1 \to Y_1\},$$

where again capital (resp. lowercase) letters are nonterminals (resp. terminals), and X_0 is the initial letter. Then

$$L(G, \varphi) = \{PP \,|\, P \in W(\{a, b\})\}. \tag{4.5}$$

The index 1 is associated with the letter a, the index 2 with the letter b. If, for some $j \geqq 0$, after the $(3+4j)$th step in a derivation one of the letters X, Y has the index 1 and the other, the index 2, that is, at the steps $(2+4j)$ and $(3+4j)$ both of the letters a, b were introduced, then the derivation terminates without producing a terminal word since it is impossible to get through the steps $(4+4j)$ and $(5+4j)$.

Thus the language (4.4) belongs to the family $\mathscr{T}$ and the language (4.5) to the family $\mathscr{T}^{\lambda}$. [In fact, if in (4.5) we assume that $P \neq \lambda$, then the language (4.5) belongs to the family $\mathscr{T}$.] Since any grammar can be regarded as a periodically time-varying grammar with period 1, the family $\mathscr{T}^{\lambda}$ (resp. the family $\mathscr{T}$) includes properly the family $\mathscr{L}_2$ (resp. the family of context-free λ-free languages).

The appearance checking interpretation in the application of productions is now extended to concern time-varying grammars.

Definition. Let (G, φ) be a time-varying grammar. Let the notations be the same as in the first definition of this section, and let F_1 be a subset of F. A binary relation $\Rightarrow_{ac}$ on the set of pairs (P, j), where P is a word over the alphabet V and j a natural number, is defined as follows: $(P, j_1) \Rightarrow_{ac} (Q, j_2)$ holds iff $(P, j_1) \Rightarrow (Q, j_2)$ holds, or else $j_2 = j_1 + 1$, $P = Q$, and there is a production $P' \to Q'$ in $F_1 \cap \varphi(j_1)$ such that P' is not a subword of P. (Thus, $\Rightarrow_{ac}$ depends also on F_1.) Let $\Rightarrow_{ac}^*$ be the reflexive transitive closure of the relation $\Rightarrow_{ac}$. The language *generated* by (G, φ) with *appearance checking* for productions in F_1 is defined by

$$L_{ac}(G, \varphi, F_1) = \{P \in W(V_T) | (X_0, 1) \Rightarrow_{ac}^* (P, j) \text{ for some } j\}. \tag{4.6}$$

The family of languages of the form (4.6), where φ is periodic and G is a context-free (resp. context-free λ-free) grammar, is denoted by $\mathscr{T}_{ac}^\lambda$ (resp. $\mathscr{T}_{ac}$). The languages in this family are referred to as *ptvcfac* (resp. *ptvcfac λ-free*) languages.

Thus the indices λ and ac have the same meaning as in connection with the $\mathscr{M}$-families. The inclusions corresponding to (3.5),

$$\mathscr{T} \subseteq \mathscr{T}^\lambda \subseteq \mathscr{T}_{ac}^\lambda, \qquad \mathscr{T} \subseteq \mathscr{T}_{ac} \subseteq \mathscr{T}_{ac}^\lambda, \tag{4.7}$$

are also now obvious by the definitions since F_1 in (4.6) can be chosen as the empty set.

Appearance checking is a very convenient tool also in connection with time-varying languages. The reader may verify this by showing that the language (3.6) considered in Example 3.2 belongs to the family $\mathscr{T}_{ac}$.

In the following two sections, we develop a general theory which shows that each of the $\mathscr{T}$-families coincides with the corresponding $\mathscr{M}$-family and that these families can be further characterized in another two essentially different ways. In addition, the family $\mathscr{T}_{ac}^\lambda$ equals the family $\mathscr{L}_0$.

Comparing $\mathscr{T}$- and $\mathscr{M}$-families, it is easy to see that each of the former is included in the corresponding one among the latter. In fact, for any (G, φ), where the period of φ equals k, it suffices to consider all matrices with k productions such that, for $j = 1, \ldots, k$, the jth production belongs to $\varphi(j)$. Thus, we can simulate (G, φ) by a matrix grammar, provided we still take care of the fact that derivations according to a matrix grammar never terminate in the middle of a matrix. This is done in detail in the sequel.

Right now we study the reverse inclusion: Is an $\mathscr{M}$-family included in the corresponding $\mathscr{T}$-family? This inclusion is not obvious because in applying a matrix one is able to "remember" which production was applied previously.

This is the reason why the matrix grammar G_1 in Example 3.1 is very simple. However, as seen in Example 4.1, the same language is generated also by a ptvcf grammar. The idea here is that only some steps in a derivation are "essential," and the remaining steps serve the purpose of finding out whether or not the essential steps were taken correctly. The same idea lies also behind the general proofs given below.

In the following theorems, our assumptions about the form of matrix grammars may seem somewhat artificial. However, we prove later that all matrix grammars can be reduced to this form.

Theorem 4.2. A language L generated by a context-free matrix grammar such that all matrices consist of two productions belongs to the family $\mathscr{T}^\lambda$.

Proof. Assume that the matrices of the matrix grammar G which generates L are

$$[X_1^i \to P_1^i, X_2^i \to P_2^i], \qquad (4.8)$$

where $i = 1, \ldots, u$, and each of the X's is a nonterminal. A ptvcf grammar (G_1, φ) is now defined in such a way that

$$L = L(G) = L(G_1, \varphi). \qquad (4.9)$$

The set of nonterminals of G_1 is obtained by adding the new nonterminals

$$Y_j^i, \qquad 1 \leqq i \leqq u, \quad 1 \leqq j \leqq 2,$$

to those of G. The set of terminals and the initial letter in G_1 equal those in G. The production set of G_1 consists of all of the following productions:

$$X_j^i \to P_j^i Y_j^i, \qquad (4.10)$$

$$Y_j^i \to Y_j^i, \qquad (4.11)$$

$$Y_j^i \to \lambda, \qquad (4.12)$$

where the X's and P's are as in (4.8), $1 \leqq i \leqq u$, and $1 \leqq j \leqq 2$.

By definition, φ will be a periodic function with the period $2u + 2$. Thus it suffices to define φ for natural numbers less than or equal to $2u + 2$. For $j = 1, 2$, $\varphi(j)$ consists of the productions (4.10) where $i = 1, \ldots, u$. For

$$v = 2u + j, \qquad 1 \leqq j \leqq 2,$$

$\varphi(v)$ consists of the productions (4.12) where $i = 1, \ldots, u$. For

$$v = 2h + j, \qquad 1 \leqq h \leqq u - 1, \quad 1 \leqq j \leqq 2,$$

$\varphi(v)$ consists of the productions (4.11), where $1 \leqq i \leqq u$ and $i \neq h$, and of the production

$$Y_{3-j}^h \to Y_{3-j}^h. \qquad (4.13)$$

The nonterminals Y_j^i are introduced in order to prevent such derivations getting through which use first and second productions from two different matrices. We now prove that (4.9) holds true.

Consider the application of the matrix (4.8) in a derivation according to G. Precisely the same effect is obtained in a derivation according to (G_1, φ) in $2u + 2$ steps. The only difference is that during the first two steps the nonterminals $Y_j^i, j = 1, 2$, are introduced and during the last two steps considered, these nonterminals are erased. Hence, any derivation according to G can be converted to a derivation according to (G_1, φ), and consequently the left side of (4.9) is included in the right side.

Any derivation according to (G_1, φ), which yields a terminal word, can be divided into subderivations, each of which consists of $2u + 2$ steps. Consider one such subderivation. If, for some i, the nonterminals Y_j^i, $j = 1, 2$, are introduced during the first two steps, then the same effect is obtained by applying the matrix (4.8). Assume, therefore, that the nonterminals Y_1^p and Y_2^q, $p \neq q$, are introduced during the first two steps. Then, by the choice of the production (4.13) to the range of $\varphi(v)$, both of the productions $Y_1^p \to Y_1^p$ and $Y_2^q \to Y_2^q$ are applicable at the same step. Consequently, for some v, no production is applicable at the vth step. (In fact, if $p \neq u$, then $v = 2p + 1$; and if $p = u$, then $v = 2q + 2$.) Thus, the derivation terminates without producing a terminal word. This implies that the right side of (4.9) is included in the left side. ∎

Theorem 4.2 is now extended to concern the appearance checking interpretation. This calls for a modification of the argument, where new nonterminals are introduced to indicate that a production $X \to P$ has been applied to a word Q by noticing that X is not a subword of Q.

Theorem 4.3. Let G be a context-free matrix grammar whose matrices are the matrices (4.8) where $i = 1, \ldots, u$. Assume that the sets of letters appearing in the first and second productions are disjoint; that is, no letter appears in both $X_1^i P_1^i$ and $X_2^j P_2^j$ where $1 \leq i, j \leq u$. Let F_1 be a subset of the set of (the occurrences of) the first productions in the matrices (4.8), and let $\Rightarrow_{ac}$ be defined with respect to this F_1. Then the language

$$\{P \in W(V_T) | X_0 s_0 \Rightarrow_{ac}^* P\}, \qquad (4.14)$$

where X_0 (resp. s_0) is one of the nonterminals appearing in the first (resp. second) productions in the matrices, belongs to the family $\mathcal{T}_{ac}^\lambda$.

Proof. Assume first that F_1 is empty. Then the language (4.14) is generated by the matrix grammar whose matrices are (4.8) and

$$[X_0' \to X_0', \ X_0' \to X_0 s_0],$$

where X_0' is the new initial letter. By Theorem 4.2, (4.14) belongs to the family $\mathscr{T}^\lambda$, and consequently to the family $\mathscr{T}_{ac}^\lambda$.

From now on we assume that F_1 consists of v (occurrences of) productions where $1 \leq v \leq u$. By a suitable renumbering, the productions in F_1 are

$$X_1^i \to P_1^i, \qquad 1 \leq i \leq v.$$

We define a ptvcf grammar (G_1, φ) and a subset F_2 of the production set of G_1 such that (4.14) equals the language $L_{ac}(G_1, \varphi, F_2)$.

The set of nonterminals of G_1 is obtained by adding new nonterminals

$$X_0', U, Z, U^i, Z^i, \quad 1 \leq i \leq v; \qquad Y_j^i, \quad 1 \leq i \leq u, \quad 1 \leq j \leq 2,$$

to those of G. The production set of G_1 consists of all productions (4.10)–(4.12) and of the following productions:

$$X_0' \to X_0 s_0 U, \tag{4.15}$$

$$U \to \lambda, \tag{4.16}$$

$$U \to U^i U Y_1^i, \qquad 1 \leq i \leq v, \tag{4.17}$$

$$X_1^i \to Z^i X_1^i, \qquad 1 \leq i \leq v, \tag{4.18}$$

$$U^i \to Z^i, \qquad 1 \leq i \leq v, \tag{4.19}$$

$$Z^i \to \lambda, \qquad 1 \leq i \leq v, \tag{4.20}$$

$$Z^i \to Z, \qquad 1 \leq i \leq v. \tag{4.21}$$

The initial letter in G_1 is X_0', and the terminals are the same as in G. The set F_2 consists of the productions (4.15), and (4.18)–(4.21).

By definition, φ is a periodic function with the period $(2u+3) + 4v$; $\varphi(1)$ consists of the production (4.15). For $j = 2, \ldots, 2u+3$, $\varphi(j)$ is defined exactly as $\varphi(j-1)$ in the proof of Theorem 4.2 with the exception that all productions (4.16) and (4.17) are added to the set $\varphi(2)$. For

$$j = (2u+3) + 1, \ldots, (2u+3) + 4v,$$

$\varphi(j)$ will consist of one production only. These productions are (4.18)–(4.21) in the following order:

$$X_1^1 \to Z^1 X_1^1, \ U^1 \to Z^1, \ Z^1 \to \lambda, \ldots, X_1^v \to Z^v X_1^v,$$

$$U^v \to Z^v, \ Z^v \to \lambda, \ Z^1 \to Z, \ldots, Z^v \to Z.$$

Having completed the definition of the triple (G_1, φ, F_2), we now prove that (4.14) equals the language $L_{ac}(G_1, \varphi, F_2)$. The production (4.15) is applied at the beginning of each derivation according to (G_1, φ), after which it is applied in the appearance checking sense only since X_0' does not occur anywhere else. To an application of a matrix (4.8) there corresponds

$(2u+2) + 4v$ steps in a derivation according to (G_1, φ). Among these only the first two steps are "essential"; the remaining ones serve the purpose of checking that the first two steps were done correctly. The role of the Y's is the same as in the proof of Theorem 4.2: They enable us to make sure that the productions applied at the first two steps come from the same matrix.

Assume that we want to apply the production

$$X_1^i \rightarrow P_1^i, \qquad 1 \leq i \leq v,$$

at the first step by noticing that X_1^i is not a subword of the word under scan. Then we apply the production (4.17). This application has been wrong iff, for some i, we have both of the letters X_1^i and U^i in the word under scan after the first step. [We are now considering a specific sequence of $(2u+2) + 4v$ steps.] By our assumption concerning the matrices, this happens exactly in case X_1^i and U^i occur in the word under scan after the $(2u+2)$th step (provided that the derivation is not terminated before that). On the other hand, this means that the nonterminal Z (which can never be eliminated) will be introduced at the steps after the $(2u+2)$th step. By the choice of F_2, this is the only case where Z will be introduced. Hence, only correct applications of (4.17) lead to terminal words.

A derivation according to (G_1, φ) is terminated by an application of (4.16). If (4.16) is used prematurely, then no terminal word will result because the Y_2^i introduced at the next step is not eliminated. ∎

The constructions of the two preceding proofs can be carried out in the λ-free case, too. This means that the auxiliary nonterminals (Y's, U's, and Z's) must be replaced by indices attached to other nonterminals. This implies the following result which we state in the general form without making additional assumptions concerning the matrices. (All matrices can be reduced to the required form similarly as in the proof of Theorem 3.3.)

Proposition 4.1. $\mathcal{M} \subseteq \mathcal{T}$ and $\mathcal{M}_{\mathrm{ac}} \subseteq \mathcal{T}_{\mathrm{ac}}$.

5. PROGRAMMED GRAMMARS

In a matrix grammar, one applies strings of productions. Once an application of a string has been started, all productions in the string have to be applied. Thus, within certain limits, in a matrix grammar each application of a production determines which productions will be applicable at the next step. Also *programmed grammars* are based on a similar method of regulating derivations. In a programmed grammar G, one is given together with each production f two subsets $\sigma(f)$ and $\varphi(f)$ of the entire production set F of G, referred to as the *success* and *failure* field of f, respectively. Any production

f can be applied both in the ordinary rewriting sense and in the appearance checking sense. If we have applied f in the former sense, then the next production to be applied must belong to $\sigma(f)$. If we have applied f in the appearance checking sense, that is, noticed that the left side of f is not a subword of the word under scan, then the next production to be applied must belong to $\varphi(f)$. The sets $\sigma(f)$ and $\varphi(f)$ are termed also the *go-to fields* of f.

It is sometimes convenient to allow the same production $P \to Q$ to possess different go-to fields in different parts of a derivation. This is affected by assigning $P \to Q$ one or more *labels*, and considering σ and φ to be mappings of the set $\text{Lab}(F)$ of all labels of the productions in F into the set of subsets of $\text{Lab}(F)$. In general, for a finite set S, we denote by $\text{Lab}(S)$ any set of labels for the elements of S such that to each label f there is associated a unique element of S, called the element *labeled* by f, and each element of S possesses at least one label. [Thus, $\text{Lab}(S)$ is an alphabet which is mapped onto the set S. It is understood that this mapping is also specified together with the set $\text{Lab}(S)$. In fact, labeling was used already in connection with matrix grammars when we spoke of the *occurrences* of the productions in the matrices.]

Definition. A *programmed grammar* of type i, $0 \leq i \leq 3$, is an ordered triple (G, σ, φ) where $G = (V_N, V_T, X_0, F)$ is a type-i grammar, and σ and φ are mappings of $\text{Lab}(F)$ into the set of subsets of $\text{Lab}(F)$ [for some fixed set $\text{Lab}(F)$ of labels for the elements of F]. Two binary relations $\Rightarrow$ and $\Rightarrow_{ac}$ on the set of all pairs (P, f), where P is a word over the alphabet $V = V_N \cup V_T$ and $f \in \text{Lab}(F)$, are defined as follows: $(P, f_1) \Rightarrow (Q, f_2)$ holds iff there are words P_1, P_2, P', and Q' such that (i) $P = P_1 P' P_2$ and $Q = P_1 Q' P_2$, (ii) the production in F labeled by f_1 is $P' \to Q'$, and (iii) f_2 belongs to the set $\sigma(f_1)$; $(P, f_1) \Rightarrow_{ac} (Q, f_2)$ holds iff $(P, f_1) \Rightarrow (Q, f_2)$ holds, or else each of the following conditions is satisfied for some words P' and Q': (i) $P = Q$, (ii) the production in F labeled by f_1 is $P' \to Q'$, (iii) P' is not a subword of P, and (iv) f_2 belongs to the set $\varphi(f_1)$. (Thus, only the relation $\Rightarrow_{ac}$ depends on the mapping φ.) Let $\Rightarrow^*$ (resp. $\Rightarrow_{ac}^*$) be the reflexive transitive closure of the relation $\Rightarrow$ (resp. $\Rightarrow_{ac}$). The language *generated* by the programmed grammar is defined by

$$L(G, \sigma) = \{P \in W(V_T) | (X_0, f) \Rightarrow^* (P, f') \text{ for some } f, f' \in \text{Lab}(F)\}.$$
$$(5.1)$$

The language *generated* by the programmed grammar with *appearance checking* in the application of productions is defined by

$$L_{ac}(G, \sigma, \varphi) = \{P \in W(V_T) | (X_0, f) \Rightarrow_{ac}^* (P, f') \text{ for some } f, f' \in \text{Lab}(F)\}.$$
$$(5.2)$$

The family of languages of the form (5.1), where G is a context-free (resp. context-free λ-free) grammar, is denoted by $\mathscr{P}^\lambda$ (resp. $\mathscr{P}$). Similarly, the family of languages of the form (5.2), where G is a context-free (resp. context-free λ-free) grammar, is denoted by $\mathcal{P}_{ac}^{\lambda}$ (resp. $\mathcal{P}_{ac}$). Equivalently, the family $\mathcal{P}^{\lambda}$ (resp. $\mathcal{P}$) may be defined as the family of languages of the form (5.2) where G is a context-free (resp. context-free λ-free) grammar and the range of the function φ is the empty set.

The inclusions

$$\mathcal{P} \subseteq \mathcal{P}^{\lambda} \subseteq \mathcal{P}_{ac}^{\lambda}, \qquad \mathcal{P} \subseteq \mathcal{P}_{ac} \subseteq \mathcal{P}_{ac}^{\lambda} \qquad (5.3)$$

are again obvious by the definitions. (Note that the indices λ and ac have the same meaning as in the two preceding sections.) Ordinary grammars are obtained as degenerate cases of programmed grammars where for each $f \in \text{Lab}(F)$, we have $\sigma(f) = \varphi(f) = \text{Lab}(F)$. Consequently, the following example shows that $\mathcal{P}^{\lambda}$ (resp. $\mathcal{P}$) properly includes the family of context-free (resp. context-free λ-free) languages.

Example 5.1. Consider the context-free λ-free programmed grammar (G, σ, φ) consisting of the productions

		σ	φ
$f_1:$	$X_0 \to XY$	$\{f_2, f_3, f_6, f_7\}$	$\varnothing$
$f_2:$	$X \to aX$	$\{f_4\}$	$\varnothing$
$f_3:$	$X \to bX$	$\{f_5\}$	$\varnothing$
$f_4:$	$Y \to aY$	$\{f_2, f_3, f_6, f_7\}$	$\varnothing$
$f_5:$	$Y \to bY$	$\{f_2, f_3, f_6, f_7\}$	$\varnothing$
$f_6:$	$X \to a$	$\{f_8\}$	$\varnothing$
$f_7:$	$X \to b$	$\{f_9\}$	$\varnothing$
$f_8:$	$Y \to a$	$\{f_1\}$	$\varnothing$
$f_9:$	$Y \to b$	$\{f_1\}$	$\varnothing$

where capital (resp. lowercase) letters are nonterminals (resp. terminals), X_0 is the initial letter, and the go-to fields are given together with each production. Obviously,

$$L(G, \sigma) = L_{ac}(G, \sigma, \varphi) = \{PP \mid P \in W(\{a, b\}), P \neq \lambda\}$$

and consequently this language belongs to the family $\mathcal{P}$.

Example 5.2. For the context-free λ-free programmed grammar (G, σ, φ) defined by

		σ	φ
$f_1:$	$X_0 \to ZZ$	$\{f_1\}$	$\{f_2, f_3\}$
$f_2:$	$Z \to X_0$	$\{f_2\}$	$\{f_1\}$
$f_3:$	$Z \to a$	$\{f_3\}$	$\varnothing$

where the notation is as in the previous example, we have

$$L_{ac}(G, \sigma, \varphi) = \{a^{2^n} | n \geq 1\}. \tag{5.4}$$

The programmed grammar for the language (5.4) is very simple. Let us compare it with the generative and matrix grammars for (essentially) the same language given in Example 2.4 in Part 1 and in Example 3.2. It is seen that the context-sensitive device of sending messages through words can be conveniently simulated by context-free productions, provided an appearance checking regulator [such as the failure fields $\varphi(f)$ or the set F_1] is added.

The following theorem is fundamental in the theory of programmed grammars.

Theorem 5.1. A language is of type 0 iff it is generated with appearance checking by a context-free programmed grammar, that is, $\mathcal{L}_0 = \mathcal{P}_{ac}^\lambda$.

Proof. The "if" part is an immediate consequence of Church's thesis. To prove the "only if" part, we consider an arbitrary type-0 language L generated by the grammar $G = (V_N, V_T, X_0, F)$. We show that L is generated (with appearance checking) by a context-free programmed grammar $G_p = (G_1, \sigma, \varphi)$.

Assume that $V_N \cup V_T = V$ consists of $m-1$ letters, $m \geq 3$. Words over V will be encoded as numbers, using a notation similar to the m-adic notation described in Part 1, Note 9.1. Thus we consider a one-to-one mapping g of V onto the set $\{1, ..., m-1\}$. The mapping g is then extended by

$$g(\lambda) = 0, \qquad g(a_1 \cdots a_n) = g(a_1)m^{n-1} + \cdots + g(a_{n-1})m + g(a_n)$$

where $n \geq 1$ and each $a_i \in V$. Since no letter of V represents the digit 0, the mapping g thus extended is a bijection of $W(V)$ into the set of nonnegative integers.

When simulating G, our programmed grammar G_p will work with the codings of the words rather than with the words themselves. Roughly, this is accomplished as follows. To begin with, G_p is given the word $A^{g(X_0)}$ where A is a new nonterminal. Consider one step

$$R_1 P' R_2 \Rightarrow R_1 Q' R_2, \qquad P' \to Q' \in F,$$

in a derivation according to G. The input to G_p is $g(R_1 P' R_2)$ copies of the special nonterminal A; G_p can break up a word in a nondeterministic fashion, after which it may scan a word with $g(R_1)$ occurrences of A, $g(P')$ occurrences of B, and $g(R_2)$ occurrences of C. (This is one possible decomposition; B and C are new nonterminals.) Now G_p can replace the $g(P')$ occurrences of B by $g(Q')$ occurrences of B. (This can be done for any production $P' \to Q'$ in F.) Then the $g(R_1)$ occurrences of A, $g(Q')$ occurrences of B, and $g(R_2)$ occurrences of C are recombined to make $g(R_1 Q' R_2)$ occurrences of A. After this G_p can either break up the word $R_1 Q' R_2$ again, or else decode the $g(R_1 Q' R_2)$ occurrences of A as the word $R_1 Q' R_2$.

The production set of G_p is divided into several parts, referred to as *subroutines*. (Of course, these can be combined to make one big list of productions.) Flow charts are used to describe the interconnection between the various subroutines. The expression "out" in a go-to field of a subroutine indicates that the next subroutine is called. An arrow pointing to a production label indicates that the subroutine is entered through that production.

In our considerations, only the number of the nonterminals such as A, B, C matters, not their order. To avoid repeating this throughout the proof, we introduce a special notation

$$P \Rightarrow^* : Q,$$

meaning the following. The subroutine under consideration generates from any word, where the numbers of occurrences of each letter (which occurs also in P) coincide with those in P, a word where the numbers of occurrences of each letter coincide with those in Q. For example, $A^2 B^3 \Rightarrow^* : ABC$ means that any word with two A's and three B's generates a word with one A, B, and C. Occurrences of letters different from A, B, C remain unaltered.

In breaking up and recombining words, some arithmetic is needed. We first define two arithmetical subroutines. For a nonnegative integer i, we denote by $[i/m]$ [resp. $\text{rem}(i/m)$] the integral part [resp. remainder] in the division of i by m. Thus,

$$i/m = [i/m] + \text{rem}(i/m)/m.$$

A subroutine $\text{DIV}(A, B)$ is now defined by

		σ	φ	
$\to d_1$	$: A \to A'$	$\{d_2\}$	$\{d_{2m}\}$	
d_i	$: A \to \lambda$	$\{d_{i+1}\}$	$\{d_{m+i-1}\}$	$i = 2, \ldots, m-1$
d_m	$: A \to \lambda$	$\{d_1\}$	$\{d_{2m-1}\}$	
d_{m+i}	$: A' \to B^i$	$\{d_{2m}\}$	$\varnothing$	$i = 1, \ldots, m-1$
d_{2m}	$: A' \to A$	$\{d_{2m}\}$	out	

It is immediately verified that $\text{DIV}(A, B)$ satisfies, for each nonnegative integer i,

$$A^i \Rightarrow^* : A^{[i/m]} B^{\text{rem}(i/m)}.$$

[Note that m is the number fixed by the cardinality of the alphabet V. Instead of A and B, some other letters may be used. Thus we may consider $\text{DIV}(C, D)$ where the corresponding alphabetic change is made in the productions.]

Another arithmetical subroutine, MULT(A, B, C), is now defined:

$$
\begin{array}{llll}
 & & \sigma & \varphi \\
\to e_1: & A \to A'A'' & \{e_1\} & \{e_2\} \\
e_2: & A'' \to \lambda & \{e_3\} & \{e_5\} \\
e_3: & B \to B'C & \{e_3\} & \{e_4\} \\
e_4: & B' \to B & \{e_4\} & \{e_2\} \\
e_5: & A' \to A & \{e_5\} & \text{out}
\end{array}
$$

This subroutine multiplies any two nonnegative integers i and j as follows:

$$A^i B^j \Rightarrow *: A^i B^j C^{ij}.$$

We list next some simple subroutines which will be useful in the sequel. In each case, we give first the name of the subroutine, followed by a description of its action, and finally its definition as a programmed grammar.

ER(A) erases all occurrences of the letter A.

$$
\begin{array}{llll}
 & & \sigma & \varphi \\
f_1: & A \to \lambda & \{f_1\} & \text{out}
\end{array}
$$

CH(A) checks the appearance or nonappearance of the letter A without changing anything. The next subroutine depends on the result of the checking.

$$
\begin{array}{llll}
 & & \sigma & \varphi \\
f_2: & A \to A & \text{out} & \text{out}
\end{array}
$$

$G_1(A, B)$ satisfies, for all $i \geq 1$, $A^i \Rightarrow *: A^i B$.

$$
\begin{array}{llll}
 & & \sigma & \varphi \\
f_3: & A \to AB & \text{out} & \text{out}
\end{array}
$$

$G_2(A, B, C)$ satisfies, for all $i \geq 1$, $A^i \Rightarrow *: A^i B^i C$.

$$
\begin{array}{llll}
 & & \sigma & \varphi \\
\to f_4: & A \to AC & \{f_5\} & \text{out} \\
f_5: & A \to A' & \{f_5\} & \{f_6\} \\
f_6: & A' \to AB & \{f_6\} & \text{out}
\end{array}
$$

$G_3(A)$ satisfies, for all $i \geq 0$, $A^i \Rightarrow *: A^{mi}$.

$$
\begin{array}{llll}
 & & \sigma & \varphi \\
\to f_7: & A \to A' & \{f_7\} & \{f_8\} \\
f_8: & A' \to A^m & \{f_8\} & \text{out}
\end{array}
$$

$G_4(A, B)$ replaces all A's by B's.

$$
\begin{array}{llll}
 & & \sigma & \varphi \\
f_9: & A \to B & \{f_9\} & \text{out}
\end{array}
$$

G_5 satisfies $X_0' \Rightarrow^* \# A^{g(X_0)}$.

$$
\begin{array}{ccc}
 & \sigma & \varphi \\
f_{10}\colon X_0' \to \# A^{g(X_0)} & \text{out} & \varnothing
\end{array}
$$

We now proceed to somewhat more complicated subroutines. The first among them, $G_6(A, B)$, serves the purpose of breaking up a word. More specifically, $G_6(A, B)$ satisfies, for all words P and Q over V with $PQ \neq \lambda$,

$$A^{g(PQ)} \Rightarrow^*\colon A^{g(P)} B^{g(Q)}.$$

The action of the subroutine is based on the equation

$$g(PQ) = g(P)m^{lg(Q)} + g(Q)$$

which is valid for any words P and Q over V. In particular, for a letter $a \in V$, this equation has the form

$$g(Pa) = g(P)m + g(a),$$

that is, $g(P)$ and $g(a)$ are the integral part and the remainder in the division of $g(Pa)$ by m. By our choice of m and the definition of g, $1 \leqq g(a) < m$. [If we use ordinary m-adic notation instead of g, then it is possible to have $g(a) = m$. The corresponding change has to be made in the division equation and the subroutine $DIV(A, B)$.]

The subroutine $G_6(A, B)$ is defined by Fig. 10. Given $A^{g(R)}$, the subroutine breaks R into two parts $R = PQ$. Initially, $Q = \lambda$. The loop in the flow diagram successively picks up a single letter from the right end of P and adds it to Q.

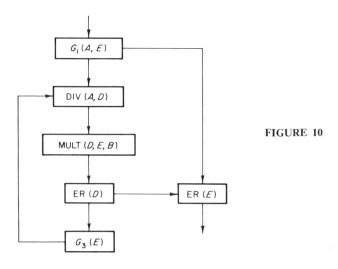

FIGURE 10

The block $\mathrm{DIV}(A, D)$ is entered with a word of the form

$$A^{g(Pa)} B^{g(Q)} E^{mlg(Q)}.$$

(Initially, $Q = \lambda$.) It is converted (in the sense of the relation $\Rightarrow *$:) by $\mathrm{DIV}(A, D)$ into the word

$$A^{g(P)} D^{g(a)} B^{g(Q)} E^{mlg(Q)}.$$

The next block produces the word

$$A^{g(P)} D^{g(a)} B^{g(Q)} E^{mlg(Q)} B^{g(a)mlg(Q)} = A^{g(P)} D^{g(a)} E^{mlg(Q)} B^{g(aQ)}$$

(equality is understood in the sense of the relation $\Rightarrow *$:). After this the D's are erased. Then either the E's are erased, which completes the routine, or else the block $\mathrm{DIV}(A, D)$ is entered with the word

$$A^{g(P)} B^{g(aQ)} E^{mlg(aQ)}.$$

which starts the loop all over again. Note that the direct path from $G_1(A, E)$ to $\mathrm{ER}(E)$ makes it possible for Q to be empty.

The next subroutine, $G_7(A, B)$, has an effect reverse to that of G_6; namely, it recombines words. For any words P and Q over V, $G_7(A, B)$ satisfies

$$A^{g(P)} B^{g(Q)} \Rightarrow *: A^{g(PQ)}.$$

$G_7(A, B)$ is defined by Fig. 11. If there are no B's present, then $Q = \lambda$ and we exit without changing the exponent of A. Otherwise, we enter the loop which produces $E^{mlg(Q)}$; that is, the block $\mathrm{MULT}(A, E, C)$ is entered with the word

$$A^{g(P)} B^{g(Q)} E^{mlg(Q)}.$$

After this block the number of C's equals $g(P)m^{lg(Q)}$ and the number of B's equals $g(Q)$. Since both B's and C's are finally converted into A's, we obtain altogether $g(PQ)$ occurrences of A.

The next subroutine, G_8, generates from the word $\# A^{g(P)}$ the word P for any $P \in W(V)$. (Here we think of the ordinary yield-relation rather than $\Rightarrow *$:.) Thus, G_8 serves the purpose of decoding words. The productions of G_8 consist of the productions of $\mathrm{DIV}(A, B)$, where $\{h_1^{\ 1}\}$ is defined to be the failure field of d_{2m}, and of the following productions:

		σ	φ	
$h_1^{\ 1}$:	$B \to \lambda$	$\{h_2^{\ 1}\}$	$\{h_1^{\ 5}\}$	
$h_i^{\ 1}$:	$B \to \lambda$	$\{h_{i+1}^{1}\}$	$\{h_{i-1}^{2}\}$	$i = 2, \ldots, m-1$
$h_m^{\ 1}$:	$B \to \lambda$	$\varnothing$	$\{h_{m-1}^{2}\}$	
$h_i^{\ 2}$:	$A \to A$	$\{h_i^{\ 3}\}$	$\{h_i^{\ 4}\}$	$i = 1, \ldots, m-1$
$h_i^{\ 3}$:	$\# \to \#g^{-1}(i)$	$\{d_1\}$	$\varnothing$	$i = 1, \ldots, m-1$
$h_i^{\ 4}$:	$\# \to g^{-1}(i)$	$\varnothing$	$\varnothing$	$i = 1, \ldots, m-1$
$h_1^{\ 5}$:	$\# \to \lambda$	$\varnothing$	$\varnothing$	

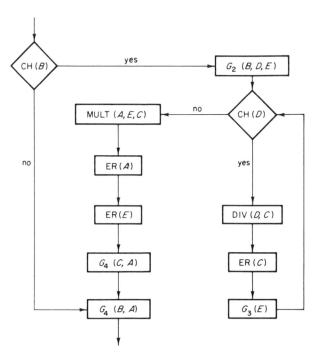

FIGURE 11

The subroutine G_8 works as follows. The part of the routine consisting of $DIV(A, B)$ is entered with a word of the form

$$\#QA^{g(Ra)}, \qquad a \in V, \quad P = RaQ.$$

It is first converted by $DIV(A, B)$ into the word

$$\#QA^{g(R)}B^{g(a)}.$$

(The mutual order of A's and B's may be different from the one indicated.) The productions $h_j{}^1$ erase the B's but their number i is retained by the different failure fields. The productions $h_j{}^2$ check whether or not any A's are present, still retaining the number of B's. Then $a = g^{-1}(i)$ is written to the right of $\#$. If there were no A's left, then also $\#$ is erased (by $h_i{}^4$). Otherwise $h_i{}^3$ is applied, after which the loop is reentered with the word

$$\#aQA^{g(R)},$$

where $R = R_1 b$ for some $b \in V$. If originally $P = \lambda$, and consequently G_8 is entered with the word $\#$, then the sequence of productions $d_1, d_{2m}, h_1{}^1, h_1{}^5$ produces λ. This is the only case where the application of $h_1{}^1$ is not successful.

Our last subroutine G_9 satisfies, for any production $P \to Q$ in F, the relation $B^{g(P)} \Rightarrow *: B^{g(Q)}$. Define

$$u = \max\{g(P)|P \to Q \text{ in } F\}.$$

For each production in F, we introduce a label. Let $t_1{}^1, ..., t_v{}^1$ be the labels thus obtained. For each $i = 1, ..., u$, let $T(i)$ be the set (maybe empty) of labels of those productions in F whose left side equals $g^{-1}(i)$. Let Q_i, $i = 1, ..., v$, be the right side of the production labeled by $t_i{}^1$. The subroutine G_9 consists of the following productions:

		σ	φ	
$t_i{}^1$	$: D \to B^{g(Q_i)}$	out	$\varnothing$	$i = 1, ..., v$
$\to t_1{}^2$	$: B \to D$	$\{t_2{}^2\}$	$\varnothing$	
$t_i{}^2$	$: B \to \lambda$	$\{t_{i+1}^2\}$	$T(i-1)$	$i = 2, ..., u$
t_{u+1}^2	$: B \to \lambda$	$\varnothing$	$T(u)$	

Since the left sides of all productions in F are distinct from λ, the application of the initial production $t_1{}^2$ is always successful. The productions $t_i{}^2$ erase the B's, retaining their number, after which the only D is rewritten as an appropriate power of B.

We are now in the position to introduce the required programmed grammar G_p. It is defined by Fig. 12 (which implicitly defines the auxiliary nonterminal and label alphabets needed). The block $G_6(A, C)$ is entered with a word of the form

$$\# A^{g(P)}, \qquad P \neq \lambda,$$

where $X_0 \Rightarrow * P$ according to the given grammar G. (Initially, an application of G_5 gives $X_0 = P$. The initial letter of G_p is X_0'.) The two blocks G_6 produce (in a nondeterministic fashion and in the sense of the relation $\Rightarrow *$:) the word

$$\# A^{g(R_1)} B^{g(P')} C^{g(R_2)}, \qquad P = R_1 P' R_2.$$

If P' is the left side of some production of G, then the block G_9 converts the word above into

$$\# A^{g(R_1)} B^{g(Q')} C^{g(R_2)}$$

where Q' is the right side of the production in question. The two blocks G_7 now produce the word

$$\# A^{g(R_1 Q' R_2)} = \# A^{g(P_1)},$$

where $P \Rightarrow P_1$ according to G, and consequently $X_0 \Rightarrow * P_1$. Then the loop may be started all over again, or else P_1 is decoded by the block G_8 and the derivation ends. (If P_1 is over the terminal alphabet, then the latter alternative must be

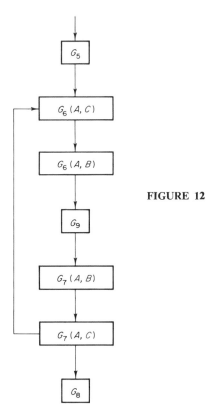

FIGURE 12

chosen in order to terminate the derivation. On the other hand, the loop must be chosen if P_1 contains at least one nonterminal.) We conclude that $L(G) = L_{ac}(G_p)$. ∎

The next theorem is an immediate corollary of Theorem 5.1.

Theorem 5.2. Any type-0 language is a homomorphic image of a language in $\mathscr{P}_{ac}$.

Proof. Let L be a type-0 language over V_T. By Theorem 5.1, there is a context-free programmed grammar (G, σ, φ) such that

$$L = L_{ac}(G, \sigma, \varphi).$$

Let (G_1, σ, φ) be the context-free λ-free programmed grammar obtained from (G, σ, φ) by adding a new terminal c, replacing every production $X \to \lambda$ with the production $X \to c$, and leaving the labels of the productions unchanged.

Let h be the homomorphism of $W(V_T \cup \{c\})$ onto $W(V_T)$ defined by

$$h(c) = \lambda, \qquad h(a) = a \qquad \text{for} \quad a \in V_T.$$

Then

$$L = h(L_{ac}(G_1, \sigma, \varphi)). \quad \blacksquare$$

The inclusion $\mathcal{M}_{ac}^\lambda \subseteq \mathcal{P}_{ac}^\lambda$ follows by Theorem 5.1 and Church's thesis. It can also be established directly.

Theorem 5.3. Each of the $\mathcal{M}$-families is included in the corresponding $\mathcal{P}$-family, that is,

$$\mathcal{M} \subseteq \mathcal{P}, \qquad \mathcal{M}_{ac} \subseteq \mathcal{P}_{ac}, \qquad \mathcal{M}^\lambda \subseteq \mathcal{P}^\lambda, \qquad \mathcal{M}_{ac}^\lambda \subseteq \mathcal{P}_{ac}^\lambda. \qquad (5.5)$$

Proof. Let $G = (V_N, V_T, X_0, M)$ be a context-free λ-free matrix grammar, and F_1 a subset of the set F of all (occurrences of) productions in the matrices. We define a context-free λ-free programmed grammar (G_1, σ, φ) such that

$$L_{ac}(G, F_1) = L_{ac}(G_1, \sigma, \varphi). \qquad (5.6)$$

Moreover, if $F_1 = \varnothing$, then also the range of φ is the empty set. This will prove the first two inclusions.

Introduce $V_1 = \{X_a | a \in V_T\}$ and denote by F' the set of productions obtained from F by replacing each $a \in V_T$ with X_a. This replacement is performed in the productions in the matrices of M, yielding a set M', after which the productions are labeled in such a way that a distinct label is attached to every occurrence of every production in some matrix. The productions in the set

$$F_2 = \{X_a \to a | a \in V_T\}$$

are used as their own labels. In this way, we obtain a context-free λ-free grammar $G_1 = (V_N \cup V_1, V_T, X_0, F' \cup F_2)$ and a set of labels, $\text{Lab}(F' \cup F_2)$. We now define the functions σ and φ. Consider an arbitrary matrix

$$[f_1: X_1 \to P_1, ..., f_n: X_n \to P_n], \qquad n \geq 1 \qquad (5.7)$$

in the set M'. [Note that we have given, together with each production, its label. The labels in (5.7) are distinct among themselves, as well as from all labels appearing in other matrices.] For $j < n$, we define $\sigma(f_j) = \{f_{j+1}\}$ and $\varphi(f_j) = \{f_{j+1}\}$ or $\varphi(f_j) = \varnothing$, depending on whether or not the production $X_j \to P_j$ belongs to F_1 (i.e., whether or not the production from which $X_j \to P_j$ results by replacing each $a \in V_T$ with X_a belongs to F_1). Let H be the subset of $\text{Lab}(F' \cup F_2)$ consisting of the labels of the first productions in the matrices of M'. Then $\sigma(f_n) = H \cup F_2$ and $\varphi(f_n) = \sigma(f_n)$ or

$\varphi(f_n) = \varnothing$, depending on whether or not the production $X_n \to P_n$ belongs to F_1. Finally, for $f \in F_2$, we define $\sigma(f) = F_2$ and $\varphi(f) = \varnothing$. It is clear that (5.6) holds true, and that the range of φ is the empty set if $F_1 = \varnothing$.

The latter two among the inclusions (5.5) are established in almost the same way. The given grammar G is now not necessarily λ-free. To define a context-free programmed grammar (G_1, σ, φ) such that (5.6) holds true, we introduce $V_1 = \{X_0', Y\}$, and label the productions in the matrices of M in such a way that a distinct label is attached to every occurrence of every production in some matrix. The productions in the set

$$F_2 = \{X_0' \to X_0 Y, \; Y \to \lambda\} \tag{5.8}$$

are used as their own labels. In this way, we obtain a context-free grammar $G_1 = (V_N \cup V_1, V_T, X_0', F \cup F_2)$ and a set of labels, $\mathrm{Lab}(F \cup F_2)$. For $f \in F_2$, we define $\varphi(f) = \varnothing$ and $\sigma(f) = \{f\}$ or $\sigma(f) = H$, depending on whether f is the second or first production in F_2. [Here H is the subset of $\mathrm{Lab}(F \cup F_2)$ consisting of the labels of the first productions in the matrices of M.] Otherwise, the definition of σ and φ is exactly as before [with F_2 in the new meaning (5.8)]. Thus (5.6) holds true now also, and the range of φ is the empty set if $F_1 = \varnothing$. ∎

In the previous proof, the nonterminals in V_1 and the productions in F_2 were introduced to prevent derivations ending with only a partial application of some matrix.

6. CONTROL LANGUAGES

Consider a grammar G with the set of productions F, and introduce $\mathrm{Lab}(F)$. Obviously, to each derivation D according to G there corresponds a word (so-called *control word*) over the alphabet $\mathrm{Lab}(F)$ consisting of labels of productions applied in D in the order of their application. Let C be a language over the alphabet $\mathrm{Lab}(F)$. The language generated by G with *control language* C is the subset of the language $L(G)$ consisting of words which possess at least one derivation with a control word in C. (In general, control words are not uniquely determined by derivations.) The application of productions can also now be understood in the narrow (rewriting only) or in the broad (both rewriting and appearance checking) sense.

Control languages provide a uniform way of describing grammars with restrictions on the use of productions, such as the ones considered in Sections 3–5, as well as a convenient method of proving results about the language families corresponding to such grammars. If we are dealing with the regulating devices introduced in Sections 3–5, it suffices to consider *regular* control languages. It turns out that, for $i = 0, 1, 2, 3$, the regulating devices increase

e generative capacity of type-$(i = 2)$ grammars only. Moreover, all of the
gulating devices considered increase the generative capacity of type-2
ammars to the same extent, that is, the $\mathcal{M}$-, $\mathcal{T}$-, and $\mathcal{P}$-families (with none
$\cdot$ some of the indices λ and ac) are all equal.
After these remarks, we now give the formal definitions.

Definition. Let $G = (V_N, V_T, X_0, F)$ be a grammar, $\text{Lab}(F)$ a set of labels
$\cdot$r the production set F, and F_1 a subset of $\text{Lab}(F)$. Let D be a derivation
cording to G and U a word over the alphabet $\text{Lab}(F)$. Then U is a *control*
ord of D iff one of the following conditions is satisfied: (i) for some
Q, P', Q', R_1, R_2, D is the derivation $P \Rightarrow Q$ and $U = f$, where $P =$
$P' R_2$, $Q = R_1 Q' R_2$, and $P' \rightarrow Q'$ possesses the label $f \in \text{Lab}(F)$; (ii) for
$\cdot$me P, P', Q', D is the derivation consisting of the word P only and $U = \lambda$,
$\cdot$ else $U = f$, where $P' \rightarrow Q'$ possesses the label $f \in F_1$ and P' is not a subword
$\cdot$ P; (iii) for some P, Q, R, U_1, U_2, D is the derivation $P \Rightarrow^* Q \Rightarrow^* R$,
$= U_1 U_2$, and U_1 is a control word of the derivation $P \Rightarrow^* Q$ and U_2 is a
$\cdot$ntrol word of the derivation $Q \Rightarrow^* R$.
Let C be a language over the alphabet $\text{Lab}(F)$. The language *generated*
$\cdot$ G with *control language* C and with *appearance checking* for productions
F_1 is defined by

$$L_{ac}(G, C, F_1) = \{P \in W(V_T) | \text{ there is a derivation}$$

$$D: X_0 \Rightarrow^* P \text{ and } U \in C \text{ such that } U \text{ is a control word of } D\}. \quad (6.1)$$

$F_1 = \varnothing$ [which implies that point (ii) in the definition of a control word may
$\cdot$ omitted], then (6.1) is termed also the language *generated* by G with
$\cdot$ntrol language C and denoted by $L(G, C)$. A language is of *type* $(i, j, 1)$ iff
$\cdot$ is of the form (6.1) where G is a type-i grammar and C a type-j language.
language is of *type* $(i, j, 0)$ iff it is of the form $L(G, C)$ where G is a type-i
ammar and C a type-j language. (For $i = 3$, G may be either right-linear or
$\cdot$t-linear.) The family of all languages of type (i, j, k) is denoted by

$$\mathcal{L}(i, j, k), \quad 0 \leq i \leq 3, \quad 0 \leq j \leq 3, \quad 0 \leq k \leq 1. \quad (6.2)$$

$\cdot$ontext-free λ-free grammars and languages are referred to, in short, as
$\cdot$pe-$(2 - \lambda)$ grammars and languages. A language is of *type* $(2 - \lambda, j, 1)$ iff it
$\cdot$ of the form (6.1) where G is a type-$(2 - \lambda)$ grammar and C a type-j language.
he type $(2 - \lambda, j, 0)$ is defined analogously, and the family notation (6.2) is
$\cdot$tended to concern the case where $i = 2 - \lambda$.

Example 6.1. Assume that a grammar G contains the following labeled
$\cdot$roductions

$$f_1: X \rightarrow X, \quad f_2: X \rightarrow X, \quad f_3: X \rightarrow aY, \quad f_4: Y \rightarrow ab, \quad f_5: X \rightarrow Y$$

where $f_2, f_5 \in F_1$. Then each of the following words

$$f_3 f_4, \qquad f_3 f_4 f_2, \qquad f_1 f_3 f_2 f_4, \qquad f_1^3 f_3 f_2^5 f_5 f_4 f_2^7$$

is a control word of the derivation $X \Rightarrow^* a^2 b$, whereas none of the words

$$f_3 f_4^2, \qquad f_1 f_5 f_3 f_4, \qquad f_3^2 f_4$$

is a control word of this derivation.

Example 6.2. In this and the following examples we use our customa\
notation: Capital (resp. lowercase) letters are nonterminals (resp. terminal\
and X_0 is the initial letter. Consider the grammar G consisting of the label\
productions

$$f_1: X_0 \to XYZ, \qquad f_2: X \to aX, \qquad f_3: Y \to bY, \qquad f_4: Z \to cZ,$$

$$f_5: X \to a, \qquad f_6: Y \to b, \qquad f_7: Z \to c.$$

Define $F_1 = \varnothing$, and let C be denoted by the regular expressic\
$f_1(f_2 f_3 f_4)^* f_5 f_6 f_7$. Then

$$L(G, C) = \{a^n b^n c^n | n \geq 1\}$$

and consequently this language belongs to the family $\mathscr{L}(2-\lambda, 3, 0)$.

Example 6.3. Let G be determined by the labeled productions

$$f_1: X_0 \to ZZ, \qquad f_2: Z \to X_0, \qquad f_3: X_0 \to a, \qquad f_4: X_0 \to Y, \qquad f_5: Z \to$$

Define $F_1 = \{f_4, f_5\}$ and $C = (f_1^* f_4 f_2^* f_5)^* f_3^*$. Then

$$L_{ac}(G, C, F_1) = \{a^{2^n} | n \geq 0\}.$$

Hence, this language belongs to the family $\mathscr{L}(2-\lambda, 3, 1)$.

Example 6.4. Here $a, b, 0, 1$ are terminals. Our grammar G consists no\
of the labeled productions

$$f_1: X_0 \to 1 X_0 X_2, \qquad f_2: X_0 \to 0 X_0, \qquad f_3: X_1 \to X_2 X_2, \qquad f_4: X_1 \to X_3$$

$$f_5: X_2 \to X_1, \qquad f_6: X_2 \to X_3, \qquad f_7: X_0 \to b, \qquad f_8: X_1 \to a.$$

Choose $F_1 = \{f_4, f_6\}$ and let C be denoted by the regular expression

$$((f_1 \cup f_2) f_3^* f_4 f_5^* f_6)^* f_7 f_8^*.$$

Then $L_{ac}(G, C, F_1)$ consists of all words of the form nba^n where n is a no\
negative binary integer.

We do not go into a detailed study of the families (6.2) in this book. Son\
of their properties are mentioned in Note 6.1. The following inclusions ho\

for all i, j, k, i_1, j_1:

$$\mathscr{L}_i \subseteq \mathscr{L}(i, j, k), \tag{6.3}$$

$$\mathscr{L}_j \subseteq \mathscr{L}(i, j, k), \tag{6.4}$$

$$\mathscr{L}(i, j, 0) \subseteq \mathscr{L}(i, j, 1), \tag{6.5}$$

$$\mathscr{L}(i, j, k) \subseteq \mathscr{L}(i, j_1, k) \qquad \text{if } j \geq j_1, \tag{6.6}$$

$$\mathscr{L}(i, j, k) \subseteq \mathscr{L}(i_1, j, k) \qquad \text{if } i \geq i_1 \text{ and not both } i = 2 \text{ and } i_1 = 1. \tag{6.7}$$

In (6.7) it is understood that $3 \geq 2 - \lambda \geq 2 \geq 1 \geq 0$. Furthermore, if in (6.4) $i = 2 - \lambda$ or in (6.7) $i_1 = 2 - \lambda$, then the left side of the inclusion is restricted to the subfamily of λ-free languages. The additional assumption concerning i and i_1 is necessary because, as is seen below,

$$\mathscr{L}(2, 3, 1) = \mathscr{L}_0 \qquad \text{and} \qquad \mathscr{L}(1, 3, 1) = \mathscr{L}_1.$$

The reason for this is that productions $X \to \lambda$ in context-free grammars added with regulating devices constitute a powerful generative tool, whereas they are "harmless" in ordinary context-free grammars.

The inclusions (6.3)–(6.7) are immediate by the definitions, with the possible exception of (6.4). To establish (6.4), we assume that C is a type-j language over the alphabet $\{f_1, \ldots, f_n\}$. Let G be the type-3 grammar consisting of the labeled productions

$$f_u: X_0 \to f_u X_0, \qquad 1 \leq u \leq n; \qquad f_{u+1}: X_0 \to \lambda. \tag{6.8}$$

Then $C = L(G, Cf_{u+1})$, which shows that any type-j language is of type $(3, j, 0)$. An obvious modification of (6.8) shows that any λ-free type-j language is of type $(2 - \lambda, j, 0)$. Hence, (6.4) follows.

We are now in the position to develop a general theory about the generative capacity of matrix, periodically time-varying, and programmed grammars, as well as of grammars with a *regular* control language. In accordance with the notations introduced in the previous sections, we denote

$$\mathscr{L}(2 - \lambda, 3, 0) = \mathscr{R}, \qquad \mathscr{L}(2, 3, 0) = \mathscr{R}^\lambda,$$

$$\mathscr{L}(2 - \lambda, 3, 1) = \mathscr{R}_{ac}, \qquad \mathscr{L}(2, 3, 1) = \mathscr{R}^\lambda_{ac}.$$

The following theorem shows that control languages cover all of the restrictive devices introduced previously.

Theorem 6.1. Any language generated (resp. generated with appearance checking) by a type-i matrix, periodically time-varying, or programmed grammar, where $i = 3, 2 - \lambda, 2, 1, 0$, belongs to the family $\mathscr{L}(i, 3, 0)$ [resp. to the family $\mathcal{L}(i, 3, 1)$]. Hence, each of the $\mathcal{M}$-, $\mathcal{T}$-, and $\mathcal{P}$-families is included in the corresponding $\mathcal{R}$-family (i.e., the family marked with the same indices λ and ac).

Proof. Consider a matrix grammar $G = (V_N, V_T, X_0, M)$. Let F be the set of (occurrences of) productions appearing in the matrices in M, and let $F_1 \subseteq F$. Label the productions in such a way that a distinct label is attached to every occurrence of every production. Let $\mathrm{Lab}(F)$ be the resulting set of labels, and let F_1' be the subset of $\mathrm{Lab}(F)$ consisting of the labels of the productions in F_1. For a matrix

$$m_i = [f_1 : P_1 \to Q_1, \ldots, f_n : P_n \to Q_n]$$

in M, we denote $\alpha_i = f_1 \cdots f_n \in W(\mathrm{Lab}(F))$. Let $\alpha_1, \ldots, \alpha_u$ be all the words obtained from the matrices in M in this fashion. Define

$$C = (\alpha_1 \cup \cdots \cup \alpha_u)^*,$$

and let G_1 be the grammar (V_N, V_T, X_0, F). Then

$$L_{ac}(G, F_1) = L_{ac}(G_1, C, F_1').$$

Since C is regular and F_1' is empty whenever F_1 is empty, we have established the assertion concerning matrix grammars. (Clearly, the type of G_1 is the same as that of G.)

Consider next a periodically time-varying grammar (G, φ) where $G = (V_N, V_T, X_0, F)$ and the period of φ equals k. Assume that $F_1 \subseteq F$. Consider the subsets $\varphi(j)$ of F, $j = 1, \ldots, k$. Label the productions in F in such a way that a distinct label is attached to every occurrence of every production in some of these sets $\varphi(j)$. Let $\mathrm{Lab}(F)$ be the resulting set of labels, and let F_1' be the subset of $\mathrm{Lab}(F)$ consisting of the labels of the productions in F_1. Denote by K_j, $j = 1, \ldots, k$, the language consisting of the labels of the productions in $\varphi(j)$. (Thus all words in K_j are of length 1.) Define

$$C = (K_1 \cdots K_k)^*(\{\lambda\} \cup K_1 \cup K_1 K_2 \cup \cdots \cup K_1 K_2 \cdots K_{k-1}).$$

Then

$$L_{ac}(G, \varphi, F_1) = L_{ac}(G, C, F_1'),$$

where F_1' is empty if F_1 is empty. Consequently, the assertion concerning periodically time-varying grammars is true.

Finally, consider a programmed grammar (G, σ, φ) where $G = (V_N, V_T, X_0, F)$, and σ and φ are mappings of the set

$$\mathrm{Lab}(F) = \{f_1, \ldots, f_n\}$$

into the set of subsets of $\text{Lab}(F)$. Assume that the production labeled by f_j is $P_j \to Q_j, j = 1, ..., n$. We introduce the grammar

$$G_1 = (V_N \cup \{Y\}, V_T, X_0, \{f_j: P_j \to Q_j | 1 \leqq j \leqq n\}$$
$$\cup \{g_j: P_j \to \alpha(Y) | 1 \leqq j \leqq n\}),$$

where $\alpha(Y) = Y$ if G is of type not equal to 1. If G is of type 1 and $P_j = \beta X \gamma$, $Q_j = \beta \delta \gamma$, we define $\alpha(Y) = \beta Y \gamma$. Together with the productions, we have indicated their labels. Thus we are considering the set

$$\{f_1, ..., f_n, g_1, ..., g_n\} \tag{6.9}$$

of labels for the productions of G_1. Mappings σ_1 and φ_1 of (6.9) into the set of subsets of (6.9) are now defined by

$$\varphi_1(f_j) = \sigma_1(g_j) = \varnothing,$$

$$\sigma_1(f_j) = \{f_u | f_u \in \sigma(f_j)\} \cup \{g_u | f_u \in \sigma(f_j)\},$$

$$\varphi_1(g_j) = \{f_u | f_u \in \varphi(f_j)\} \cup \{g_u | f_u \in \varphi(f_j)\},$$

for $j = 1, ..., n$. In this way, we obtain a programmed grammar $(G_1, \sigma_1, \varphi_1)$ for which clearly

$$L_{ac}(G, \sigma, \varphi) = L_{ac}(G_1, \sigma_1, \varphi_1). \tag{6.10}$$

Moreover, the range of φ_1 is the empty set if the range of φ is the empty set, and if G is of any of the types i mentioned in the statement of the theorem, then also G_1 is of type i.

A binary relation R on the finite set (6.9) is defined as follows. For any elements α and β of (6.9), $\alpha R \beta$ holds iff $\beta \in \sigma_1(\alpha) \cup \varphi_1(\alpha)$ (i.e., the production labeled by β is in a go-to field of the production labeled by α). Let C be the language over the alphabet (6.9) consisting of all words $a_1 \cdots a_m$ where $m \geqq 1$, the a's are letters, and $a_j R a_{j+1}$ holds for $j = 1, ..., m-1$. By Theorem 2.1, C is regular. We obtain

$$L_{ac}(G_1, \sigma_1, \varphi_1) = L_{ac}(G_1, C, \{g_1, ..., g_n\}). \tag{6.11}$$

In fact, since the nonterminal Y can never be eliminated, productions labeled by g's have to be applied in the appearance checking sense only.

It is obvious that in (6.11) the set $\{g_1, ..., g_n\}$ can be replaced by the empty set if the range of φ (and thus also the range of φ_1) is the empty set. Consequently, by (6.10) and (6.11), we conclude that the assertion concerning programmed grammars is true. ∎

The next step in our theory is to study how the generative capacity of type-i grammars is affected if grammars are provided with regular control languages.

It is a consequence of (6.3) that the generative capacity either remains un-altered or increases. Hence, by Church's thesis, the following theorem is obvious.

Theorem 6.2. The family $\mathscr{L}(0,3,1)$ equals the family $\mathscr{L}_0$ of type-0 languages.

The next two theorems show that the corresponding result holds true also for type-1 and type-3 grammars.

Theorem 6.3. The family $\mathscr{L}(1,3,1)$ equals the family $\mathscr{L}_1$ of context-sensitive languages.

Proof. It suffices to prove that an arbitrary language

$$L = L_{ac}(G, C, F_1), \tag{6.12}$$

where $G = (V_N, V_T, X_0, F)$ is of type 1, C is regular, and $F_1 \subseteq \text{Lab}(F)$, is context-sensitive. This is done in two steps. During the first step, the appearance checking is eliminated and, during the second step, the control language is eliminated.

Without loss of generality, we assume that $X_0 \to \lambda$ does not belong to F. For we can first find out, by inspecting C, whether or not $\lambda \in L$. If $L - \{\lambda\}$ is context-sensitive, then so is L. On the other hand, the production $X_0 \to \lambda$ is applied in derivations of nonempty words of L in the appearance checking sense only. Hence, this production may be replaced by the production $X_0 \to Y$ where Y is a new nonterminal without affecting the set of nonempty words in L.

To eliminate appearance checking, we now introduce a length-increasing grammar G_1 and a regular control language C_1 such that

$$L(G_1, C_1) = \{bPb \mid P \in L_{ac}(G, C, F_1)\} \tag{6.13}$$

where b is a new terminal letter. The set of nonterminals of G_1 is the union

$$V_N' = V_N \cup \{Y_0, B\} \cup \{[\alpha, f] \mid \alpha \in V_N \cup V_T, f \in F_1\}.$$

The terminal alphabet of G_1 is $V_T \cup \{b\}$, and the initial letter is Y_0.

We now define the production set of G_1. It consists of (i) the productions in F, labeled in the same way as before, (ii) the two labeled productions

$$g_1: Y_0 \to BX_0 B, \qquad g_2: B \to b,$$

and (iii) for each $f \in F_1$, three sets of productions A_f, E_f, and B_f defined below. (The productions in A_f, E_f, and B_f are used as their own labels, and thus we have also given a labeling of the productions of G_1.) Consider an arbitrary $f \in F_1$. Let $P \to Q$ be the production labeled by f, and assume that

$P = x_1 \cdots x_r$, $r \geq 1$, where each x is a letter of $V_N \cup V_T$. The set A_f consists of all productions

$$[\alpha, f]\beta \to \alpha[\beta, f], \qquad \alpha, \beta \in V_N \cup V_T, \quad \alpha \neq x_1,$$

$$[x_1, f]\beta \to x_1[\beta, f], \qquad \beta \in (V_N \cup V_T) - \{x_2\},$$

$$[x_1, f]x_2\beta \to x_1[x_2, f]\beta, \qquad \beta \in (V_N \cup V_T) - \{x_3\},$$

$$\vdots$$

$$[x_1, f]x_2 \cdots x_{r-1}\beta \to x_1[x_2, f] \cdots x_{r-1}\beta, \qquad \beta \in (V_N \cup V_T) - \{x_r\}.$$

The set E_f consists of the productions

$$[\alpha, f]B \to \alpha B, \qquad \alpha \in V_N \cup V_T,$$

$$\text{if not both} \quad r = 1 \quad \text{and} \quad \alpha = x_1,$$

$$[\alpha_1, f]\alpha_2 B \to \alpha_1\alpha_2 B, \qquad \alpha_i \in V_N \cup V_T, \quad r > 2,$$

$$\vdots$$

$$[\alpha_1, f]\alpha_2 \cdots \alpha_{r-1}B \to \alpha_1\alpha_2 \cdots \alpha_{r-1}B, \qquad \alpha_i \in V_N \cup V_T, \quad r > 2.$$

Finally, B_f consists of the productions

$$B\alpha \to B[\alpha, f], \qquad \alpha \in V_N \cup V_T.$$

Having completed the definition of G_1, we now introduce a regular substitution σ on the elements of $\mathrm{Lab}(F)$ by

$$\sigma(f) = \begin{cases} f & \text{if } f \in \mathrm{Lab}(F) - F_1, \\ f \cup B_f(A_f)^*E_f & \text{if } f \in F_1. \end{cases}$$

We now define

$$C_1 = g_1\sigma(C)g_2^2.$$

Clearly, C_1 is regular.

It is now easy to verify that (6.13) holds true. Since g_1 begins every word of C_1, one first introduces the two boundary markers B. The definition of σ makes it possible to simulate the application of productions labeled by $f \in F_1$ either in the rewriting or in the appearance checking sense. For the latter purpose, one begins with a production in B_f, introducing a nonterminal $[\alpha, f]$. Productions in A_f are then applied to move the bracketed nonterminal toward the right end where it can be eliminated by a production in E_f. If the left side of the production labeled by f appears as a subword of the word under scan, then no production in E_f can become applicable, and the derivation terminates without producing a terminal word. Finally, the boundary markers B are replaced by the terminals b.

We now eliminate the control language. More specifically, we introduce a length-increasing grammar G_2 such that

$$L(G_2) = \{bbPb|P \in L_{ac}(G, C, F_1)\} \qquad (6.14)$$

where b is a new terminal letter. This implies, by (6.12) and Theorem 10.4 in Part 1, that L is context-sensitive.

We return to the equation (6.13). Since C_1 is regular, it is accepted by a finite deterministic automaton $(S, V_1, s_0, S_1, \varphi)$ where V_1 is the set of labels introduced for the productions of G_1. Define

$$G_2 = (V_N' \cup S \cup \{Z_0\}, V_T \cup \{b\}, Z_0, F_2)$$

where

$$F_2 = \{sP \to \varphi(s,f)Q|s \in S \text{ and } P \to Q \text{ is a production of } G_1,$$

$$\text{labeled by } f \in V_1\} \cup \{s\alpha \to \alpha s, \alpha s \to s\alpha|s \in S, \alpha \in V_N' \cup V_T\}$$

$$\cup \{sb \to bb|s \in S_1\} \cup \{Z_0 \to s_0 Y_0\}.$$

It can now be verified that (6.14) holds true. In fact, productions in the first set of the union keep track of the control word, whereas productions in the second set serve the purpose of looking for a suitable position to continue the derivation. The remaining productions introduce and eliminate the state symbol. (Note that the rightmost B must be replaced by b before the leftmost one since the state symbol cannot pass the terminal letter b.) ∎

Theorem 6.4. The family $\mathscr{L}(3,3,1)$ equals the family $\mathscr{L}_3$ of regular languages.

Proof. It suffices to prove that an arbitrary language in the family $\mathscr{L}(3,3,1)$ is of type 3. To do this, we assume that

$$L = L_{ac}(G, C, F_1)$$

where $G = (V_N, V_T, X_0, F)$ is right-linear, C is regular, and $F_1 \subseteq \text{Lab}(F)$. (The proof for a left-linear G is quite similar.) We construct a generalized sequential machine GSM such that

$$L = \text{GSM}(C). \qquad (6.15)$$

This implies, by Theorem 2.2, that L is of type 3.

The state, input, and output alphabets of GSM are $V_N \cup \{U\}$, $\text{Lab}(F)$, and V_T, respectively. The initial state is X_0, the final state set being $\{U\}$. The productions of GSM are defined as follows. For every production

$$f: X \to PY, \qquad X, Y \in V_N, \quad P \in W(V_T), \quad f \in \text{Lab}(F),$$

in F, GSM contains the production

$$Xf \to PY \qquad (6.16)$$

and furthermore, provided $f \in F_1$, the productions

$$Zf \to Z, \qquad Z \in V_N \cup \{U\}, \quad Z \neq X. \qquad (6.17)$$

For every production

$$g: X \to P, \qquad X \in V_N, \quad P \in W(V_T), \quad g \in \mathrm{Lab}(F),$$

in F, GSM contains the production

$$Xg \to PU, \qquad (6.18)$$

and furthermore, provided $g \in F_1$, the productions

$$Zg \to Z, \qquad Z \in V_N \cup \{U\}, \quad Z \neq X. \qquad (6.19)$$

It is now easy to see that (6.15) holds. In fact, since the number of non-terminals in derivations according to G never becomes greater than one, control words make nonterminals superfluous. Rewriting is simulated by (6.16) and (6.18), and appearance checking by (6.17) and (6.19). ∎

The following theorem is an immediate corollary of Theorems 6.1–6.4. It shows that the regulating devices we have introduced do not add anything to the generative capacity of type-i grammars if $i \neq 2$.

Theorem 6.5. For $i = 0, 1, 3$, each of the following language families equals the family $\mathscr{L}_i$ of type-i languages: The family of languages generated (with appearance checking) by type-i matrix grammars, the family of languages generated (with appearance checking) by type-i periodically time-varying grammars, and the family of languages generated (with appearance checking) by type-i programmed grammars.

There remains the case where the core productions are context-free. It turns out that the $\mathscr{M}$-, $\mathscr{T}$-, $\mathscr{P}$-, and $\mathscr{R}$-families are all equal (if they are provided with the same indices). Moreover, $\mathscr{R}_{ac}^\lambda$ equals the family $\mathscr{L}_0$, both of the families $\mathscr{R}$ and $\mathscr{R}_{ac}$ are properly between $\mathscr{L}_2$ and $\mathscr{L}_1$, whereas it is not known how large the family $\mathscr{R}^\lambda$ is.

It was seen in Theorem 6.1 how matrices can be replaced by a regular control language. We show now how a regular control language can be replaced by matrices.

Theorem 6.6. Any language in the family $\mathscr{L}(2, 3, 0) = \mathscr{R}^\lambda$ is generated by a context-free matrix grammar, all of whose matrices consist of two productions. Any language in the family $\mathcal{L}(2, 3, 1) = \mathcal{R}^\lambda_{ac}$ is of the form (4.14) for some context-free matrix grammar G satisfying the assumptions of Theorem 4.3.

Proof. We prove first the second sentence of the theorem. Assume that L is in the family $\mathcal{R}^\lambda_{ac}$, that is,

$$L = L_{ac}(G_1, C, F_2)$$

where $G_1 = (V_N, V_T, X_0, F)$ is a context-free grammar, C is a regular language over the alphabet $\text{Lab}(F)$, and F_2 is a subset of $\text{Lab}(F)$. Hence, C is accepted by a finite deterministic automaton $A = (S, \text{Lab}(F), s_0, S_1, \varphi)$. Consider the (context-free) matrix grammar

$$G = (V_N \cup S, V_T, X_0, M)$$

where M is defined as follows. Assume that

$$\text{Lab}(F) = \{f_1, ..., f_u\}$$

and that the production labeled by f_j is $X_j \to P_j$, $j = 1, ..., u$. Then M consists of the matrices

$$[X_j \to P_j, s \to \varphi(s, f_j)], \quad s \in S, \quad 1 \leqq j \leqq u,$$

$$[X_j \to P_j, s \to \lambda] \quad \text{for} \quad s \in S, \quad 1 \leqq j \leqq u, \quad \text{such that} \quad \varphi(s, f_j) \in S_1.$$

Let F_1 be the set consisting of all productions $X_j \to P_j$ such that $f_j \in F_2$. (Indeed, F_1 is a set of occurrences of productions because $X_j \to P_j$ and $X_k \to P_k$, $j \neq k$, may be identical and $f_j \in F_2$, $f_k \notin F_2$.) Then G is a matrix grammar satisfying the hypothesis of Theorem 4.3. Moreover, for this G, L is the language (4.14). This follows because the second productions in the matrices serve the purpose of finding out whether or not the control word drives the automaton A from s_0 to a state in S_1.

The proof of the first sentence of the theorem is quite similar. Now F_2 is empty. The definition of G remains the same except that a new nonterminal Y_0, which is also the initial letter, and the matrix

$$[Y_0 \to Y_0, \ Y_0 \to X_0 s_0]$$

are added. The set F_1 is, of course, empty; L is the language generated by this matrix grammar, all of whose matrices consist of two productions. ∎

Theorem 6.7. Each of the families $\mathcal{M}^\lambda_{ac}$, $\mathcal{T}^\lambda_{ac}$, $\mathcal{P}^\lambda_{ac}$, and $\mathcal{R}^\lambda_{ac}$ equals the family $\mathcal{L}_0$ of type-0 languages. Consequently, every type-0 language is ptvcfac. Moreover, all of the families $\mathcal{M}^\lambda$, $\mathcal{T}^\lambda$, $\mathcal{P}^\lambda$, and $\mathcal{R}^\lambda$ are equal.

Proof. The inclusions

$$\mathcal{M}^\lambda_{ac}, \mathcal{T}^\lambda_{ac}, \mathcal{P}^\lambda_{ac} \subseteq \mathcal{R}^\lambda_{ac} \quad \text{and} \quad \mathcal{M}^\lambda, \mathcal{T}^\lambda, \mathcal{P}^\lambda \subseteq \mathcal{R}^\lambda$$

follow by Theorem 6.1. The inclusions

$$\mathscr{R}^\lambda \subseteq \mathscr{M}^\lambda \subseteq \mathscr{T}^\lambda \quad \text{and} \quad \mathscr{R}^\lambda_{ac} \subseteq \mathscr{M}^\lambda_{ac} \subseteq \mathscr{T}^\lambda_{ac}$$

follow by Theorems 6.6, 6.1, 4.2, and 4.3. [For the first of the latter inclusions, we notice that a language of the form (4.14) belongs to the family $\mathscr{M}^\lambda_{ac}$.] Since, by Theorem 5.3,

$$\mathscr{M}^\lambda \subseteq \mathscr{P}^\lambda \quad \text{and} \quad \mathscr{M}^\lambda_{ac} \subseteq \mathscr{P}^\lambda_{ac},$$

we obtain the equations

$$\mathscr{T}^\lambda = \mathscr{M}^\lambda = \mathscr{P}^\lambda = \mathscr{R}^\lambda \quad \text{and} \quad \mathscr{T}^\lambda_{ac} = \mathscr{M}^\lambda_{ac} = \mathscr{P}^\lambda_{ac} = \mathscr{R}^\lambda_{ac}.$$

Theorem 6.7 now follows by Theorem 5.1. ∎

The following theorem is an immediate corollary of Theorems 6.1 and 6.6.

Theorem 6.8. Any language generated (resp. generated with appearance checking) by a context-free matrix grammar is generated (resp. generated with appearance checking) by a context-free matrix grammar, all of whose matrices consist of two productions.

Theorem 6.8 holds true also in the λ-free case, that is, for the families $\mathscr{M}$ and $\mathscr{M}_{ac}$.

Our next theorem is implied by Theorems 6.1 and 6.3.

Theorem 6.9. All languages in the families $\mathscr{T}_{ac}$, $\mathscr{M}_{ac}$, $\mathscr{P}_{ac}$, and $\mathscr{R}_{ac}$ are context-sensitive. Consequently, all languages in the families $\mathscr{T}$, $\mathscr{M}$, $\mathscr{P}$, and $\mathscr{R}$ are context-sensitive.

The following result is easily established by Theorem 3.2 and Theorem 9.9 in Part 1.

Theorem 6.10. $\mathscr{M}^\lambda_{left} = \mathscr{L}_0$.

It can also be shown that the λ-free families among the $\mathscr{T}$-, $\mathscr{M}$-, $\mathscr{P}$-, and $\mathscr{R}$-families are equal. The core of this proof consists of Proposition 4.1. Moreover, there are (λ-free) context-sensitive languages which do not belong to these families.

Proposition 6.1. $\mathscr{T} = \mathscr{M} = \mathscr{P} = \mathscr{R}$ and $\mathscr{T}_{ac} = \mathscr{M}_{ac} = \mathscr{P}_{ac} = \mathscr{R}_{ac}$. All of these families are properly included in the family of λ-free context-sensitive languages. The family $\mathscr{R}_{ac}$ is an AFL which is closed under substitution and restricted homomorphism.

It is not known whether or not the inclusion $\mathscr{R} \subseteq \mathscr{R}_{ac}$ is proper. It is also not known how large the family $\mathscr{R}^\lambda$ is when compared, for instance, with the family $\mathscr{L}_1$ or $\mathscr{R}_{ac}$. The families $\mathscr{R}$ and $\mathscr{R}^\lambda$ are known to be closed under AFL operations other than (possibly) λ-free catenation closure.

Note 6.1. Tables 3 and 4 summarize the known results concerning the mutual relations between the families $\mathscr{L}(i, j, k)$ and $\mathscr{L}_i$. In the tables, $\mathscr{REC}$

TABLE 3

$$\mathscr{L} = \mathscr{L}(i, j, 0)$$

			j	
i	0	1	2	3
0	$\mathscr{L} = \mathscr{L}_0$	$\mathscr{L} = \mathscr{L}_0$	$\mathscr{L} = \mathscr{L}_0$	$\mathscr{L} = \mathscr{L}_0$
1	$\mathscr{L} = \mathscr{L}_0$	$\mathscr{L} = \mathscr{L}_0$	$\mathscr{L}_1 \subseteq \mathscr{L} \subset \mathscr{REC}$	$\mathscr{L} = \mathscr{L}_1$
2	$\mathscr{L} = \mathscr{L}_0$	$\mathscr{L} = \mathscr{L}_0$	$\mathscr{L}_2 \subset \mathscr{L}$	$\mathscr{L}_2 \subset \mathscr{L}$
$2-\lambda$	$\mathscr{L} = \mathscr{L}_0{}'$	$\mathscr{L} = \mathscr{L}_0{}'$	$\mathscr{L}_2{}' \subset \mathscr{L} \subset \mathscr{REC}'$	$\mathscr{L}_2{}' \subset \mathscr{L} \subset \mathscr{L}_1{}'$
3	$\mathscr{L} = \mathscr{L}_0$	$\mathscr{L} = \mathscr{L}_0$	$\mathscr{L} = \mathscr{L}_2$	$\mathscr{L} = \mathscr{L}_3$

TABLE 4

$$\mathscr{L} = \mathscr{L}(i, j, 1)$$

			j	
i	0	1	2	3
0	$\mathscr{L} = \mathscr{L}_0$	$\mathscr{L} = \mathscr{L}_0$	$\mathscr{L} = \mathscr{L}_0$	$\mathscr{L} = \mathscr{L}_0$
1	$\mathscr{L} = \mathscr{L}_0$	$\mathscr{L} = \mathscr{L}_0$	$\mathscr{L}_1 \subseteq \mathscr{L} \subset \mathscr{REC}$	$\mathscr{L} = \mathscr{L}_1$
2	$\mathscr{L} = \mathscr{L}_0$	$\mathscr{L} = \mathscr{L}_0$	$\mathscr{L} = \mathscr{L}_0$	$\mathscr{L} = \mathscr{L}_0$
$2-\lambda$	$\mathscr{L} = \mathscr{L}_0{}'$	$\mathscr{L} = \mathscr{L}_0{}'$	$\mathscr{L}_2{}' \subset \mathscr{L} \subset \mathscr{REC}'$	$\mathscr{L}_2{}' \subset \mathscr{L} \subset \mathscr{L}_1{}'$
3	$\mathscr{L} = \mathscr{L}_0$	$\mathscr{L} = \mathscr{L}_0$	$\mathscr{L} = \mathscr{L}_2$	$\mathscr{L} = \mathscr{L}_3$

denotes the family of recursive languages. Primes (′) indicate that the sub-family consisting of λ-free languages is considered. See also inclusions (6.3)–(6.7) and Exercises 6–9. In our estimation, the most interesting open problems are (i) to characterize the family $\mathscr{L}(2, 3, 0)$ and (ii) to determine whether or not $\mathscr{L}_1 = \mathscr{L}(1, 2, 0)$.

Denote by $\mathscr{L}(i, \mathscr{C}, 0)$, $0 \leq i \leq 3$, the family of languages of the form $L(G, C)$ where G is a type-i grammar and the control language C belongs to the family $\mathscr{C}$. The notation $\mathscr{L}(i, \mathscr{C}, 1)$ is used similarly for the family of languages $L_{ac}(G, C, F_1)$. Then (i) the family $\mathscr{L}(i, \mathscr{C}, k)$, $0 \leq i, k \leq 1$, is an AFL if $\mathscr{C}$ is closed under the operations of union, catenation, and λ-free catenation closure, (ii) the family $\mathscr{L}(2, \mathscr{C}, 1)$ is a full AFL if $\mathscr{C}$ is closed under the operations of union, catenation, λ-free catenation closure, and λ-free regular substitution, and (iii)

$$\mathscr{L}(3, \mathscr{C}, 1) = \mathscr{L}(3, \mathscr{C}, 0) = \mathscr{C}$$

if $\mathscr{C}$ is a full AFL.

Note 6.2. When defining a control language, we specified a set of strings of productions and considered those words which possess at least one derivation with a control word in this set. Thus, in this approach, the control language determines the generated language. One can also reverse this approach: Study the control language determined by the generated language. This means that for a grammar $G = (V_N, V_T, X_0, F)$, one considers the language $Sz(G)$ over the alphabet F consisting of all control words of all derivations of words in $L(G)$. [It is assumed that $\mathrm{Lab}(F) = F$ and $F_1 = \varnothing$.] $Sz(G)$ is termed the *Szilard language* of the grammar G. For instance, if G is determined by the productions $X_0 \to aX_0 b$ and $X_0 \to ab$, denoted by f_1 and f_2, respectively, then $Sz(G)$ is denoted by the regular expression $f_1 {}^* f_2$.

It can be immediately verified that the Szilard language of a type-3 grammar is of type 3. Moreover, the Szilard language of any grammar is of type 1. This is seen roughly as follows. Given a grammar $G = (V_N, V_T, X_0, F)$, one constructs a length-increasing grammar G_1 such that $L(G_1)$ contains, for every $P \in L(G)$ and every Q which is a control word of a derivation of P, a word $Q \# P_1 \#$ where $\#$ is a boundary marker and P is obtained from P_1 by erasing all occurrences of an auxiliary letter d. Furthermore, the length of P_1 is linearly bounded by that of Q. [A derivation according to G_1 begins with $\# X_0 \#$. A production $f \colon P' \to Q'$ in G is replaced in G_1 by $P' \to X_f Q' d^i$ where i is big enough to make the production length-increasing. Before this production in G_1 can be applied, a messenger travels between the boundary markers to find out that there are no production indicators, such as X_f, present. Finally, the indicator X_f travels to the left of the leftmost marker $\#$ where it becomes f. The linear bound required is the greatest among the differences $lg(Q') - lg(P')$, where $P' \to Q'$ ranges through the productions in F, added with a constant to take care of the auxiliary nonterminals and boundary markers.] Thus, the workspace theorem can be applied to show that the language consisting of all words Q is context-sensitive.

On the other hand, the Szilard language may be non-context-free even for a context-free grammar G. Consider the grammar G determined by the productions

$$X_0 \to X_1 X_0 X_2, \qquad X_1 \to \lambda, \qquad X_2 \to \lambda, \qquad X_0 \to P,$$

where P is a word over the terminal alphabet. By Example 6.2 and Theorem 6.7 in Part 1, the language $Sz(G)$ is not context-free. Using this example, the following stronger result also can be established: For every nonempty context-free language L, there is a type-2 grammar G such that $L = L(G)$ and $Sz(G)$ is not of type 2. If one considers leftmost derivations only, then the corresponding leftmost Szilard language $Sz_{left}(G)$ is context-free for any G. (The notion of a leftmost derivation is defined in exact terms in Section 10. It is then assumed that no terminal appears on the left side of any production.) Furthermore, there is an algorithm for deciding whether or not $Sz_{left}(G)$ for an arbitrary G is regular. Since $Sz_{left}(G)$ is context-free, for any G, and $\mathscr{L}_2$ is closed under homomorphism, the language generated by leftmost derivations according to a type-0 grammar G (with no terminals on the left sides of the productions) is context-free for any G. A slightly more general result is established by a different method in Theorem 10.3.

It was seen above that the Szilard language of a context-free grammar is not necessarily context-free. It is possible to give an exact characterization for those context-free grammars which possess a context-free (resp. regular) Szilard language. The characterization shows that there are context-free languages L such that no grammar for L has a context-free Szilard language. If a language L is not ultralinear, then no grammar for L has a regular Szilard language. (The notion of ultralinearity is introduced in Section 10.) There is an algorithm for deciding for an arbitrary context-free grammar G whether $Sz(G)$ is (i) regular, or (ii) context-free.

One can also pose the general problem: What conditions must a language L satisfy to be the Szilard language of some grammar G? So far no results have been presented in this direction.

7.   ORDERED GRAMMARS

We consider now another very natural restriction on the use of productions: ordering. A partial order, denoted by $>$, is defined on the set of productions. A production f can be applied to a word P only if no production f' such that $f' > f$ is applicable to P. Here application is understood in the rewriting sense only. (If the application of f were understood also in the appearance checking sense, then productions f_1 such that $f > f_1$ could never be applied.)

Definition. An *ordered grammar* of type i, $i = 3, 2 - \lambda, 2, 1, 0$, is a pair $(G, >)$ where $G = (V_N, V_T, X_0, F)$ is a type-i grammar and $>$ is a partial order on the set F. A binary relation $\Rightarrow$ on the set $W(V_N \cup V_T)$ is defined as follows. For any P and Q, $P \Rightarrow Q$ holds iff there are words R_1, R_2, P', Q' such that $P = R_1 P' R_2$, $Q = R_1 Q' R_2$, the production $P' \to Q'$ (denoted by f) is in F, and furthermore there is in F no production $f' > f$ whose left side is a subword of P. Let $\Rightarrow^*$ be the reflexive transitive closure of the relation $\Rightarrow$. The language *generated* by the ordered grammar $(G, >)$ is defined by

$$L(G, >) = \{P \in W(V_T)|X_0 \Rightarrow^* P\}.$$

By choosing $>$ as the empty relation, it is seen that every type-i language is generated by an ordered grammar of type i. The next example shows that the family of languages generated by context-free [resp. context-free λ-free] ordered grammars properly includes the family of type-2 [resp. type-$(2-\lambda)$] languages.

Example 7.1. Consider the type-$(2-\lambda)$ grammar G determined by the productions

(1)	$X_0 \to XYZ,$	(2)	$X \to aX_1,$	(3)	$X \to X_2,$
(4)	$X \to U_1,$	(5)	$Y \to bY_1,$	(6)	$Y \to Y_2,$
(7)	$Y \to U_1,$	(8)	$Z \to cZ_1,$	(9)	$Z \to Z_2,$
(10)	$Z \to U_1,$	(11)	$X_1 \to X,$	(12)	$X_1 \to U_1,$
(13)	$X_1 \to U_2,$	(14)	$Y_1 \to Y,$	(15)	$Y_1 \to U_1,$
(16)	$Y_1 \to U_2,$	(17)	$Z_1 \to Z,$	(18)	$Z_1 \to U_1,$
(19)	$X_2 \to a,$	(20)	$X_2 \to U_1,$	(21)	$Y_2 \to b,$
(22)	$Y_2 \to U_1,$	(23)	$Z_2 \to c.$		

The relation $>$ is defined by listing all pairs for which it holds:

$$18 > 2, 3; \qquad 4 > 20 > 5; \qquad 4 > 12 > 6; \qquad 13 > 14;$$
$$7 > 22 > 8; \qquad 7 > 15 > 9; \qquad 16 > 17; \qquad 10 > 11, 19, 21.$$

We claim that

$$L(G, >) = \{a^n b^n c^n | n \geq 1\}. \tag{7.1}$$

Consider derivations leading to a terminal word from the word $a^j Xb^j Yc^j Z$ where $j \geq 0$. [Initially, by production (1), we have $j = 0$.] Productions (2)–(10) are applicable to this word. However, the ordering excludes the productions (5), (6), (8), and (9). Productions (4), (7), and (10) introduce the nonterminal U_1 which cannot be eliminated. This leaves us only the productions (2) and (3).

Assume first that (2) is applied, yielding $a^{j+1} X_1 b^j Yc^j Z$. Then the next productions must be (5), (8), (11), (14), and (17), in this order. The reader may verify this in the same way as above, that is, by finding out (i) which productions have such a nonterminal on their left side which occurs in the word under scan, (ii) which among these productions are eliminated by the ordering, and (iii) which of the remaining productions are eliminated by the fact that they introduce one of the nonterminals U. It turns out that at each step only one production is possible, namely, the ones listed above. After applying these productions, we have the word $a^{j+1} Xb^{j+1} Yc^{j+1} Z$ which is of our original form.

Second, assume that (3) is applied, yielding $a^j X_2 b^j Y c^j Z$. Then the next productions must be (6) and (9), yielding $a^j X_2 b^j Y_2 c^j Z_2$. After this the productions (19), (21), and (23) must be applied in some order, yielding finally $a^{j+1} b^{j+1} c^{j+1}$

If it is assumed that the ordering relation $>$ is *total* (i.e., linear), this causes severe restrictions on the generative capacity of ordered grammars. It is not true that every type-i language is generated by a type-i ordered grammar $(G, >)$ where the relation $>$ is total. For instance, the reader may verify that the language $\{a, b\}$ is generated by no type-1 ordered grammar $(G, >)$ where $>$ is total. We now give an example of a length-increasing ordered grammar with a total order among the productions.

Example 7.2 (due to Seppo Lampila). Consider the grammar G determined by the productions

(1)	$X_0 \to XX,$	(2)	$X \to W,$	(3)	$XW \to ABC,$
(4)	$WX \to XYXYXM,$	(5)	$XYX \to XZX,$	(6)	$XZX \to XABCX,$
(7)	$XABC \to ABCXY,$	(8)	$CA \to AC,$	(9)	$BA \to AB.$
(10)	$CB \to BC,$	(11)	$ZXM \to ZTM,$	(12)	$XZT \to XST,$
(13)	$YXS \to YMS,$	(14)	$XYM \to XTM,$	(15)	$XT \to ST,$
(16)	$M \to C,$	(17)	$T \to B,$	(18)	$S \to A,$
(19)	$A \to a,$	(20)	$B \to b,$	(21)	$C \to c.$

The order relation $>$ is defined by

$$1 > 3 > 4 > 11 > 12 > 13 > 14 > 15 > 6 > 7 > 8 > 9 > 10$$

$$> 5 > 2 > 16 > 17 > 18 > 19 > 20 > 21.$$

The reader may verify that (7.1) holds true also for this $(G, >)$.

The following theorem relates ordered grammars with regular control languages.

Theorem 7.1. A language generated by an ordered grammar of type i $(i = 3, 2 - \lambda, 2, 1, 0)$ belongs to the family $\mathscr{L}(i, 3, 1)$.

Proof. Let $(G, >)$ be an ordered grammar where $G = (V_N, V_T, X_0, F)$ is of type i. Assume that

$$f_j \colon P_j \to Q_j, \qquad 1 \leqq j \leqq n, \tag{7.2}$$

are all the productions in F. Denote by F' the set consisting of the productions

$$g_j \colon P_j \to \alpha(Y), \qquad 1 \leqq j \leqq n, \tag{7.3}$$

where Y is a new nonterminal and $\alpha(Y)$ is defined (depending on the type of G) as in the proof of Theorem 6.1. Define

$$G_1 = (V_N \cup \{Y\}, V_T, X_0, F \cup F'),$$

and let $\mathrm{Lab}(F \cup F')$ consist of the letters f_j and g_j as indicated in (7.2) and (7.3). Furthermore, let F_1 consist of the labels g_j, $1 \leq j \leq n$. Clearly G_1 is of type i (or length-increasing, for $i = 1$).

We now define the control language C. For any $j = 1, \ldots, n$, we define a word α_j over $\mathrm{Lab}(F \cup F')$ as follows. The last letter of α_j is f_j. It is preceded by all letters g_k such that $f_k > f_j$. (The mutual order of the letters g_k in α_j is immaterial. If there are no productions $f_k > f_j$, then $\alpha_j = f_j$.) The language C is denoted by the regular expression $(\alpha_1 \cup \cdots \cup \alpha_n)^*$. Clearly,

$$L(G, >) = L_{ac}(G_1, C, F_1). \quad \blacksquare$$

The next theorem is an immediate corollary of Theorems 6.2–6.4 and 7.1.

Theorem 7.2. A language is of type i, where $i = 0, 1, 3$, iff it is generated by an ordered grammar of type i. Any language generated by an ordered grammar of type $(2 - \lambda)$ is context-sensitive.

It is not known how large a family is generated by ordered type-2 grammars. By Proposition 6.1, the following strengthening of the second sentence of Theorem 7.2 is obtained. (The first inclusion mentioned in Proposition 7.1 is obvious by Example 7.1.)

Proposition 7.1. The family of languages generated by ordered type-$(2 - \lambda)$ grammars includes properly the family of context-free λ-free languages and is properly included in the family of context-sensitive λ-free languages.

Consider a production f in an ordered grammar $(G, >)$. Let $P_1, \ldots, P_k$ be the left sides of the productions f_j such that $f_j > f$. Then f is applicable to a word Q iff Q belongs to the language

$$V^* - \bigcup_{j=1}^{k} V^* P_j V^* \tag{7.4}$$

where V is the union of the nonterminal and terminal alphabets of G. Clearly, the language (7.4) is regular. This suggests the following generalization of an ordered grammar: For each production f of a grammar G, one specifies a regular language $\rho(f)$ such that f is applicable only to words in $\rho(f)$.

Definition. A type-i *grammar with regular restrictions* is a pair (G, ρ) where $G = (V_N, V_T, X_0, F)$ is a type-i grammar ($i = 3, 2 - \lambda, 2, 1, 0$) and ρ is a mapping of F into the family of regular languages over $V_N \cup V_T = V$. A binary relation $\Rightarrow$ on $W(V)$ is defined as follows. For any P and Q, $P \Rightarrow Q$ holds iff there are words R_1, R_2, P', Q' such that $P = R_1 P' R_2$, $Q = R_1 Q' R_2$, the production $P' \to Q'$ is in F, and furthermore

$$P \in \rho(P' \to Q').$$

The language *generated* by (G, ρ) is defined by

$$L(G, \rho) = \{P \in W(V_T) | X_0 \Rightarrow^* P\},$$

where $\Rightarrow^*$ is the reflexive transitive closure of $\Rightarrow$.

Theorem 7.3. A language generated by a type-1 grammar with regular restrictions is context-sensitive. Any λ-free context-sensitive language is generated by a type-$(2-\lambda)$ grammar with regular restrictions.

Proof. To prove the first sentence, we consider a type-1 grammar with regular restrictions, (G, ρ), and use the notations of the preceding definition. Without loss of generality, we assume that F does not contain the production $X_0 \to \lambda$. If $f_1, \dots, f_n$ are the productions in F, every $\rho(f_j)$ is accepted by a finite deterministic automaton

$$A_j = (S^j, V, s_0{}^j, S_1{}^j, \varphi^j), \qquad j = 1, \dots, n.$$

We may assume that the sets S^j are pairwise disjoint. Let f_j be the production $P_j \to Q_j, j = 1, \dots, n$. Consider the grammar

$$G_1 = \left(V_N \cup \bigcup_{j=1}^{n} S^j \cup \{Y_j | 1 \leqq j \leqq n\} \cup \{Z_0, Y, B\}, V_T, Z_0, F_1 \right),$$

where

$$F_1 = \{Z_0 \to BYX_0 B, \; B \to \lambda, \; Y \to \lambda\} \cup \{\alpha Y \to Y\alpha | \alpha \in V\}$$

$$\cup \{BY \to Bs_0{}^j | 1 \leqq j \leqq n\} \cup \{s^j \alpha \to \alpha\varphi^j(s^j, \alpha) | \alpha \in V, \; 1 \leqq j \leqq n,$$

$$s^j \in S^j\} \cup \{s_1{}^j B \to Y_j B | 1 \leqq j \leqq n, \; s_1{}^j \in S_1{}^j\}$$

$$\cup \{\alpha Y_j \to Y_j \alpha | \alpha \in V, \; 1 \leqq j \leqq n\} \cup \{Y_j P_j \to YQ_j | 1 \leqq j \leqq n\}.$$

It is easy to verify that $L(G_1) = L(G, \rho)$. (The construction resembles many of our previous ones. First the boundary markers B and the general-purpose scanner Y are introduced. In the position adjacent to the leftmost B, Y can be converted to the initial state of A_j. If the word between the boundary markers is accepted by A_j, the production marker Y_j is introduced. This makes an application of f_j possible.) Since G is of type 1, we conclude by the workspace theorem that $L(G, \rho)$ is context-sensitive.

To prove the second sentence, we consider a λ-free language L generated by a type-1 grammar $G = (V_N, V_T, X_0, F)$. For every production

$$f: P^f X^f Q^f \to P^f R^f Q^f, \qquad X^f \in V_N, \qquad R^f \neq \lambda$$

in F, we introduce a new nonterminal Y^f and productions

$$u_f: X^f \to Y^f, \qquad v_f: Y^f \to R^f.$$

Then the language L is generated by the type-$(2-\lambda)$ grammar (G_1, ρ) where

$$G_1 = (V_N \cup \{Y^f | f \in F\}, V_T, X_0, \{u_f | f \in F\} \cup \{v_f | f \in F\})$$

and the regular restrictions are defined by

$$\rho(g) = V^* \cup \bigcup_{f \in F} (V^* P^f Y^f Q^f V^*), \qquad V = V_N \cup V_T,$$

for every production g of G_1. ∎

It is seen from the preceding proof that the first sentence of Theorem 7.3 remains valid if a length-increasing grammar is considered instead of a type-1 grammar. (This remark applies also to Theorem 6.3.) For a modification of the second sentence, see Exercise 12.

EXERCISES

1. Prove that the languages considered in Examples 2.3 and 2.5 of Part 1 belong to the family $\mathscr{P}_{ac}$.

2. Define and study language families bearing the same relation to $\mathscr{T}$-, $\mathscr{P}$-, and $\mathscr{R}$-families as $\mathscr{M}_{left}^\lambda$ and $\mathscr{M}_{left}$ do to $\mathscr{M}$-families. Introduce leftmost restriction in such a way that the equality between $\mathscr{M}$-, $\mathscr{T}$-, $\mathscr{P}$-, and $\mathscr{R}$-families results.

3. An *unconditional transfer* programmed grammar is a programmed grammar with $\sigma(f) = \varphi(f)$ for all f. Prove that if (G, σ, φ) is an unconditional transfer context-free programmed grammar, then there is an algorithm for deciding whether or not $L_{ac}(G, \sigma, \varphi)$ is empty.

4. Prove that every type-0 language can be expressed in the form $h(L_{ac}(G, \sigma, \varphi) \cap L_1)$ where (G, σ, φ) is an unconditional transfer context-free λ-free programmed grammar, L_1 is a minimal linear language, and h is a homomorphism.

5. The language $L = \{a^m b^n | m \geq 1, 1 \leq n \leq 2^m\}$ is not context-free since it is not letter-equivalent to any regular language. Prove that L is of type $(2-\lambda, 3, 0)$.

6. Prove that every language of the form $L_{ac}(G, C, F_1)$, where C is regular and G is a linear grammar, is linear.

7. Establish the first two columns in Tables 3 and 4 given in Note 6.1. [The essential tool for type-$(i, 1, k)$ languages is Theorem 9.9 in Part 1.]

8. Using the method of Theorem 6.3, prove that

$$\mathscr{L}(1,2,0) = \mathscr{L}(1,2,1).$$

9. Prove that every language in the family $\mathscr{L}(1,2,1)$ is recursive.

10. Prove that each of the families

$$\mathscr{L}(2-\lambda,3,1), \qquad \mathscr{L}(2-\lambda,2,1), \qquad \mathscr{L}(1,2,0)$$

is an AFL.

11. Consider ordered grammars $(G, >)$ where $>$ is a total order. Give examples of finite languages which cannot be generated by such ordered grammars of type 1. Prove that any type-0 language can be generated by such an ordered grammar of type 0.

12. Prove that any type-0 language is generated by a type-2 grammar with regular restrictions.

13. In Sections 3–6, the set $\mathrm{Lab}(F)$ rather than F was used in defining $\mathscr{M}$-, $\mathscr{P}$-, and $\mathscr{R}$-families but not in defining $\mathscr{T}$-families. Show that none of the $\mathscr{M}$-, $\mathscr{P}$-, and $\mathscr{R}$-families decreases if $\mathrm{Lab}(F)$ is not introduced and it is always assumed that $F_1 \subseteq F$. [If $\mathrm{Lab}(F)$ is not introduced, it is not possible to "duplicate" productions and use the different copies in a different way.]

BIBLIOGRAPHICAL REMARKS

Matrix grammars were introduced by Ábrahám (1965). For an interesting special case, see Ibarra (1970). Appearance checking was defined in Salomaa (1969) and the leftmost restriction in Salomaa (1972). For similar orientation devices, see also Kasai (1970) and Rozenberg (1972). The material concerning time-varying grammars is from Salomaa (1970a). For corresponding results concerning automata, see Baer and Spanier (1969) and Salomaa (1968). The notion of a programmed grammar as well as the main results are due to Rosenkrantz (1969). (His notion differs from the one defined in Section 5 in that Rosenkrantz requires that a production is applied to the leftmost occurrence of its left side.) An early version of the notion of control language is in Altman and Banerji (1965). Ginsburg and Spanier (1968) restrict their attention to leftmost derivations only. The control languages discussed in Section 6 were developed in Friant (1968), Stotskij (1967, 1968, 1971a,b) and Salomaa (1969 and 1970b). The equivalence of the various types of restrictive devices (also in cases mentioned as propositions in Section 6) was shown in Salomaa (1970a). Other similar restrictive devices have been introduced by Nash and Cohen (1969) and Mayer (1972). For Szilard languages, see Moriya (1972), as well as the references given therein. Ordered grammars are due to Friš (1968). Friant (1968) has considered various extensions. Regular restrictions were discussed in more detail by Král (1970). Lepistö (1971) has investigated the possibility of removing the appearance checking from Theorem 7.1. We have not discussed above the two-level grammars introduced by Van Wijngaarden in connection with ALGOL 68. Basically, in a two-level grammar the productions are generated by means of another grammar. The reader is referred to Maurer (1969) and Koster (1970) and the references given therein.

BIBLIOGRAPHY

S. Ábrahám. Some questions of phrase structure grammars. *Computational Linguistics* **4** (1965) 61–70.

E. Altman and R. Banerji. Some problems of finite representability. *Information Control* **8** (1965) 251–263.

R. Baer and E. Spanier. Referenced automata and metaregular families. *J. Comput. System Sci.* **3** (1969) 423–446.

J. Friant. Grammaires ordonnees—grammaires matricielles. Univ. de Montréal MA-101 (1968).

J. Friš. Grammars with partial ordering of the rules. *Information Control* **12** (1968) 415–425.

S. Ginsburg and E. Spanier. Control sets on grammars. *Math. Systems Theory* **2** (1968) 159–177.

O. Ibarra. Simple matrix languages. *Information Control* **17** (1970) 359–394.

T. Kasai. An hierarchy between context-free and context-sensitive languages. *J. Comput. System Sci.* **4** (1970) 492–508.

C. H. A. Koster. Two-level grammars. *Seminar on Automata Theory and Mathematical Linguistics*, Utrecht, Abstract no. 11 (1970).

J. Král. A Note on Grammars with Regular Restrictions. Manuscript (1970).

T. Lepistö. On Ordered Context-Free Grammars. Manuscript (1971).

H. Maurer. *"Theoretische Grundlagen der Programmiersprachen."* Hochschultaschen-bücher 404, Bibliographisches Inst., 1969.

O. Mayer. Some restrictive devices for context-free grammars. *Information Control* **20** (1972) 69–92.

E. Moriya. The associate language and the derivation properties of formal grammars. *Information Control* (1972) (to appear).

B. Nash and R. Cohen. Parallel leveled grammars. *IEEE Conf. Record 10th Ann. Symp. Switching Automata Theory* (1969) 263–276.

D. Rosenkrantz. Programmed grammars and classes of formal languages. *J. Assoc. Comput. Mach.* **16** (1969) 107–131.

G. Rozenberg. Direction controlled programmed grammars. *Acta Informatica* **1** (1972) 242–252.

A. Salomaa. On finite automata with a time-variant structure. *Information Control* **13** (1968) 85–98.

A. Salomaa. On grammars with restricted use of productions. *Ann. Acad. Sci. Fennicae, Ser. AI.* **454** (1969).

A. Salomaa. Periodically time-variant context-free grammars. *Information Control* **17** (1970a) 294–311.

A. Salomaa. On some families of formal languages obtained by regulated derivations. *Ann. Acad. Sci. Fennicae, Ser. AI.* **479** (1970b).

A. Salomaa. Matrix grammars with a leftmost restriction. *Information Control* **20** (1972) 143–149.

E. D. Stotskij. O nekotorykh ogranichenijakh na sposob vyvoda v grammatikakh neposredstvennykh sostavljajushchikh. *Akad. Nauk SSSR Nauchno-Tekhn. Inform. Ser.* **2** (1967) 35–38.

E. D. Stotskij. Porozhdajushchie grammatiki i upravlenie vyvodom. *Akad. Nauk SSSR Nauchno-Tekhn. Inform. Ser.* **2** (1968) 28–31.

E. D. Stotskij. Formalnye grammatiki i ogranichenija na vyvod. *Probl. Pered. Inform.* **7,1** (1971a) 87–101.

E. D. Stotskij. Upravlenie vyvodom v formalnykh grammatikakh. *Probl. Pered. Inform.* **7,3** (1971b) 87–102.

Chapter VI

Context-Free Languages Revisited

We now return to the discussion of the family $\mathscr{L}_2$. New aspects are presented about the definition, ambiguity, parsing, bounds in derivations, as well as subfamilies of context-free languages.

8. FORMAL POWER SERIES

Any language can be defined in terms of a formal power series in associative but noncommutative variables. By this approach, a unified treatment can be given to some problems and in some cases also results from classical mathematical analysis become applicable.

Let V_T be an alphabet and φ a mapping of the set $W(V_T)$ into the set of integers. Such a mapping can represented by

$$\varphi = \sum \varphi(P) P = \varphi(P_1) P_1 + \varphi(P_2) P_2 + \cdots, \tag{8.1}$$

where the sum is taken over all words $P \in W(V_T)$. The series (8.1) is referred to as a *formal power series* in the associative but noncommutative variables a of V_T. The *support* of φ, in symbols, $\text{supt}(\varphi)$, is defined by

$$\text{supt}(\varphi) = \{P \in W(V_T) | \varphi(P) \neq 0\}. \tag{8.2}$$

Thus, $\text{supt}(\varphi)$ consists of words whose coefficients in (8.1) are distinct from zero. Clearly, any language over V_T is of the form (8.2) for some suitably chosen φ. If for each $P \in W(V_T)$, $\varphi(P)$ equals 0 or 1, we say that (8.1) is the *characteristic* formal power series of its support. The set of all formal power series (resp. all formal power series with nonnegative coefficients) over V_T is denoted by $Z(V_T)$ [resp. by $N(V_T)$].

The following interpretation can be given for the coefficients of a formal power series φ. Consider a generative device G for a language L over V_T. Then every word $P \in W(V_T)$ is assigned some structural descriptions (like generation trees) according to G. Let $\varphi(P)$ be the number of these descriptions. Hence, for every $P \in W(V_T)$, $\varphi(P) \geq 0$ and $\varphi(P) > 0$ iff $P \in L$. In this interpretation, $\varphi(P)$ expresses the "degree" of structural ambiguity of P with respect to G. [For instance, if G is a context-free grammar, $\varphi(P)$ is the number of leftmost derivations of P according to G.] The interpretation is applicable for series in $N(V_T)$ only. For $\varphi \in Z(V_T)$, we can regard $\varphi(P)$ as the difference between the number of times that P is generated by two fixed generative devices G_1 and G_2, that is, the difference between the number of structural descriptions assigned to P according to G_1 and that assigned to P according to G_2.

We now define some operations for formal power series. If φ is a formal power series and n an integer, the *product* $n\varphi$ is the formal power series such that, for every $P \in W(V_T)$, $(n\varphi)(P) = n(\varphi(P))$. For two formal power series φ and φ', the coefficients of their *sum* and *Cauchy product* are defined by

$$(\varphi + \varphi')(P) = \varphi(P) + \varphi'(P); \qquad (\varphi\varphi')(P) = \sum_{P_1 P_2 = P} (\varphi(P_1)\varphi'(P_2)),$$

for every $P \in W(V_T)$. Clearly, if φ and φ' are in $Z(V_T)$ or in $N(V_T)$, then so are $\varphi + \varphi'$ and $\varphi\varphi'$ also. [Moreover, $Z(V_T)$ is a ring with respect to sum and Cauchy product.] Any two formal power series φ and φ' in $N(V_T)$ satisfy

$$\text{supt}(\varphi + \varphi') = \text{supt}(\varphi) \cup \text{supt}(\varphi'), \tag{8.3}$$

$$\text{supt}(\varphi\varphi') = (\text{supt}(\varphi))(\text{supt}(\varphi')). \tag{8.4}$$

Since the Cauchy product clearly is associative, we may use the notation φ^k, $k \geq 1$, in its customary sense. Furthermore, the formal power series

$$\varphi^+ = \lim_{m \to \infty} \sum_{k=1}^{m} \varphi^k$$

is well defined for each formal power series φ such that $\varphi(\lambda) = 0$. The series φ^+ is called the *quasi-inverse* of φ. It satisfies the equations $\varphi + \varphi^+\varphi = \varphi + \varphi\varphi^+ = \varphi^+$. If φ is an element of $N(V_T)$, then so is φ^+, and

$$\text{supt}(\varphi^+) = (\text{supt}(\varphi))^+, \tag{8.5}$$

where on the right side superscript plus denotes λ-free catenation closure. [The notion of a quasi-inverse is interrelated with the familiar notion of an inverse as follows. Denote by λ the formal power series in which the coefficient of the empty word is 1, the other coefficients being 0. Let φ' be an arbitrary formal power series such that $\varphi'(\lambda) = 1$. Then $\varphi' = \lambda + (-1)\varphi$ where φ satisfies the condition $\varphi(\lambda) = 0$. Consequently, φ^+ exists. Denote $\varphi'' = \lambda + \varphi^+$. Then

$$\varphi'\varphi'' = (\lambda - \varphi)(\lambda + \varphi^+) = \lambda + (\varphi^+ - \varphi - \varphi\varphi^+) = \lambda = \varphi''\varphi',$$

i.e., φ'' is the inverse of φ'.]

For $a \in V_T$, we denote by a also the formal power series in which the coefficient of a equals 1, the other coefficients being 0. (Note that a is the characteristic series of the language $\{a\}$.) We say that a collection of formal power series is *rationally closed* iff it contains the element φ^+ for every φ satisfying the condition $\varphi(\lambda) = 0$. The collection of *rational* [resp. *rational nonnegative*] formal power series over V_T, in symbols, $\mathrm{rat}(V_T)$ [resp. $\mathrm{rat}^+(V_T)$], is the smallest rationally closed set which contains λ and each $a \in V_T$, and is closed under product [resp. product $n\varphi$ where $n \geqq 0$], sum, and Cauchy product.

The following theorem is an immediate consequence of the equations (8.3)–(8.5).

Theorem 8.1. A language over V_T is regular iff it equals the support of some formal power series in $\mathrm{rat}^+(V_T)$.

A convenient characterization for the elements of $\mathrm{rat}^+(V_T)$ can be given in terms of matrices. Let μ be a mapping of V_T into the set of n-dimensional square matrices whose components are nonnegative integers. The mapping μ is extended in a natural way into a homomorphism of $W(V_T)$ by defining $\mu(\lambda)$ to be the identity matrix, and $\mu(aP) = \mu(a)\mu(P)$ for $a \in V_T$ and $P \in W(V_T)$. An element φ of $N(V_T)$ is said to possess a *matrix representation* iff there exist an integer $n \geqq 1$ and a mapping μ as above such that, for any nonempty word P over V_T, $\varphi(P)$ equals the $(1, n)$th entry in the matrix $\mu(P)$.

Proposition 8.1. A formal power series in $N(V_T)$ is rational iff it possesses a matrix representation.

So far we have not discussed the problem of how a formal power series φ is obtained for a language L, that is, a formal power series φ satisfying $\mathrm{supt}(\varphi) = L$. If L is defined by a *context-free* grammar, then φ is obtained by an iterative procedure described below. (The procedure is closely related to matters discussed in Note 6.1 of Part 1.)

Let G be a context-free grammar with the nonterminals $X_0, \ldots, X_n$, $n \geqq 0$.
For $i = 0, \ldots, n$, let $P_1^i, \ldots, P_{m_i}^i$ be all the words appearing on the right sides
of the productions with X_i on the left side. (We assume that $m_i \geqq 1$ for all
i.) We associate with G the system of (formal) equations

$$X_i = P_1^i + \cdots + P_{m_i}^i = \alpha_i, \qquad i = 0, \ldots, n. \tag{8.6}$$

Given G, the system (8.6) can be immediately written and, conversely, (8.6)
determines G uniquely.

We assume now that G does not contain any productions $X \to Y$ or $X \to \lambda$
where X and Y are nonterminals. (This does not affect the generative capacity
except possibly with respect to the empty word.) Let $\varphi(P)$ be equal to the
number of generation trees of P according to G for $P \in W(V_{\mathrm{T}})$. The formal
power series

$$\varphi = \sum \varphi(P) P$$

is now constructed. Define formal power series φ_j^k for $0 \leqq j \leqq n$ and $k \geqq 0$
as follows. [We are considering the system (8.6) for G.] For all j, $\varphi_j^0 = 0$
(i.e., φ_j^0 equals the series, all of whose coefficients equal zero). For $k > 0$
and all j, φ_j^k is obtained from α_j by replacing each nonterminal X_i,
$0 \leqq i \leqq n$, with the series φ_i^{k-1}. (In the resulting expression, letters a of V_{T}
are considered as formal power series in the way indicated above; $+$ and
juxtaposition denote the operations of sum and Cauchy product, respectively.
Since every φ_i^k has only finitely many nonzero coefficients, it can be considered
as a *polynomial*.) Clearly,

$$\varphi = \lim_{k \to \infty} \varphi_0^k. \tag{8.7}$$

In fact, for each u and P with $lg(P) \leqq u$, the coefficient of P in the series
$\varphi_0^{2^u-1}$ equals the coefficient $\varphi(P)$ of P in the series φ (cf. Exercise 1). Here
the assumption that productions $X \to Y$ and $X \to \lambda$ are not present is essential.
The formal power series (8.7) obtained in this fashion from a system (8.6) is
termed *context-free*. The next theorem is an immediate consequence of the
definitions.

Theorem 8.2. A context-free language is unambiguous iff its characteristic
formal power series is context-free.

Example 8.1. Consider the λ-free Dyck language generated by the grammar

$$G = (\{X_0\}, \{a, b\}, X_0, \{X_0 \to X_0 X_0, X_0 \to a X_0 b, X_0 \to ab\}).$$

The system (8.6) consists now of the single equation

$$X_0 = X_0 X_0 + a X_0 b + ab.$$

The first among the polynomials $\varphi_j{}^k$ are

$$\varphi_0{}^0 = 0, \qquad \varphi_0{}^1 = ab, \qquad \varphi_0{}^2 = abab + aabb + ab,$$

$$\varphi_0{}^3 = (abab + aabb + ab)^2 + a(abab + aabb + ab)b + ab$$

$$= abababab + ababaabb + aabbaabb + aabbabab + 2ababab$$

$$+ aabbab + abaabb + aababb + aaabbb + abab + aabb + ab.$$

The coefficient of any word of length less than or equal to $2k$ in the formal power series φ is seen from the polynomial $\varphi_0{}^k$. This is established by an obvious induction on k.

Example 8.2. Consider the grammar G determined by the equations

$$X_0 = aX_1 + aX_2 + aX_3 + a, \qquad X_1 = aX_0, \qquad X_2 = aX_0, \qquad X_3 = b.$$

Now the first polynomials are

$$\varphi_j{}^0 = 0 \qquad \text{for} \quad 0 \leq j \leq 3,$$

$$\varphi_0{}^1 = a,$$
$$\varphi_0{}^2 = ab + a,$$
$$\varphi_0{}^3 = 2aaa + ab + a,$$
$$\varphi_0{}^4 = 2aaab + 2aaa + ab + a.$$

$$\varphi_1{}^1 = \varphi_2{}^1 = 0,$$
$$\varphi_1{}^2 = \varphi_2{}^2 = aa,$$
$$\varphi_1{}^3 = \varphi_2{}^3 = aab + aa,$$

$$\varphi_3{}^1 = b,$$
$$\varphi_3{}^2 = b,$$
$$\varphi_3{}^3 = b,$$

It is easy to verify inductively that

$$\varphi = \lim_{k \to \infty} \varphi_0{}^k = \sum_{m=1}^{\infty} 2^{m-1} a^{2m-1}(b + \lambda).$$

The coefficients of the words P on the right sides of the equations (8.6) are all positive. (In fact, they are all equal to 1.) The iterative procedure described above for obtaining the formal power series φ is applicable also in the case where the coefficients are arbitrary integers. (We assume also now that neither a single nonterminal nor λ is among the words P.) A formal power series φ obtained in this fashion is termed *algebraic*. The *Hadamard product* of two formal power series φ and φ' is a formal power series where, for any $P \in W(V_T)$, the coefficient of P equals the product of $\varphi(P)$ and $\varphi'(P)$.

Proposition 8.2. The Hadamard product of a rational and of an algebraic formal power series is algebraic.

Note that Theorem 6.7 in Part 1 is obtained as a special case of Proposition 8.2.

We now apply techniques similar to the ones used in the iterative procedure above to obtain another normal form for context-free grammars. However, formal power series are not used in this development.

Definition. A context-free grammar $G = (V_N, V_T, X_0, F)$ is in the *Greibach normal form* iff all productions in F are of the form

$$X \to aP, \qquad X \in V_N, \quad a \in V_T, \quad P \in W(V_N \cup V_T).$$

It is obvious that if G is in the Greibach normal form, then $\lambda \notin L(G)$. We show that any λ-free context-free language is generated by a grammar in the Greibach normal form. The next theorem is a lemma which asserts that substitutions may be performed in equations of (8.6) without affecting the language generated.

Theorem 8.3. Let G be the context-free grammar associated with the system of equations (8.6). Let G' be the context-free grammar associated with the system obtained from (8.6) by replacing, for some i and j, some occurrence of X_j in α_i with α_j (and applying the distributive law to the resulting expression). Then $L(G) = L(G')$.

Proof. G' is obtained from G as follows. Some production $X_i \to Q_1 X_j Q_2$ is replaced by the productions

$$X_i \to Q_1 P_1^{\,j} Q_2, ..., X_i \to Q_1 P_{m_j}^{\,j} Q_2$$

where the P's are the right sides of the productions with X_j on the left side. Clearly $L(G') \subseteq L(G)$ since the application of a production $X_i \to Q_1 P_k^{\,j} Q_2$ belonging to G' can be replaced by the two steps

$$X_i \Rightarrow Q_1 X_j Q_2 \Rightarrow Q_1 P_k^{\,j} Q_2$$

in a derivation according to G. To establish the reverse inclusion $L(G) \subseteq L(G')$, we note that if the production $X_i \to Q_1 X_j Q_2$ is used in a derivation according to G, then a production $X_j \to P_k^{\,j}$ must be applied at some later step of the derivation. These two steps may be replaced by an application of the production $X_i \to Q_1 P_k^{\,j} Q_2$. ∎

Example 8.3. Consider the grammar G determined by the equations

$$X_0 = X_0 X_1 + X_0 X_0 + a + b,$$

$$X_1 = X_1 X_0 + X_0 X_0 + b.$$

These equations can be expressed in the matrix form:

$$(X_0, X_1) = (a+b, b) + (X_0, X_1) \begin{pmatrix} X_0 + X_1 & X_0 \\ \varnothing & X_0 \end{pmatrix}$$

or, in short,

$$A = B + AD.$$

Successive applications of Theorem 8.3 yield the equation

$$A = B + (B + AD)D = B + BD + AD^2$$

which can then be rewritten as two equations for X_0 and X_1.

Theorem 8.4. Any context-free λ-free language L is generated by a grammar in the Greibach normal form.

Proof. By Theorem 6.3 in Part 1, we assume that the given language L is generated by a grammar $G = (V_N, V_T, X_0, F)$ in the Chomsky normal form. Let (8.6) be the system of equations associated with G. Consequently, each of the words P consists of either two nonterminals or one terminal. Denoting

$$A = (X_0, ..., X_n),$$

we write (8.6) in the matrix form

$$A = B + AD, \qquad B = (b_j)_{0 \leq j \leq n}, \qquad D = (d_{ij})_{0 \leq i,j \leq n}$$

such that each b_j is the sum of some letters of V_T and each d_{ij} is the sum of some letters of V_N. (The "empty sum" $\varnothing$ is possible.) By Theorem 8.3, the grammar G_1 associated with the equation

$$A = B + BD + AD^2$$

satisfies $L = L(G_1)$. By successive substitutions, we conclude that for every $u \geq 1$, the grammar G_u associated with the equation

$$A = B + BD + BD^2 + \cdots + BD^{v-1} + AD^v,$$

where $v = 2^u$, satisfies $L = L(G_u)$. For every $u \geq 1$, we denote by G_u' the grammar associated with the equation

$$A = B + BD + BD^2 + \cdots + BD^{v-1}, \qquad v = 2^u.$$

Since G_u' results from G_u by omitting some productions, we obtain

$$L(G_u') \subseteq L(G_u) = L(G), \qquad u \geq 1. \tag{8.8}$$

We now introduce $(n+1)^2$ new nonterminals Y_{ij}, where $0 \leq i, j \leq n$, and let Y be the matrix (Y_{ij}). Consider the grammar H associated with the system of equations in the matrix form

$$A = B + BY, \qquad Y = D + DY. \tag{8.9}$$

For every $u \geq 1$, we denote by H_u the grammar associated with the system of equations in the matrix form

$$A = B + BD + \cdots + BD^{v-1} + BD^{v-1}Y, \qquad Y = D + DY,$$

where $v = 2^u$. By Theorem 8.3, $L(H) = L(H_u)$ for every $u \geq 1$. Since H_u

contains all of the productions of $G_u{}'$, we conclude that

$$L(G_u{}') \subseteq L(H_u) = L(H), \qquad u \geqq 1. \tag{8.10}$$

Using (8.8) and (8.10), we now prove that

$$L(H) = L(G) = L. \tag{8.11}$$

For every $v \geqq 1$, every entry in the matrix D^v is a sum of words of length v over V_N. (The empty sum $\varnothing$ is again possible.) This follows by the remark concerning the elements d_{ij}. Consequently, the right sides of the productions resulting from the matrices AD^v and $BD^{v-1}Y$ are of length $v+1$. This means that these productions cannot be applied in the derivation of words of length $\leqq v$. Thus if P is a word of length $v \geqq 1$ which is in $L(G)$ or in $L(H)$ and if $2^u \geqq v$, then P is in $L(G_u{}')$. This fact together with (8.8) and (8.10) proves (8.11).

We now rewrite (8.9) in the form

$$A = B + BY, \qquad Y^{(i)} = D^{(i)} + D^{(i)}Y, \qquad i = 0, \dots, n,$$

where $Y^{(i)}$ [resp. $D^{(i)}$] is the $(i+1)$th row of Y [resp. D]. On the other hand, $D^{(i)} = AT_i$ for some square matrix T_i (all of whose components are either λ or $\varnothing$). Thus (8.9) can be written

$$A = B + BY, \qquad Y^{(i)} = AT_i + AT_iY, \qquad i = 0, \dots, n.$$

By Theorem 8.3, the grammar $H_1{}'$ associated with the system of equations (in the matrix form)

$$A = B + BY, \qquad Y^{(i)} = BT_i + BYT_i + BT_iY + BYT_iY, \qquad i = 0, \dots, n, \tag{8.12}$$

satisfies $L(H_1{}') = L(H)$ and hence, by (8.11), $L(H_1{}') = L$. Clearly, $H_1{}'$ is in the Greibach normal form. ∎

Our next theorem is an immediate consequence of the definition of $H_1{}'$ in the previous proof.

Theorem 8.5. Any context-free λ-free language is generated by a grammar, all of whose productions are of the form $X \to aP$ where X is a nonterminal, a is a terminal, and P is a word over the nonterminal alphabet satisfying $0 \leqq lg(P) \leqq 2$.

Example 8.4. We reduce the grammar G of Example 8.3 into the Greibach normal form. By (8.12), we obtain

$$(X_0, X_1) = (a+b, b) + (a+b, b)\begin{pmatrix} Y_{00} & Y_{01} \\ Y_{10} & Y_{11} \end{pmatrix},$$

$$(Y_{00}, Y_{01}) = (a+b, b)\left[\begin{pmatrix} \lambda & \lambda \\ \lambda & \varnothing \end{pmatrix}\right.$$

$$+ \begin{pmatrix} Y_{00} & Y_{01} \\ Y_{10} & Y_{11} \end{pmatrix}\begin{pmatrix} \lambda & \lambda \\ \lambda & \varnothing \end{pmatrix} + \begin{pmatrix} \lambda & \lambda \\ \lambda & \varnothing \end{pmatrix}\begin{pmatrix} Y_{00} & Y_{01} \\ Y_{10} & Y_{11} \end{pmatrix}$$

$$\left. + \begin{pmatrix} Y_{00} & Y_{01} \\ Y_{10} & Y_{11} \end{pmatrix}\begin{pmatrix} \lambda & \lambda \\ \lambda & \varnothing \end{pmatrix}\begin{pmatrix} Y_{00} & Y_{01} \\ Y_{10} & Y_{11} \end{pmatrix}\right],$$

$$(Y_{10}, Y_{11}) = (a+b, b)\left[\begin{pmatrix} \varnothing & \lambda \\ \varnothing & \varnothing \end{pmatrix}\right.$$

$$+ \begin{pmatrix} Y_{00} & Y_{01} \\ Y_{10} & Y_{11} \end{pmatrix}\begin{pmatrix} \varnothing & \lambda \\ \varnothing & \varnothing \end{pmatrix} + \begin{pmatrix} \varnothing & \lambda \\ \varnothing & \varnothing \end{pmatrix}\begin{pmatrix} Y_{00} & Y_{01} \\ Y_{10} & Y_{11} \end{pmatrix}$$

$$\left. + \begin{pmatrix} Y_{00} & Y_{01} \\ Y_{10} & Y_{11} \end{pmatrix}\begin{pmatrix} \varnothing & \lambda \\ \varnothing & \varnothing \end{pmatrix}\begin{pmatrix} Y_{00} & Y_{01} \\ Y_{10} & Y_{11} \end{pmatrix}\right].$$

Eliminating the matrices, we get the following system of equations:

$$X_0 = a + b + aY_{00} + bY_{00} + bY_{10},$$

$$X_1 = b + aY_{01} + bY_{01} + bY_{11},$$

$$Y_{00} = a + b + aY_{00} + aY_{01} + aY_{10} + bY_{00} + bY_{01} + bY_{10} + bY_{11}$$
$$\quad + aY_{00}^2 + aY_{00}Y_{10} + aY_{01}Y_{00} + bY_{00}^2 + bY_{00}Y_{10} + bY_{01}Y_{00}$$
$$\quad + bY_{10}Y_{00} + bY_{10}^2 + bY_{11}Y_{00},$$

$$Y_{01} = a + b + aY_{00} + aY_{01} + aY_{11} + bY_{00} + bY_{01} + bY_{11} + bY_{10}$$
$$\quad + aY_{00}Y_{01} + aY_{00}Y_{11} + aY_{01}^2 + bY_{00}Y_{01} + bY_{00}Y_{11} + bY_{01}^2$$
$$\quad + bY_{10}Y_{01} + bY_{10}Y_{11} + bY_{11}Y_{01},$$

$$Y_{10} = aY_{10} + bY_{10} + aY_{00}Y_{10} + bY_{00}Y_{10} + bY_{10}^2,$$

$$Y_{11} = a + b + aY_{00} + aY_{11} + bY_{00} + bY_{11} + bY_{10} + aY_{00}Y_{11}$$
$$\quad + bY_{00}Y_{11} + bY_{10}Y_{11}.$$

The productions of a grammar G_1 in the Greibach normal form such that $L(G_1) = L(G)$ are immediately seen from these equations. It is to be noted that, in constructing G_1, we have followed the general algorithm of Theorem 8.4 and consequently G_1 is very complicated. One can, of course, make use of various shortcuts. In this case, an obvious shortcut would be to notice what the language $L(G)$ is.

The following theorem is an immediate consequence of Theorems 8.3 and 8.4 above, and of Theorem 6.2 in Part 1.

Theorem 8.6. Let L be a context-free language. Then for any k there is a grammar $G = (V_N, V_T, X_0, F)$ generating L such that all productions of G are of the two forms $X \to P$ and $X \to QR$ where $X \in V_N$, P and Q are words over V_T, and $lg(Q) > k$, whereas R is a word over $V_N \cup V_T$.

As regards pushdown automata, Theorem 8.4 may be interpreted as follows. For every pushdown automaton, there is an equivalent pushdown automaton which expends an input letter at each step of the computation; that is, all productions are of the form (4.15) in the numbering of Part 1.

9. AMBIGUITY

The notion of ambiguity of context-free grammars and languages was defined in Section 6 of Part 1. We now establish the existence of inherently ambiguous languages. Before the general result, we consider a special case. One can relativize the notion of ambiguity with respect to subclasses of context-free grammars (such as the ones considered in Section 8 of Part 1) and study whether or not all grammars within the subclass generating a given language L are ambiguous. If this is the case, then L is inherently ambiguous with respect to this subclass. An example is given in the following theorem.

Theorem 9.1. There is a minimal linear language L such that (i) every minimal linear grammar generating L is ambiguous and (ii) L is generated by an unambiguous linear grammar.

Proof. Consider the language $L = \{a^m c a^n | m \geq n \geq 0\}$ generated by the minimal linear grammar

$$G = (\{X_0\}, \{a, c\}, X_0, \{X_0 \to aX_0 a, \ X_0 \to aX_0, \ X_0 \to c\}).$$

Clearly, G is ambiguous, the ambiguity being due to the fact that the order of application of the first two productions is arbitrary. [For any m and n satisfying $m \geq n \geq 0$, the word $a^m c a^n$ possesses $\binom{m}{n}$ leftmost derivations.] The language L satisfies condition (ii), the required grammar being determined by the productions

$$X_0 \to aX_0 a, \qquad X_0 \to aX_1, \qquad X_1 \to aX_1, \qquad X_0 \to c, \qquad X_1 \to c.$$

To prove that L satisfies condition (i) also, we note that the productions of any minimal linear grammar G_1 generating L must be of the two forms

$$X_0 \to a^i X_0 a^j, \qquad i \geq j \geq 0; \qquad X_0 \to c.$$

Since the words ac and aca belong to L, the first two productions of G (and consequently all productions of G) must be among the productions of G_1. Thus any word has at least as many derivations according to G_1 as it has according to G. This implies that G_1 is ambiguous. ∎

We now return to the general notion of ambiguity of languages. We are going to show that the language

$$L = \{a^m b^n c^n | m, n \geq 1\} \cup \{a^m b^m c^n | m, n \geq 1\} \qquad (9.1)$$

is inherently ambiguous, that is, every context-free grammar generating L is ambiguous. (The language L is context-free because it is the union of two languages which were shown to be context-free in the proof of Theorem 6.6 in Part 1.) We first establish a lemma concerning unambiguous grammars. For a context-free grammar $G = (V_N, V_T, X_0, F)$, we denote

$$U(G) = \{X \in V_N | X \Rightarrow_G^* PXQ \text{ for some } P, Q \in W(V_T) \text{ such that } PQ \neq \lambda\}.$$

We say that G is *almost looping* iff each of the following conditions (i)–(iv) is satisfied.

(i)   For every $X \in V_N$, there is a word $P \in W(V_T)$ such that $X \Rightarrow^* P$.

(ii)   For every $X \in V_N - \{X_0\}$, there are words P and Q such that $X_0 \Rightarrow^* PXQ$.

(iii)   Either $X_0 \in U(G)$ or else X_0 occurs exactly once in every derivation of every word $P \in L(G)$.

(iv)   Every $X \in V_N - \{X_0\}$ is contained in $U(G)$.

[Note that (iv) is the actual "looping" condition.]

Theorem 9.2. For every unambiguous context-free grammar $G = (V_N, V_T, X_0, F)$ with $L(G) \neq \varnothing$, there is an equivalent unambiguous almost looping grammar G'.

Proof. Without loss of generality, we assume that the given grammar G satisfies the conditions (i) and (ii) above. For if this is not the case originally, then we remove all the nonterminals in question, as well as all productions containing some of these nonterminals. The generated language is not affected. [Note that the assumption $L(G) \neq \varnothing$ is needed to assure that we do not have to remove everything.] If the resulting grammar were ambiguous, this would be true also of G.

If G does not satisfy condition (iii), we have $X_0 \Rightarrow^* X_0$ where the length of the derivation is at least 1. For any $P \in L(G)$, we obtain now two leftmost derivations

$$X_0 \Rightarrow^* P \qquad \text{and} \qquad X_0 \Rightarrow^* X_0 \Rightarrow^* P.$$

This implies that G is ambiguous, which is against the hypothesis. Consequently, G satisfies (iii) also.

To obtain an unambiguous grammar $G' = (V_N', V_T, X_0, F')$ satisfying (i)–(iv), we proceed as follows. Assume that

$$V_N = \{X_0, X_1, \ldots, X_k\}, \qquad k \geq 0.$$

If $k = 0$, we choose $G' = G$. Condition (iv) holds vacuously in this case. If $k > 0$, we introduce a sequence of grammars

$$G_0 = G, G_1, \ldots, G_k = G'$$

in the following way. Consider a fixed j, $1 \leq j \leq k$, and assume that the grammar $G_{j-1} = (V_N^{j-1}, V_T, X_0, F^{j-1})$ has already been defined and that G_{j-1} is unambiguous and satisfies (i)–(iii). (We have shown that this holds for G_0.) If $X_j \in U(G_{j-1})$, we define $G_j = G_{j-1}$. Otherwise, let

$$X_j \to P_1, \ldots, X_j \to P_r \qquad (9.2)$$

be all the productions in F^{j-1} with X_j on the left side. Then $r \geq 1$ (since X_j generates at least one terminal word) and X_j is not a subword of the word $P_1 \cdots P_r$. [Since G_{j-1} satisfies (i) and (ii) and is unambiguous, the derivation $X_j \Rightarrow^* X_j$ with length ≥ 1 is not possible. Thus if X_j is a subword of $P_1 \cdots P_r$, then $X_j \in U(G_{j-1})$.] To obtain G_j, we first define $V_N^j = V_N^{j-1} - \{X_j\}$. The production set F^j is obtained from F^{j-1} by removing the productions (9.2) and replacing in the remaining productions every occurrence of X_j, independently of other occurrences, with each of the words $P_1, \ldots, P_r$. (Thus in an equation $X = Q_1 + \cdots + Q_m$ corresponding to a nonterminal $X \neq X_j$, we replace every occurrence of X_j on the right side by $P_1 + \cdots + P_r$.) We have now defined the grammar G_j. Clearly, G_j and G_{j-1} are equivalent. The ambiguity of G_j would imply the ambiguity of G_{j-1}, and consequently G_j is unambiguous. It is also obvious that G_j satisfies (i)–(iii) because G_{j-1} satisfies these conditions. Moreover, V_N^j contains the nonterminal X_i, $1 \leq i \leq j$, iff $X_i \in U(G) = U(G_j)$. This implies that $G_k = G'$ satisfies conditions (i)–(iv) and consequently is almost looping. ∎

Theorem 9.3. The language (9.1) is inherently ambiguous.

Proof. Assume the contrary. By Theorem 9.2, L is generated by an unambiguous almost looping grammar $G = (V_N, V_T, X_0, F)$. We establish next three facts (I–III) concerning G.

I.   Every nonterminal $X \neq X_0$ is of exactly one of the following types.

Type 1. There is a natural number m and words P and Q such that $X \Rightarrow^* PXQ$ and either $PQ = a^m$ or $PQ = c^m$.

Type 2. There is a natural number m such that $X \Rightarrow^* a^m X b^m$.
Type 3. There is a natural number m such that $X \Rightarrow^* b^m X c^m$.

To prove assertion I, we consider a nonterminal $X \neq X_0$ and note first that since G is almost looping, there are words P_1 and Q_1 over V_T such that $X \Rightarrow^* P_1 X Q_1$ and $P_1 Q_1 \neq \lambda$. The letters a, b, c always occur in the alphabetical order in the words of L, that is, an occurrence of b never precedes an occurrence of a and an occurrence of c never precedes an occurrence of a or b. Since we also have $X \Rightarrow^* P_1{}^2 X Q_1{}^2$, both of the words P_1 and Q_1 contain at most one of the letters a, b, c. We prove now that X is of at least one of the types $1, 2, 3$. Since G is almost looping, we also have a derivation

$$X_0 \Rightarrow^* R_1 X R_2 \Rightarrow^* a^r b^s c^t \tag{9.3}$$

where $r, s, t \geq 1$ and either $r = s$ or $s = t$.

Assume that $P_1 = a^m$ where $m > 0$. Consider (9.3). If $Q_1 = c^n$ where $n > 0$, then L contains, for every $q \geq 0$, the word $a^{r+qm} b^s c^{t+qn}$, which is impossible. If $Q_1 = b^n$ where $m \neq n \geq 1$, then L contains, for every $q \geq 0$, the word $a^{r+qm} b^{s+qn} c^t$, which is also impossible. Consequently, either $Q_1 = b^m$ or $Q_1 = a^n$ where $n \geq 0$; that is, X is of type 1 or 2.

Assume that $P_1 = b^m$ where $m > 0$. Then Q_1 cannot be of the form a^n with $n > 0$ because this would violate the alphabetical order of the letters a, b, c in the words of L. If $Q_1 = b^n$ where $n \geq 0$, then L contains, for every $q \geq 0$, the word $a^r b^{s+q(m+n)} c^t$, which is impossible. If $Q_1 = c^n$ where $n \neq m$, then L contains, for every $q \geq 0$, the word $a^r b^{s+qm} c^{t+qn}$, which is also impossible. Consequently, $Q_1 = c^m$ and X is of type 3.

Assume that $P_1 = c^m$ where $m > 0$. By the alphabetical order of the letters a, b, c in the words of L, we conclude that $Q_1 = c^n$ with $n \geq 0$, and X is of type 1.

Finally, assume that $P_1 = \lambda$. Then Q_1 is a positive power of one of the letters a, b, c. If $Q_1 = b^n$ where $n > 0$, then L contains, for every $q \geq 0$, the word $a^r b^{s+qn} c^t$, which is impossible. This implies that X is of type 1.

Having established that X is of at least one of the types 1–3, we now prove that X cannot be of two of the types mentioned. Assume that X is of the types 1 and 2. Thus $X \Rightarrow^* PXQ$ and $X \Rightarrow^* a^n X b^n$ where $PQ = x^m$, m and n are natural numbers, and $x = a$ or $x = c$. Combining these derivations, we obtain

$$X \Rightarrow^* a^n x^{m_1} X x^{m_2} b^n, \qquad m_1 + m_2 = m.$$

As before, we conclude that each of the words $a^n x^{m_1}$ and $x^{m_2} b^n$ is a power of one of the letters a, b, c. This implies that $x = a$ and $m_2 = 0$. However, this was shown impossible above when we assumed that $P_1 = a^m$. Consequently, X is not of both of the types 1 and 2. Similarly we conclude that X is not of both of the types 1 and 3. Assume, finally, that X is of the types 2 and 3. Then we obtain

$$X \Rightarrow^* a^m b^n X c^n b^m, \qquad m \geq 1, \quad n \geq 1,$$

which contradicts the alphabetical order of the letters a, b, c in the words of L. Hence, assertion I follows.

II.   The initial letter X_0 occurs exactly once in every derivation according to G of every word $P \in L$.

Assuming the contrary, we conclude by condition (iii) in the definition of almost looping grammars that

$$X_0 \Rightarrow^* P X_0 Q, \qquad PQ \neq \lambda, \quad P, Q \in W(V_T).$$

This implies that both of the words P and Q are powers of one of the letters a, b, c. Since all words in L begin with the letter a and end with c, there are only the following possibilities:

$$P = a^m, \qquad m \geq 1; \qquad Q = \lambda, \tag{9.4}$$

$$P = \lambda; \qquad\qquad Q = c^m, \qquad m \geq 1, \tag{9.5}$$

$$P = a^m, \qquad m \geq 1; \qquad Q = c^n, \qquad n \geq 1. \tag{9.6}$$

Since $abc^2 \in L$, (9.4) implies that $a^{m+1} bc^2 \in L$, which is absurd. Since $a^2 bc \in L$, (9.5) implies that $a^2 bc^{m+1} \in L$, which is also absurd. Finally, since $abc \in L$, (9.6) implies that $a^{m+1} bc^{n+1} \in L$. Thus, a contradiction arises in every case. We conclude that II holds.

III.   There exists a natural number v such that every word $P \in L$, possessing a derivation which does not contain nonterminals of types 2 and 3, contains less than v b's.

In fact, by II, if there are u_1 nonterminals of type 1 and u_2 is the maximum number of b's appearing on the right side of some production, we may choose $v = (u_1 + 1)u_2$. Thus, assertion III is true.

For every nonterminal X of type 2 or 3, we fix now a natural number $m(X)$ satisfying the condition mentioned in the definition of the types. Let u be the least common multiple of all of the integers $m(X)$. Choose an integer $p > v$ such that p is divisible by u. Consider the word $R_1 = a^p b^p c^{2p}$ which belongs to L. If we have, for some words R' and R'' and some type-3 nonterminal X,

$$X_0 \Rightarrow^* R' X R'' \Rightarrow^* R_1, \tag{9.7}$$

then we also have

$$X_0 \Rightarrow^* R' X R'' \Rightarrow^* R' b^p X c^p R'' \Rightarrow^* a^p b^{2p} c^{3p} \notin L.$$

(Here the last portion of the derivation is understood as follows: If the derivation leads to a terminal word, where a, b, c appear in the alphabetical order, then this word is necessarily $a^p b^{2p} c^{3p}$. This remark is applicable also elsewhere in this proof.) Consequently, no type-3 nonterminal appears in any derivation of R_1. By III, since $p > v$, (9.7) must hold for some R' and R'' and type-2 nonterminal X. For this X, we have $X \Rightarrow^* a^p X b^p$. [Remember that p is divisible by each of the numbers $m(X)$.] In the latter derivation, no type-3 nonterminals occur. Thus

$$X_0 \Rightarrow^* R'XR'' \Rightarrow^* R'a^p X b^p R'' \Rightarrow^* a^{2p} b^{2p} c^{2p} \tag{9.8}$$

is a derivation containing a type-2 nonterminal X but no nonterminals of type 3.

Similarly, beginning with the word $R_2 = a^{2p} b^p c^p$, we obtain a derivation

$$X_0 \Rightarrow^* R_3 X_1 R_4 \Rightarrow^* R_3 b^p X_1 c^p R_4 \Rightarrow^* a^{2p} b^{2p} c^{2p}, \tag{9.9}$$

which contains a type-3 nonterminal X_1 but does not contain any nonterminals of type 2. By I, the leftmost derivations resulting from (9.8) and (9.9) are different. After all, G is ambiguous. ∎

Note 9.1. The *degree of ambiguity* of a context-free grammar G is·defined as follows: G is *ambiguous of degree* $n \geqq 1$ (in short, an *n-grammar*) iff at least one word $P \in L(G)$ possesses n distinct leftmost derivations according to G, and no word $Q \in L(G)$ possesses more than. n distinct leftmost derivations according to G. If no such n exists, then G is ambiguous of degree ∞. Thus if the formal power series $\varphi \neq 0$ is defined by (8.7), then G is ambiguous of degree $n = \lim \sup \varphi(P)$ where P ranges over all words of V_T. Thus G is unambiguous iff it is ambiguous of degree 1.

A language is *inherently ambiguous of degree* $n \geqq 1$ iff it is generated by an *n*-grammar but is generated by no *m*-grammar with $m < n$. A context-free language L is inherently ambiguous of degree ∞ iff, for no n, L is generated by an *n*-grammar. For instance, the language

$$\{a^r b^s c^t \mid r, s, t \geqq 1, \text{ and } r = s \text{ or } r = t \text{ or } s = t\}$$

is inherently ambiguous of degree 3. For any u, including $u = \infty$, there is a language inherently ambiguous of degree u.

Note 9.2. Considering closure properties of language families such as the ones deduced earlier, unambiguity (or ambiguity) is a weak hypothesis. For instance, the following examples show that this hypothesis does not imply anything as regards the problem of whether the complement of the language is context-free. The language

$$\{a^p b^q c^r d^s e^t \mid (p = q \wedge r = s) \vee (q = r \wedge s = t)\}$$

is inherently ambiguous but its complement is context-free. The language

$$\{a^p b^q c^r d^s |((10p < q < 12p \vee 10q < p < 12q) \wedge (10r < s < 12r$$

$$\vee 10s < r < 12s)) \vee (10q < r < 12q \wedge 6p < s < 8p)\}$$

is unambiguous but its complement is not context-free.

10.   RESTRICTIONS ON DERIVATIONS

The most important problems concerning formal languages deal with ambiguity and complexity of derivations. Having studied ambiguity, we now consider a particular aspect of complexity of context-free derivations, namely, the maximum number of occurrences of nonterminals at any step of a derivation when, for each terminal word, a derivation has been chosen where this number is minimal.

More specifically, let $G = (V_N, V_T, X_0, F)$ be a context-free grammar. For a word P over the alphabet $V = V_N \cup V_T$, we denote by $N(P)$ the word obtained from P by erasing all letters of V_T. The *index* of a derivation

$$D: X_0 = P_0 \Rightarrow P_1 \Rightarrow \cdots \Rightarrow P_r = Q$$

according to G is defined by

$$\mathrm{ind}(D) = \max_{0 \leqslant j \leqslant r} lg(N(P_j)).$$

For a word $Q \in L(G)$, we define

$$\mathrm{ind}(Q, G) = \min_D \mathrm{ind}(D)$$

where D ranges over all derivations of Q according to G. The *index* of G, in symbols, $\mathrm{ind}(G)$, is the smallest natural number u such that, for all $Q \in L(G)$, $\mathrm{ind}(Q, G) \leqq u$. If no such u exists, G is said to be of *infinite index*. Finally, the *index* of a context-free *language* L is defined by

$$\mathrm{ind}(L) = \min_G \mathrm{ind}(G),$$

where G ranges over all context-free grammars generating L.

Example 10.1. The grammar

$$G = (\{X_0\}, \{a, a'\}, X_0, \{X_0 \to \lambda, X_0 \to aX_0 a', X_0 \to X_0 X_0\})$$

generates the Dyck language D_1 over the alphabet $\{a, a'\}$. Consider the following infinite sequence of words:

$$Q_0 = \lambda; \qquad Q_{i+1} = aQ_i a'aQ_i a', \qquad i \geqq 0.$$

We show by induction on i that for each i,

$$\text{ind}(Q_i, G) = i + 1. \tag{10.1}$$

Clearly, (10.1) holds for $i = 0$. Assume that it holds for a fixed value of $i \geqq 0$. Since the word $Q_i a' a Q_i$ does not belong to D_1, any derivation of Q_{i+1} begins with an application of the production $X_0 \to X_0 X_0$. The only proper initial subword of Q_{i+1} which belongs to D_1 is the word $a Q_i a'$. Furthermore, any derivation from X_0 of the word $a Q_i a'$ begins with an application of the production $X_0 \to a X_0 a'$ (apart from derivations beginning with an application of $X_0 \to X_0 X_0$ where one of the X_0's on the right side is later reduced to λ). By these observations and by our inductive hypothesis, we conclude that (10.1) holds also when i is replaced by $i+1$. Hence, (10.1) holds for all i. This implies that G is of infinite index.

Example 10.2. Also the grammar

$$G = (\{X_0\}, \{a, b\}, X_0, \{X_0 \to a X_0 X_0, X_0 \to b\})$$

is of infinite index. The verification of this is left to the reader. The grammar (8.8) in Part 1 is of index $k + 1$.

Thus it is easy to present examples of grammars of any previously given index. As regards languages, such examples can also be given but the construction is not so straightforward.

Proposition 10.1. For any $u \geqq 1$, there is a language of index u. The Dyck language D_1 is of infinite index.

We denote by $\mathscr{F}\mathscr{I}$ the family of languages of finite index. Proposition 10.1 implies that $\mathscr{F}\mathscr{I}$ is a proper subfamily of $\mathscr{L}_2$. We now introduce two language families which turn out to be equal with $\mathscr{F}\mathscr{I}$.

A context-free grammar G is termed *nonexpansive* if there is no non-terminal X such that $X \Rightarrow^* P$ where P contains two occurrences of X. Otherwise, G is *expansive*. The family of languages generated by nonexpansive grammars is denoted by $\mathscr{N}\mathscr{E}$. Finally, let $\mathscr{S}\mathscr{L}$ be the smallest family which contains all linear languages and is closed under substitution.

Theorem 10.1. $\mathscr{N}\mathscr{E} \subseteq \mathscr{S}\mathscr{L} \subseteq \mathscr{F}\mathscr{I}$.

Proof. To establish the first inclusion, consider a nonempty language L generated by a nonexpansive grammar $G = (V_N, V_T, X_0, F)$. We prove that L is in $\mathscr{S}\mathscr{L}$. If V_N consists of only one letter, then G must be linear. Consequently, in this case L is in $\mathscr{S}\mathscr{L}$. We now make the following inductive hypothesis: The assertion is true for grammars with less than n ($\geqq 2$) nonterminals. Assume that G contains n nonterminals. Without loss of generality, we also assume that G satisfies conditions (i) and (ii) given in the definition of almost looping grammars in Section 9. (Otherwise, G is replaced by an equivalent grammar G' satisfying these conditions. In the transition from G to G', some nonterminals and productions are removed without adding anything. Consequently, G' is also nonexpansive.) Let U consist of all nonterminals X such that $X \Rightarrow^* P_1 X_0 P_2$ for some words P_1 and P_2. Clearly, $X_0 \in U$. Consider the grammar

$$G_1 = (U, V_T \cup (V_N - U), X_0, F_1)$$

where F_1 consists of all productions $X \to P$ in F such that $X \in U$. Since G is nonexpansive, so also is the grammar G_1. We claim that G_1 is linear. Assume the contrary. Then F_1 contains a production $X \to P_1 X_1 P_2 X_2 P_3$ where X_1 and X_2 belong to U and consequently,

$$X_1 \Rightarrow^* P_4 X_0 P_5 \quad \text{and} \quad X_2 \Rightarrow^* P_6 X_0 P_7, \tag{10.2}$$

for some P_4, P_5, P_6, P_7. Since a word containing X is derivable from X_0, (10.2) implies that G_1 is expansive. This contradiction shows that G_1 is linear. If $U = V_N$, then $G = G_1$ is linear, and consequently L is in $\mathscr{SL}$. Otherwise we consider, for each X in $V_N - U$, the grammar $G_X = (V_N - U, V_T, X, F - F_1)$. ($G_X$ is indeed a grammar since if $F - F_1$ contains a production $X_1 \to P_1 X_2 P_2$ where $X_2 \in U$, then also $X_1 \in U$, which is a contradiction.) Since G is nonexpansive, so is G_X also. Since $X_0 \in U$, G_X has fewer than n nonterminals. By our inductive hypothesis, $L(G_X)$ is in $\mathscr{SL}$. But clearly $L = \sigma(L(G_1))$ where the substitution σ is defined by

$$\sigma(a) = \{a\} \quad \text{for} \quad a \in V_T; \quad \sigma(X) = L(G_X) \quad \text{for} \quad X \in V_N - U.$$

Thus the first inclusion follows.

To prove the second inclusion, we note first that $\mathscr{FI}$ contains all linear languages. Hence, it suffices to show that $\mathscr{FI}$ is closed under substitution. Assume that L is a language in $\mathscr{FI}$ over the alphabet V_T and σ is a substitution such that, for each $a \in V_T$, the language $\sigma(a)$ is in $\mathscr{FI}$. Thus, L is generated by a grammar $G = (V_N, V_T, X_0, F)$ of index k and for each $a \in V_T$, $\sigma(a)$ is generated by a grammar $G_a = (V_N{}^a, V_T{}^a, X_0{}^a, F^a)$ of index k_a. Without loss of generality, we assume that the nonterminal alphabets in all these grammars are pairwise disjoint. Define a homomorphism h of $V_N \cup V_T$ by

$$h(a) = X_0{}^a \quad \text{for} \quad a \in V_T; \quad h(X) = X \quad \text{for} \quad X \in V_N.$$

Let V_N' be the union of V_N and the alphabets $V_N{}^a$, and let V_T' be the union of the alphabets $V_T{}^a$. Finally, let F_1 be the union of the sets F^a. Consider the grammar

$$G_1 = (V_N', V_T', X_0, F_1 \cup \{X \to h(P) | X \to P \text{ is in } F\}).$$

Obviously $L(G_1) = \sigma(L)$. It is also easy to verify that G_1 is of finite index. Thus $\sigma(L)$ is in $\mathscr{FI}$. ∎

We omit the proof of the inclusion which shows that the families of Theorem 10.1 are, in fact, equal:

Proposition 10.2. $\mathscr{FI} \subseteq \mathscr{NE}$.

If we are dealing with *unambiguous* grammars, then Proposition 10.2 is very easily established by an argument similar to the one in Example 10.1. To investigate the rate of growth of $\mathrm{ind}(Q, G)$, we introduce the function

$$M(G, n) = \max_{\substack{Q \in L(G) \\ lg(Q) \leqslant n}} \mathrm{ind}(Q, G), \qquad n = 1, 2, \ldots.$$

By considering derivation trees, it is easy to see that for any G, the function $M(G, n)$ is asymptotically less than or equal to $\log(n)$.

A context-free grammar $G = (V_N, V_T, X_0, F)$ is said to be *ultralinear* iff there exists a natural number k such that any word P satisfying $X_0 \Rightarrow^* P$ contains at most k nonterminals. A language is *ultralinear* iff it is generated by an ultralinear grammar.

Example 10.3. Clearly, every ultralinear grammar is of finite index. The converse does not hold true. The grammar

$$G = (\{X\}, \{a, b\}, X, \{X \to \lambda, X \to XX, X \to aXb, X \to bXa\})$$

is not ultralinear but is of finite index. It is left to the reader to determine the index of G. It can be shown that the language $(\{a^n b^n | n \geq 0\} c)^*$ is not ultralinear, although it is of finite index.

The notion of index is readily extended to concern all grammars (not necessarily context-free). Let G be a type-0 grammar such that no terminal appears on the left side of any production. Then $\mathrm{ind}(D)$, $\mathrm{ind}(Q, G)$, and $\mathrm{ind}(G)$ are defined exactly as above. A language L is said to be of *finite index in the general sense* iff L is generated by a grammar G such that $\mathrm{ind}(G)$ is finite. Thus, by definition, any language in $\mathscr{FI}$ is of finite index in the general sense. But also the converse holds true:

Proposition 10.3. If a language is of finite index in the general sense, then it belongs to $\mathscr{FI}$.

In the balance of this section, we consider the familiar restriction of a derivation being leftmost or rightmost. We prove the interesting result that for any type-0 grammar, the language generated by leftmost or rightmost derivations (or by derivations obtained by mixing leftmost and rightmost derivations) is, in fact, context-free. The essential tool in this proof is the following theorem which is a stronger version of Theorem 10.7 in Part 1. This stronger version is established without using the workspace theorem.

Theorem 10.2. Assume that $G = (V_N, V_T, X_0, F)$ is a type-0 grammar where no terminal occurs on the left side of any production but the right side of every production contains at least one terminal letter. Then $L(G)$ is context-free.

Proof. The idea behind the proof is to replace productions of the form

$$X_1 \cdots X_k \to P_1 b P_2, \qquad X_i \in V_N, \quad b \in V_T, \tag{10.3}$$

by a set of context-free productions

$$X_1 \to P_1 a_1, \; X_2 \to a_2, \; ..., \; X_{k-1} \to a_{k-1}, \; X_k \to a_k P_2$$

where the a's are new terminals. The original language $L(G)$ is then obtained from the resulting context-free language by operations preserving the property of being context-free.

We first replace G by a grammar G_1 where the left side of every production contains at most two letters. Every production in F satisfying this condition is also a production of G_1. Consider a production (10.3) in F where $k > 2$. Introduce new nonterminals $Y_1, ..., Y_{k-2}$ and new terminals $b_1, ..., b_{k-2}$. Replace (10.3) by the productions

$$X_1 X_2 \to P_1 b_1 Y_1, \; Y_1 X_3 \to b_2 Y_2, \; ..., \; Y_{k-2} X_k \to b P_2.$$

Repeat this procedure for every production (10.3) in F where $k > 2$. (New nonterminals Y_i and terminals b_i are introduced in such a way that they are distinct for every production.) In the resulting grammar

$$G_1 = (V_N^1, V_T^1, X_0, F_1),$$

the left side of every production contains at most two letters. Moreover,

$$L(G) = h(L(G_1)) \tag{10.4}$$

where the homomorphism h maps the letters of V_T into themselves and all of the new terminals (i.e., letters in $V_T^1 - V_T$) into λ. Clearly, G_1 also satisfies the hypothesis of Theorem 10.2.

We next replace G_1 by an equivalent grammar $G_2 = (V_N^2, V_T^1, X_0, F_2)$ where each production is of the form

$$P_1^{(i)} \to P_2^{(i)} b^{(i)} P_3^{(i)}, \qquad P_j^{(i)} \in W(V_N^2), \quad b^{(i)} \in V_T^1, \quad lg(P_1^{(i)}) \leqq 2. \tag{10.5}$$

This is accomplished by the construction presented in Chapter I: If some production in G_1 is not of the form (10.5), that is, it has more than one terminal on the right side, then each of the additional terminals a is replaced by a new nonterminal X_a, and productions $X_a \to a$ are added. By (10.4), we obtain

$$L(G) = h(L(G_2)). \tag{10.6}$$

Assume that F_2 contains n productions. Denote

$$V_T^3 = \{a_i | 1 \le i \le n\} \cup \{a_i' | 1 \le i \le n\},$$

and let F_3 be the set of productions obtained from F_2 as follows. Assume that (10.5) is the ith production in F_2, $1 \le i \le n$. Replace it by the production $P_1^{(i)} \to P_2^{(i)} a_i a_i' P_3^{(i)}$. Repeat this procedure for every i, $1 \le i \le n$. Consider the grammar $G_3 = (V_N^2, V_T^3, X_0, F_3)$. Thus,

$$F_3 = \{P_1^{(i)} \to P_2^{(i)} a_i a_i' P_3^{(i)} | 1 \le i \le n\}$$

where all of the words P are over V_N^2 and $lg(P_1^{(i)}) \le 2$ for $1 \le i \le n$. Let h_1 be the homomorphism defined by

$$h_1(a_i) = b^{(i)}, \qquad h_1(a_i') = \lambda, \qquad 1 \le i \le n.$$

Then it is obvious that

$$L(G_2) = h_1(L(G_3)). \tag{10.7}$$

The final step in our construction is to introduce a context-free grammar G_5 which is equivalent to G_3. It then follows by (10.6), (10.7), and Theorem 1.5 that $L(G)$ is context-free.

We define $G_4 = (V_N^2, V_T^3, X_0, F_4)$ where F_4 is obtained from F_3 by replacing every production

$$P_1^{(i)} \to P_2^{(i)} a_i a_i' P_3^{(i)}, \qquad P_1^{(i)} = X_1^{(i)} X_2^{(i)}, \quad X_j^{(i)} \in V_N^2,$$

with the two productions

$$X_1^{(i)} \to P_2^{(i)} a_i, \qquad X_2^{(i)} \to a_i' P_3^{(i)}$$

[Thus the productions in F_3, where $lg(P_1^{(i)}) = 1$, belong to F_4.] By definition, G_4 is context-free. It is obvious that $L(G_3) \subseteq L(G_4)$. Consider the regular language

$$R = \{a_i a_i' | 1 \le i \le n\}^*.$$

By Theorem 6.7 in Part 1, the language $L(G_4) \cap R$ is generated by a context-free grammar G_5. Since clearly $L(G_3) \subseteq R$, we obtain

$$L(G_3) \subseteq L(G_4) \cap R = L(G_5).$$

To establish the reverse inclusion $L(G_4) \cap R \subseteq L(G_3)$, it suffices to show by induction on r that whenever

$$Q_0 \Rightarrow_{G_4} Q_1 \Rightarrow_{G_4} \cdots \Rightarrow_{G_4} Q_r, \qquad Q_r \in R, \quad Q_0 \in (R \cup V_N^2)^*,$$

then there is a derivation $Q_0 \Rightarrow^* Q_r$ of length $\leq r$ according to G_3. The details of this induction (which is analogous to the one given in the proof of Theorem 7.4 in Part 1) are left to the reader. Hence, $L(G_3) = L(G_5)$. ∎

Let now $G = (V_N, V_T, X_0, F)$ be a type-0 grammar such that no terminal appears on the left side of any production. Define two binary relations $\Rightarrow_{\text{left}}$ and $\Rightarrow_{\text{right}}$ on the set of all words over $V = V_N \cup V_T$ as follows: $P \Rightarrow_{\text{left}} Q$ (resp. $P \Rightarrow_{\text{right}} Q$) holds iff there is a production $P' \to Q'$ in F and words R_1, R_2 where R_1 is over V_T (resp. R_2 is over V_T) such that $P = R_1 P' R_2$ and $Q = R_1 Q' R_2$. Let $\Rightarrow_{\text{LR}}$ be the binary relation such that $P \Rightarrow_{\text{LR}} Q$ holds iff $P \Rightarrow_{\text{left}} Q$ or $P \Rightarrow_{\text{right}} Q$. Finally, let $\Rightarrow_{\text{LR}}^*$ be the reflexive transitive closure of $\Rightarrow_{\text{LR}}$.

Theorem 10.3. For any type-0 grammar $G = (V_N, V_T, X_0, F)$ (such that no terminal appears on the left side of any production), the language

$$L_{\text{LR}}(G) = \{P \in W(V_T) | X_0 \Rightarrow_{\text{LR}}^* P\}$$

is context-free.

Proof. Without loss of generality (using Theorem 3.1 in Part 1 if necessary), we assume that the right side of every production in F is either a word over V_N or a nonempty word over V_T. Consider the grammar

$$G_1 = (V_N \cup \{X_0', Y_1, Y_2\}, V_T \cup \{c\}, X_0', F_1),$$

where

$$F_1 = \{X_0' \to c Y_1 X_0 Y_2, \; Y_1 \to c, \; Y_2 \to c\}$$
$$\cup \; \{Y_1 P \to c Y_1 Q, \; P Y_2 \to Q Y_2 c | P \to Q \text{ in } F \text{ and } Q \in W(V_N)\}$$
$$\cup \; \{Y_1 P \to Q Y_1, \; P Y_2 \to Y_2 Q | P \to Q \text{ in } F \text{ and } Q \in W(V_T), \; Q \neq \lambda\}.$$

By Theorem 10.2, $L(G_1)$ is context-free. Let h be the homomorphism of $V_T \cup \{c\}$, defined by

$$h(c) = \lambda, \qquad h(a) = a \quad \text{for} \quad a \in V_T.$$

Then $L_{\text{LR}}(G) = h(L(G_1))$, which proves that $L_{\text{LR}}(G)$ is context-free. ∎

In a similar fashion one can prove that for any G the language generated by leftmost (or rightmost) derivations is context-free.

11. REGULAR-LIKE EXPRESSIONS

A simple property-specifying device for a class of languages has the definite advantage that each language in the class can be defined explicitly by the device, in contrast to the implicit representation of languages by grammars. The best illustration of this is the simple definition of type-3 languages by regular expressions. Such a simple characterization would be very desirable for the family of context-free languages, too. However, no such characterization is known, and one can hardly expect to get anything so elegant and simple as regular expressions for type-3 languages.

In this section, context-free languages are characterized using "regular-like" expressions involving the operations of union, catenation, and a new catenation closure involving an auxiliary symbol. We now proceed to the formal definitions.

Let a be a letter, and let L and L_1 be languages. The *a-substitution* of L_1 into L, in symbols, $L\,S_a\,L_1$, is defined by

$$L\,S_a\,L_1 = \{P\,|\,P = P_1\,Q_1\,P_2 \cdots P_k\,Q_k\,P_{k+1},\, k \geq 0,$$

$$P_1\,a\,P_2 \cdots P_k\,a\,P_{k+1} \in L,\, a \text{ is not a subword of } P_1\,P_2 \cdots P_{k+1}$$

$$\text{and } Q_j \in L_1, \text{ for } 1 \leq j \leq k\}.$$

It is immediately verified that, for each a, S_a is an associative operation. Consequently, we may write "products" associatively, for instance,

$$L\,S_a\,L_1\,S_a\,L_2\,S_a\,L_1$$

(without specifying by parentheses the order in which the operations S_a are applied). The notation $S_a(L^i)$ means the S_a-product with $i \geq 2$ factors L. By definition, $S_a(L^1) = L$. The *iterated a-substitution closure* of L, in symbols, L^{+a}, consists of all words P which satisfy the following two conditions: (i) For some $i \geq 1$, $P \in S_a(L^i)$, and (ii) a is not a subword of P.

The iterated a-substitution closure is closely related to the operations superscript asterisk and plus. It is an immediate consequence of the definition that if L is a language over an alphabet not containing a, then

$$L^* = (La \cup \{\lambda\})^{+a}, \qquad L^+ = (La \cup L)^{+a}.$$

We are going to show that the operations of union, catenation, and iterated a-substitution closure bear the same relation to the family of context-free languages as regular operations do to the family of type-3 languages: Exactly all context-free languages are obtained from languages of the form $\varnothing$, $\{b\}$, and $\{\lambda\}$ where b is a letter, by these operations. More specifically, let U be an infinite set of letters. Denote by $\mathscr{L}(U)$ the smallest family of languages which (i) contains $\varnothing$, $\{\lambda\}$, and $\{a\}$ for each $a \in U$, and (ii) is closed under union, catenation, and iterated a-substitution closure for each $a \in U$. We now prove that a language belongs to the family $\mathscr{L}(U)$ iff it is a context-free language over some subalphabet of U.

Before the actual proof, we first establish a lemma.

Theorem 11.1. If $a \in U$ and L_1 and L_2 belong to the family $\mathscr{L}(U)$, then $L_1 S_a L_2 \in \mathscr{L}(U)$.

Proof. Every language in $\mathscr{L}(U)$ is obtained from a finite number of "basic" languages [cf. point (i) above] by applying the operations (ii) finitely many times. We use induction on the number n of applications of operations (ii) in the construction of L_1. Assume that $n = 0$, that is, L_1 is one of the basic languages (i). Then $L_1 S_a L_2$ is either one of the basic languages or L_2 and consequently,

$$L_1 S_a L_2 \in \mathscr{L}(U). \tag{11.1}$$

We now make the following inductive hypothesis: (11.1) holds for any L_1, a, and L_2 such that in the construction of L_1 at most n applications of operations (ii) have taken place. Consider the case where L_1 is obtained by applying the operations $n+1$ times. Consequently, one of the following alternatives is true:

$$L_1 = L_3 \cup L_4, \qquad L_1 = L_3 L_4, \qquad L_1 = L_3^{+b}, \tag{11.2}$$

where L_3 and L_4 are obtained by applying the operations at most n times and $b \in U$. Since b does not occur in any word of the language L_3^{+b}, we assume without loss of generality that b does not belong to the alphabet of L_2 and also that $b \neq a$. Using (11.2), our inductive hypothesis and the obvious formulas

$$(L_3 \cup L_4) S_a L_2 = L_3 S_a L_2 \cup L_4 S_a L_2,$$

$$(L_3 L_4) S_a L_2 = (L_3 S_a L_2)(L_4 S_a L_2),$$

$$L_3^{+b} S_a L_2 = (L_3 S_a L_2)^{+b},$$

we see that (11.1) holds now also, which completes the induction. ∎

Theorem 11.2. Every language in $\mathscr{L}(U)$ is context-free.

Proof. Since the basic languages are context-free and $\mathscr{L}_2$ is closed under union and catenation, it suffices to prove that $\mathscr{L}_2$ is closed under iterated a-substitution closure. Assume that $L \in \mathscr{L}_2$. Then L is generated by a context-free grammar $G = (V_N, V_T, X_0, F)$ such that all productions in F containing terminals are of the form

$$X_b \to b, \qquad b \in V_T, \qquad X_b \in V_N,$$

where the correspondence between terminals b and nonterminals X_b is one-to-one. [Cf. (3.1) in the proof of Theorem 3.1 in Part 1.] Consider the language L^{+a} where $a \in U$. If $a \notin V_T$, then $L^{+a} = L$. Otherwise, L^{+a} is generated by the context-free grammar $G_1 = (V_N, V_T - \{a\}, X_0, F_1)$ where F_1 is obtained from F by replacing the production $X_a \to a$ with the production $X_a \to X_0$. This proves that $\mathscr{L}_2$ is closed under iterated a-substitution closure. ∎

Theorem 11.3. Every context-free language L over an alphabet $V_T \subset U$ is in $\mathscr{L}(U)$.

Proof. By the definition of $\mathscr{L}(U)$, $\varnothing$ is in $\mathscr{L}(U)$. Let L be a nonempty language generated by the context-free grammar

$$G = (V_N, V_T, X_0, F), \qquad V_N = \{X_0, X_1, ..., X_n\}, \qquad n \geqq 0.$$

Since U is infinite, we may assume without loss of generality that $X_i \in U$ for $i = 0, ..., n$. We also assume without loss of generality that for each i, X_i generates a word over V_T and X_0 generates a word containing X_i.

For $0 \leqq i \leqq n$, we denote

$$V_i = \{X_j | i \leqq j \leqq n\}, \qquad F_i = \{Y \to P | Y \in V_i, \ Y \to P \text{ in } F\},$$

$$G_i = (V_i, V_T \cup (V_N - V_i), X_i, F_i).$$

Thus, $G_0 = G$. We also consider the languages L_{ij}, where $i \leqq j$ and $0 \leqq j \leqq n$, defined as follows:

$$L_{in} = \{P | X_i \to P \text{ in } F\}, \qquad 0 \leqq i \leqq n,$$

$$L_{i(j-1)} = L_{ij} S_{X_j} L_{jj}^{+X_j}, \qquad 0 \leqq i < j \leqq n.$$

Thus, each L_{ij} is a language over $V = V_N \cup V_T$. Since the languages L_{in} are finite, it follows by the definition of $\mathscr{L}(U)$ and by Theorem 11.1 that each of the languages L_{ij} is in $\mathscr{L}(U)$. To establish Theorem 11.3, it suffices to show that

$$L(G_0) = L_{00}^{+X_0}. \tag{11.3}$$

We prove (11.3) by showing by downward induction from n that

$$L(G_i) = L_{ii}^{+X_i}, \tag{11.4}$$

for $0 \leqq i \leqq n$. By the definition of L_{nn} and the operation $+X_n$, (11.4) holds for $i = n$. We now make the following inductive hypothesis: For some k with $0 < k \leqq n$, (11.4) holds whenever $k \leqq i (\leqq n)$. To complete the induction, we show that

$$L(G_{k-1}) = L_{(k-1)(k-1)}^{+X_{k-1}}. \tag{11.5}$$

We establish (11.5) by proving inclusion in both directions. By the definition of L_{ij} and by our inductive hypothesis,

$$L_{(k-1)(k-1)} = L_{(k-1)k} S_{X_k} L_{kk}^{+X_k} = L_{(k-1)k} S_{X_k} L(G_k)$$

and in general, for any t with $k-1 \leqq t < n$,

$$L_{(k-1)t} = L_{(k-1)(t+1)} S_{X_{t+1}} L_{(t+1)(t+1)}^{+X_{t+1}}$$

$$= L_{(k-1)(t+1)} S_{X_{t+1}} L(G_{t+1}).$$

Consequently, any word $Q \in L_{(k-1)(k-1)}$ possesses a derivation

$$X_{k-1} \Rightarrow_{G_{k-1}} P \Rightarrow_{G_n}^* Q_n \Rightarrow_{G_{n-1}}^* Q_{n-1} \Rightarrow_{G_{n-2}}^* \cdots \Rightarrow_{G_k}^* Q_k = Q$$

where Q_j does not contain any letters of V_j for $j = n, \ldots, k$. This implies, by the definition of the operation $+X_{k-1}$, that the right side of (11.5) is included in the left side.

To establish the reverse inclusion, we consider an arbitrary word $Q \in L(G_{k-1})$. It possesses a derivation

$$X_{k-1} \Rightarrow P = P_1 \Rightarrow P_2 \Rightarrow \cdots \Rightarrow P_m = Q \tag{11.6}$$

according to G_{k-1} such that in each P_j, $1 \leqq j < m$, one of the nonterminals with the greatest index is rewritten. (In other words, $P_j = P_1^j X_u P_2^j$, $P_{j+1} = P_1^j P' P_2^j$, and P_j does not contain any nonterminals X_t with $t > u$. Clearly, any context-free derivation can be replaced by one which satisfies the required condition, making suitable changes in the order of steps.) Since $Q \in L(G_{k-1})$, P_m does not contain any letters belonging to V_{k-1}. If $m = 1$, then clearly $Q \in L_{(k-1)(k-1)}^{+X_{k-1}}$ because $Q \in L_{(k-1)n}$ and Q does not contain letters of V_{k-1}. Suppose, therefore, that $m \geqq 2$.

We assume first that all of the words P_j, $1 \leqq j < m$, contain at least one letter of V_k. Let X_h be the nonterminal in P_{m-1} with the greatest index. Hence, $k \leqq h \leqq n$. There are integers $t(j)$, $n \geqq j \geqq h$, satisfying

$$1 = t(n) \leqq t(n-1) \leqq \cdots \leqq t(h) = m - 1$$

such that in (11.6)

$$X_{k-1} \Rightarrow P_{t(n)} \Rightarrow^* P_{t(n-1)} \Rightarrow^* \cdots \Rightarrow^* P_{t(h)} \Rightarrow P_m = Q, \tag{11.7}$$

where $P_{t(j-1)}$ is obtained from $P_{t(j)}$ by replacing all occurrences of X_j with words in the language

$$L(G_j) = L_{jj}^{+X_j}$$

for all $j = n, \ldots, h+1$. [If X_j does not occur in $P_{t(j)}$, then $P_{t(j-1)} = P_{t(j)}$.] Derivation (11.7) is due to the fact that in (11.6) one of the nonterminals with the greatest index is always rewritten. By the definition of the languages L_{ij},

$$P_{t(n)} \in L_{(k-1)n}, \quad P_{t(n-1)} \in L_{(k-1)(n-1)}, \quad \ldots, \quad P_{t(h)} \in L_{(k-1)h}.$$

Consequently, $P_m \in L_{(k-1)(h-1)}$ because P_m is obtained from $P_{t(h)}$ by replacing an occurrence of X_h with a word in the language

$$L(G_h) = L_{hh}^{+X_h}.$$

Since P_m does not contain letters of V_{k-1}, we have

$$P_m \in L_{(k-1)(k-1)} \tag{11.8}$$

and also

$$Q = P_m \in L_{(k-1)(k-1)}^{+X_{k-1}}. \tag{11.9}$$

Assume, secondly, that the words $P_{e(1)}, \ldots, P_{e(v)}$, where $v \geq 1$ and $1 \leq e(1) \leq \cdots \leq e(v) < m$, contain no nonterminals other than X_{k-1}. We have shown that (11.9) holds if $v = 0$. Proceeding now inductively also, we assume that we already have considered the value $v-1$ and shown that (11.9) holds for this value. Thus (11.6) is now written

$$X_{k-1} \Rightarrow^* P_{e(1)} \Rightarrow^* \cdots \Rightarrow^* P_{e(v)} \Rightarrow^* Q.$$

Using the same argument as in (11.8), we conclude that

$$P_{e(1)} \in L_{(k-1)(k-1)}.$$

On the other hand, Q is obtained from $P_{e(1)}$ by replacing every occurrence of X_{k-1} with a word in $L(G_{k-1})$. But by our inductive hypothesis (the recent one) these words are in $L_{(k-1)(k-1)}^{+X_{k-1}}$. This implies that (11.9) holds also now. Thus, we have shown that the left side of (11.5) is included in the right side. ∎

Definition. Assume that V and $V' = \{\cup, +, \varnothing, \lambda, (,)\}$ are disjoint alphabets. A word P over $V \cup V'$ is a *regular-like expression* over V iff

(i) P is $\varnothing$, λ, or a letter of V, or else
(ii) P is of one of the forms $(Q \cup R)$, (QR), or $(Q)^{+a}$ where $a \in V$ and Q and R are regular-like expressions over V.

Each regular-like expression P over V denotes a language $|P|$ over V according to the following conventions:

(i)   The language denoted by $\varnothing$ is empty. The language denoted by λ consists of the empty word.
(ii)   The language denoted by $a \in V$ consists of the word a.
(iii)   For regular-like expressions P and Q over V,

$$|(P \cup Q)| = |P| \cup |Q|, \qquad |(PQ)| = |P||Q|, \qquad |P^{+a}| = |P|^{+a}.$$

The following theorem is an immediate corollary of Theorems 11.2 and 11.3.

Theorem 11.4. Any language denoted by a regular-like expression is context-free. Any context-free language over an alphabet V_T is denoted by a regular-like expression over an alphabet $V \supseteq V_T$. Hence, $\mathcal{L}_2$ equals the family of languages denoted by regular-like expressions.

Example 11.1. The language $\{a^i b^i | i \geq 1\}$ is denoted by the regular-like expression $(acb \cup ab)^{+c}$. (Note that we have omitted, for convenience, unnecessary parentheses.) The language $\{P \operatorname{mi}(P) | P \in W(\{a, b\})\}$ is denoted by the regular-like expression $(aca \cup bcb \cup \lambda)^{+c}$. The simple form of these expressions is due to the fact that only one nonterminal is needed in the grammar generating the language.

Example 11.2. Consider the grammar G determined by the equations

$$X_0 = aX_0 b + ba^2 X_1 ba, \qquad X_1 = a^2 X_1 b + ba^3 X_2 ba,$$
$$X_2 = a^3 X_2 b + baX_0 ba + b.$$

The languages L_{ij} (cf. the proof of Theorem 11.3) are now

$$L_{22} = \{a^3 X_2 b, baX_0 ba, b\},$$
$$L_{12} = \{a^2 X_1 b, ba^3 X_2 ba\},$$
$$L_{02} = \{aX_0 b, ba^2 X_1 ba\} = L_{01},$$
$$L_{11} = \{a^2 X_1 b\} \cup ba^3 (a^3 X_2 b \cup baX_0 ba \cup b)^{+X_2} ba.$$

Hence, $L(G) = L_{00}^{+X_0}$ is denoted by the regular-like expression

$$\left(aX_0 b \cup ba^2 (a^2 X_1 b \cup ba^3 (a^3 X_2 b \cup baX_0 ba \cup b)^{+X_2} ba)^{+X_1} ba\right)^{+X_0}.$$

The letter X_1 may be replaced by X_2 without changing the denoted language and thus two different plus-operations are sufficient.

Denote by $\mathcal{L}_2(i, j)$ the family of such context-free languages over the alphabet $V_T = \{a_1, \ldots, a_i\}$ which are denoted by regular-like expressions over an alphabet with $i+j$ letters. Hence, for any context-free language L over V_T, there is a j such that $L \in \mathcal{L}_2(i, j)$. On the other hand, it is not known whether there exists a j such that all context-free languages over V_T are in $\mathcal{L}_2(i, j)$. Here we assume that $i \geq 2$. For $i = 1$, see Exercise 11.

The operations $+a$ in regular-like expressions and nonterminals in grammars play slightly different roles. This is seen as follows. Assume that $i = 2$. Then for any n, there is a linear language L_n over $\{a_1, a_2\}$ which cannot be generated by any context-free grammar with less than n nonterminals. On the other hand, all linear languages over $\{a_1, a_2\}$ belong to $\mathcal{L}_2(2, 2)$. Even the following stronger result holds true.

Proposition 11.1. Every language of finite index over the alphabet $\{a_1, \ldots, a_i\}$ belongs to the family $\mathcal{L}_2(i, 2)$.

12. LR(k) AND LL(k) GRAMMARS

We now study context-free grammars which are unambiguous in a certain strong sense. Consider an analytic context-free grammar G. In a derivation according to G, at every step a subword is rewritten as a nonterminal until finally the initial letter is obtained. In general, there are many subwords which can be replaced by a nonterminal. We are now going to introduce a class of grammars where this process can be carried out in a simple and deterministic manner. These grammars are called LR(k), which is an abbreviation for left to right parsing with a k letter lookahead: A given word P over the terminal alphabet can be parsed (i.e., a derivation from P to the initial letter can be found) by reading letters from left to right and looking k letters ahead, without ever backing up to consider a previous decision.

The study of LR(k) grammars is a part of the broad field of research in the area of parsing. The research deals with efficient parsing algorithms and classes of languages admitting fast and efficient parsing methods. It is of considerable practical significance in parsing and translation of programming languages. Apart from the following short discussion of certain fundamental notions, this broad field lies outside the scope of this book. For both theory and applications, the reader is referred to Aho and Ullman (1972).

The following formal definition of LR(k) grammars is given in terms of generative grammars. Let $\Rightarrow_{\text{right}}$ and $\Rightarrow_{\text{right}}^*$ be the relations corresponding to *rightmost* derivations according to a context-free grammar G. (Thus, $P \Rightarrow_{\text{right}} Q$ holds iff there are words R_1, R_2, X, Q' such that $P = R_1 X R_2$, $Q = R_1 Q' R_2$, $X \rightarrow Q'$ is a production of G and R_2 is over the terminal alphabet; $\Rightarrow_{\text{right}}^*$ is the reflexive transitive closure of $\Rightarrow_{\text{right}}$.) For a word P and a nonnegative integer k, we define

$$k : P = \begin{cases} P & \text{if} \quad lg(P) < k, \\ \text{the initial subword of } P \text{ of length } k & \text{if} \quad lg(P) \geq k. \end{cases}$$

Definition. Assume that $k \geq 0$. A context-free grammar $G = (V_N, V_T, X_0, F)$ is $LR(k)$ iff F does not contain the production $X_0 \rightarrow X_0$ and, for all words P_1, P_1', P_2, and P_2' over $V_N \cup V_T$, all words P_3 and P_3' over V_T, and all nonterminals X and X', the conditions

$$X_0 \Rightarrow_{\text{right}}^* P_1 X P_3 \Rightarrow_{\text{right}} P_1 P_2 P_3, \tag{12.1}$$

$$X_0 \Rightarrow_{\text{right}}^* P_1' X' P_3' \Rightarrow_{\text{right}} P_1' P_2' P_3', \tag{12.2}$$

$$(lg(P_1 P_2) + k) : P_1 P_2 P_3 = (lg(P_1 P_2) + k) : P_1' P_2' P_3' \tag{12.3}$$

imply the conditions

$$P_1 = P_1', \quad X = X', \quad P_2 = P_2'. \tag{12.4}$$

A language L is LR(k) iff there exists an LR(k) grammar generating L.

Example 12.1. Consider the grammar

$$(\{X_0, X\}, \{a, b, c\}, X_0, \{X_0 \to aXc, X \to bXb, X \to b\}) \qquad (12.5)$$

generating the language $\{ab^{2n+1}c \mid n \geq 0\}$. For any $k \geq 0$, the rightmost derivations

$$X_0 \Rightarrow^* ab^k Xb^k c \Rightarrow ab^{2k+1}c, \qquad X_0 \Rightarrow^* ab^{k+1} Xb^{k+1} c \Rightarrow ab^{2k+3}c$$

violate the definition of an $LR(k)$ grammar. Hence, (12.5) is not $LR(k)$ for any k. From the point of view of parsing, this is interpreted as follows. Having read (from left to right) the initial subword ab^m, no definite information about replacing the last b with X is provided by the next k letters; parsing must wait until the final c has been read.

Example 12.2. The grammar

$$(\{X_0, X\}, \{a, b, c\}, X_0, \{X_0 \to aXc, X \to Xbb, X \to b\})$$

is equivalent to (12.5) and, moreover, $LR(0)$. These simple examples show that $LR(k)$ is a property of the grammar, not of the language alone.

Theorem 12.1. Every $LR(k)$ grammar is unambiguous. Consequently, every $LR(k)$ language is unambiguous.

Proof. Assume that $G = (V_N, V_T, X_0, F)$ is $LR(k)$, for some $k \geq 0$, and $P \in L(G)$. If

$$X_0 = P_0 \Rightarrow_{\text{right}} P_1 \Rightarrow_{\text{right}} \cdots \Rightarrow_{\text{right}} P_{m-1} \Rightarrow_{\text{right}} P_m = P \qquad (12.6)$$

is a rightmost derivation of P, then P_{m-1} is unique by the $LR(k)$ condition. (In other words, if

$$X_0 \Rightarrow_{\text{right}} Q_1 \Rightarrow_{\text{right}} \cdots \Rightarrow_{\text{right}} Q_{n-1} \Rightarrow_{\text{right}} Q_n = P$$

is a derivation according to G, then $P_{m-1} = Q_{n-1}$.) Similarly, we conclude that the uniqueness of P_j implies the uniqueness of P_{j-1} for $j = 1, \ldots, m$. Since G does not contain the production $X_0 \to X_0$, we conclude by induction that (12.6) is the only rightmost derivation of P. Thus P possesses only one generation tree and consequently only one leftmost derivation. ∎

It follows by Example 12.1 that the converse of Theorem 12.1 is not true. $LR(k)$ grammars form an important subclass of unambiguous grammars because one can give the following test for the $LR(k)$ condition.

Theorem 12.2. There is an algorithm for deciding for a given context-free grammar G and a given k, whether or not G is $LR(k)$.

Proof. Consider a context-free grammar $G = (V_N, V_T, X_0, F)$ with $V = V_N \cup V_T$ and a fixed $k \geq 0$. For each production $f \in F$ and each word P of length k belonging to $W(V_T) W(\#)$, we define the right-linear grammar

$$G(f, P) = (\{[X, Q] | X \in V_N, \ Q \in W(V_T) W(\#), \ lg(Q) = k\},$$

$$V_N \cup V_T \cup \{\#\}, [X_0, \#^k], F_1),$$

where F_1 consists of the production $[Z, P] \to UP$, provided f is the production $Z \to U$, and of all productions of the following form. Assume that $Y \to Y_1 \cdots Y_m$ is in F where $m \geq 1$ and each Y_j is in $V_N \cup V_T$. Then F_1 contains all productions

$$[Y, Q] \to Y_1 \cdots Y_{i-1} [Y_i, Q_1] \tag{12.7}$$

where $1 \leq i \leq m$, $Y_i \in V_N$, and the word $Y_{i+1} \cdots Y_m Q$ generates according to G the word $Q_1 Q_2$ for some $Q_2 \in W(V_T) W(\#)$. (Of course, the lengths of Q and Q_1 must be equal to k because otherwise the brackets are not defined. In derivations according to G, $\#$ is considered to be a terminal.) Clearly, each of the finitely many productions (12.7) can be determined for any given production $Y \to Y_1 \cdots Y_m$.

We now prove two assertions I and II which lead to the required algorithm.

I. For any $X \in V_N$, $Q \in W(V_T) W(\#)$ with $lg(Q) = k$ and $R \in W(V)$

$$[X_0, \#^k] \Rightarrow^*_{G(f, P)} R[X, Q] \tag{12.8}$$

iff

$$X_0 \#^k \Rightarrow^*_{\text{right}} RXQQ_1 \tag{12.9}$$

according to G for some $Q_1 \in W(V_T) W(\#)$.

The "only if" part of assertion I is obvious by the definition of $G(f, P)$. The proof, of the "if" part is by induction on the length u of the derivation (12.9). For $u = 1$, (12.8) holds. Assuming that (12.8) holds whenever the length of (12.9) is less than u (≥ 2), we consider the case where the length of (12.9) equals u. We write (12.9) in the form

$$X_0 \#^k \Rightarrow^*_{\text{right}} R_1 X_1 Q_2 Q_3 \Rightarrow_{\text{right}} R_1 R_2 Q_2 Q_3 = RXQQ_1, \tag{12.10}$$

where $X_1 \in V_N$, $Q_2 Q_3 \in W(V_T) W(\#)$, and $lg(Q_2) = k$.

Assume first that R_2 contains a nonterminal. Then $R_2 = R_2' X R_2''$ where $R_2' \in W(V)$ and $R_2'' \in W(V_T) W(\#)$. Consequently, $R = R_1 R_2'$, $QQ_1 = R_2'' Q_2 Q_3$, and the production $[X_1, Q_2] \to R_2'[X, Q]$ is in F_1. By the inductive hypothesis,

$$[X_0, \#^k] \Rightarrow^*_{G(f, P)} R_1 [X_1, Q_2].$$

Hence, (12.8) holds.

Second, assume that R_2 does not contain any nonterminals. Then $R_1 = RXQ_4$ for some $Q_4 \in W(V_T)$. The nonterminal X (i.e., the particular occurrence of X we are considering) is introduced in (12.10) by applying some production $X_2 \to R_3 X R_4$ where $R_3 \in W(V)$ and $R_4 \in W(V)W(\#)$. By the inductive hypothesis,

$$[X_0, \#^k] \Rightarrow^*_{G(f, P)} R_5[X_2, Q_5]$$

for some $R_5 \in W(V)$ and $Q_5 \in W(V_T)W(\#)$ such that $lg(Q_5) = k$ and $R_5 R_3 = R$. Moreover, the production $[X_2, Q_5] \to R_3[X, Q]$ is in F_1. Thus, (12.8) holds also now, which proves our assertion I.

II. G is LR(k) iff, for all P_1, P_2, Q, Q_1, f, g, the conditions

$$Q \in L(G(f, P_1)), \qquad QQ_1 \in L(G(g, P_2)) \tag{12.11}$$

imply the conditions

$$Q_1 = \lambda, \qquad P_1 = P_2, \qquad f = g. \tag{12.12}$$

To prove assertion II, we conclude first by I that the language $L(G(f, P))$ consists of all words of the form RUP where $R \in W(V)$ and

$$X_0 \#^k \Rightarrow^*_{\text{right}} RZPQ_1$$

according to G for some $Q_1 \in W(V_T)W(\#)$. (Recall that f is the production $Z \to U$.)

Assume first that G is LR(k) and that conditions (12.11) are satisfied. Let f be the production $Z \to U$ and g the production $Z_1 \to U_1$. Consequently,

$$X_0 \#^k \Rightarrow^*_{\text{right}} RZP_1 Q_2 \Rightarrow_{\text{right}} RUP_1 Q_2 = QQ_2,$$

$$X_0 \#^k \Rightarrow^*_{\text{right}} R_1 Z_1 P_2 Q_3 \Rightarrow_{\text{right}} R_1 U_1 P_2 Q_3 = QQ_1 Q_3$$

according to G for some $R, R_1 \in W(V)$ and $Q_2, Q_3 \in W(V_T)W(\#)$. Since Q is an initial subword of $QQ_1 Q_3$ with length $lg(RU) + k$, we conclude by the LR(k) condition that $R = R_1$, $Z = Z_1$, and $U = U_1$. Hence, $f = g$. The equations

$$Q = RUP_1 = R_1 U_1 P_1, \qquad QQ_1 = R_1 U_1 P_2, \qquad lg(P_1) = lg(P_2)$$

imply the equations $Q_1 = \lambda$ and $P_1 = P_2$.

Second, assume that (12.11) always implies (12.12). Assume, furthermore, that the hypotheses (12.1)–(12.3) are satisfied for some P_1, P_2, P_3, X, P_1', P_2', P_3', X' (where P_3 and P_3' are over V_T). Consequently,

$$X_0 \#^k \Rightarrow^*_{\text{right}} P_1 X P_4 \Rightarrow_{\text{right}} P_1 P_2 P_4, \qquad P_4 \in W(V_T)W(\#), \quad lg(P_4) \geqq k, \tag{12.13}$$

$$X_0 \#^k \Rightarrow^*_{\text{right}} P_1' X' P_4' \Rightarrow_{\text{right}} P_1' P_2' P_4', \qquad P_4' \in W(V_T)W(\#), \quad lg(P_4') \geqq k. \tag{12.14}$$

We write

$$P_4 = P_5 P_6, \qquad P_4' = P_5'P_6', \qquad lg(P_5) = lg(P_5') = k. \qquad (12.15)$$

By (12.3),

$$P_1'P_2'P_4' = P_1'P_2'P_5'P_6' = P_1 P_2 P_5 P_7 \qquad (12.16)$$

for some P_7. By (12.13)–(12.15),

$$P_1 P_2 P_5 \in L(G(f, P_5)), \qquad P_1'P_2'P_5' \in L(G(f', P_5')) \qquad (12.17)$$

where f is the production $X \to P_2$ and f' the production $X' \to P_2'$. By (12.16), one of the words $P_1 P_2 P_5$ and $P_1'P_2'P_5'$ is an initial subword of the other. (Thus, they can be expressed in the form Q and QQ_1.) Since (12.11) always implies (12.12), we conclude by (12.17) that

$$P_1 P_2 P_5 = P_1'P_2'P_5', \qquad P_5 = P_5', \qquad X = X', \qquad P_2 = P_2'$$

and consequently $P_1 = P_1'$. Thus, (12.4) is satisfied and we conclude that assertion II is true.

By assertion II, to decide whether G is LR(k) it suffices to test whether one of finitely many regular languages $K_1, \ldots, K_t$ contains a word which is an initial subword of some word in some K_j. Clearly, an algorithm for $t = 2$ gives also an algorithm for the general case. Assume that K_1 and K_2 are regular languages over V_1. One of them contains an initial subword of some word in the other iff the regular language

$$(K_1/V_1^* \cap K_2) \cup (K_2/V_1^* \cap K_1)$$

is nonempty. (For $K_1 = K_2$, V_1^+ is taken instead of V_1^*.) ∎

Example 12.3. Consider the grammar G given in Example 12.2. For $k = 0$, the languages K_1, K_2, K_3 of the form $L(G(f, P))$ are denoted by the regular expressions

$$aXc, \qquad aXb^2, \qquad ab.$$

Clearly, $Q \in K_i$ and $QQ_1 \in K_j$ imply $Q_1 = \lambda$ and $i = j$. Hence, G is LR(0). Consider next the grammar G given in Example 12.1 and any fixed $k \geqq 0$. One of the languages $L(G(f, P))$ (in fact, the one with $P = b^k$ and $f : X \to b$) is denoted by the regular expression $ab^k b^* b b^k$. Since the words $Q = ab^{2k+1}$ and QQ_1 with $Q_1 = b$ belong to this language, G is not LR(k). Hence, in this particular case, we are able to conclude that G is not LR(k) for any k. However, the general algorithm of Theorem 12.2 is applicable for given values of k only. In fact, there is no algorithm for deciding whether or not there exists a k such that a given G is LR(k).

The recognition device corresponding to an LR(k) grammar is the deterministic pushdown automaton.

Proposition 12.1. If G is LR(k), then $L(G)$ is deterministic. Every deterministic language has an LR(1) grammar. Consequently, every LR(k) language has an LR(1) grammar.

The discussions above deal with "bottom-up" rather than "top-down" parsing. In introducing this terminology, one has in mind a generation tree with the root at the top (such as the tree of Fig. 1). The terms "bottom-up" and "top-down" refer to the direction in which one tries to reconstruct the tree when parsing a given word. Thus, in top-down (left–right) parsing, one attempts to generate the given word from the initial letter, using leftmost derivations in a left–right way. Whereas LR(k) grammars are suitable for deterministic bottom-up parsing, the LL(k) grammars introduced below have the same property as regards top-down parsing. (Parsing is deterministic iff there is only one valid production to be used at any point. This requirement is stronger than the unambiguity of a grammar which means that as soon as a parse is found, it is the only one.)

In the following definition, $\Rightarrow_{\text{left}}$ and $\Rightarrow_{\text{left}}^*$ refer to leftmost derivations.

Definition. Assume that $k \geqq 0$. A context-free grammar $G = (V_N, V_T, X_0, F)$ is LL(k) iff, for all words P_1, P_4, P_4' over V_T, all words P_2, P_2', P_3, P_3' over $V_N \cup V_T$, and all nonterminals X, the conditions

$$X_0 \Rightarrow_{\text{left}}^* P_1 X P_3 \Rightarrow_{\text{left}} P_1 P_2 P_3 \Rightarrow_{\text{left}}^* P_1 P_4,$$

$$X_0 \Rightarrow_{\text{left}}^* P_1 X P_3' \Rightarrow_{\text{left}} P_1 P_2' P_3' \Rightarrow_{\text{left}}^* P_1 P_4',$$

$$k: P_4 = k: P_4'$$

imply the equation $P_2 = P_2'$. A language is LL(k) iff there exists an LL(k) grammar generating it.

Thus for any word P generated by an LL(k) grammar, each production in its leftmost derivation can be identified by inspecting P from left to right to the kth symbol beyond the leftmost descendant of the production. Similar to the way we have defined LR(k) and LL(k) grammars, one can define RL(k) and RR(k) grammars by reversing the roles of left and right. Since an ambiguity would lead into contradiction with the LL(k) condition, we obtain the following.

Theorem 12.3. Every LL(k) grammar is unambiguous.

Example 12.4. Consider the grammar G determined by the productions

$$X_0 \to aX_1, \qquad X_0 \to \lambda, \qquad X_1 \to aX_0 bb, \qquad X_1 \to \lambda.$$

Clearly, G is LL(1). On the other hand, the grammar G_1 determined by the equations

$$X_0 = X_1 + X_2, \qquad X_1 = aX_1 b + ab, \qquad X_2 = aX_2 c + ac$$

is not LL(k) for any k.

Example 12.5. The grammar G determined by the productions

$$X_0 \rightarrow a^2 X_0 b^2, \qquad X_0 \rightarrow a, \qquad X_0 \rightarrow \lambda \qquad\qquad (12.18)$$

is LL(2). In fact, $L(G) = \{a^{2m+1} b^{2m} | m \geqq 0\} \cup \{a^{2m} b^{2m} | m \geqq 0\}$. Which of the productions (12.18) is applied can be seen by looking two letters ahead: First, second, and third productions correspond to two a's, one a but not two, and no a's, respectively. An equivalent LL(1) grammar is determined by the equations

$$X_0 = aX_1 + \lambda, \qquad X_1 = aX_2 b + \lambda, \qquad X_2 = aX_1 b + b.$$

It is clear that the language generated by an LL(0) grammar consists of at most one word. Instead of LL(0) grammars, one usually considers s-grammars. By definition, a grammar is an *s-grammar* iff all of its productions are of the form

$$X \rightarrow aP, \qquad X \in V_{\mathrm{N}}, \qquad a \in V_{\mathrm{T}}, \qquad P \in W(V), \qquad (12.19)$$

where for each pair (X, a), the grammar contains at most one production (12.19). Clearly, every s-grammar is LL(1) and in Greibach normal form. Languages generated by s-grammars are referred to as *s-languages*.

Example 12.6. For $n \geqq 1$, the s-grammar determined by the productions

$$X_0 \rightarrow a_i X_i X_0, \qquad X_j \rightarrow a_i X_i X_j, \qquad X_i \rightarrow a_i', \qquad X_0 \rightarrow \#, \qquad 1 \leqq i,j \leqq n,$$

generates the language $D_n \#$. (Here D_n is the Dyck language.)

Comparing LL(k) and LR(k) grammars, the following result can be obtained.

Proposition 12.2. Every LL(k) grammar is LR(k).

As regards decision methods, Theorem 12.2 is valid also for LL(k) grammars.

Proposition 12.3. There is an algorithm to decide for a given context-free grammar G and a given k, whether or not G is LL(k). Furthermore, there is an algorithm for deciding whether or not two LL(k) grammars generate the same language.

The second sentence of Proposition 12.3 is especially interesting because $LL(k)$ grammars form the largest known class for which the equivalence problem is decidable. The decidability of the equivalence problem for $LR(1)$ grammars is unknown.

In contrast to $LR(k)$ languages, $LL(k)$ languages form a proper hierarchy of language families.

Proposition 12.4. For every $k > 1$, the family of $LL(k)$ languages includes properly the family of $LL(k-1)$ languages. The family of $LL(1)$ languages includes properly the family of s-languages. For every $k > 1$, any language generated by a λ-free $LL(k)$ grammar is $LL(k-1)$.

EXERCISES

1. Prove the statement concerning $\varphi(P)$ made after (8.7).

2. Determine the degree of ambiguity of the grammar in Example 8.1.

3. Consider the grammar determined by the equation $X_0 = a + X_0 b X_0$. Prove that the corresponding formal power series is

$$\varphi = \sum_{n=0}^{\infty} \binom{2n}{n} (n+1)^{-1} (ab)^n a$$

where $\binom{2n}{n}$ is the binomial coefficient. [Cf. Chomsky-Schützenberger (1963).]

4. Prove that every context-free λ-free language is generated by a grammar G, all of whose productions are of the form $X \to P$ where X is a nonterminal and P both begins and ends with a terminal letter. (Prove first the weaker statement, where the words "both begins and" are omitted.)

5. Give an upper bound, as sharp as possible, for the index of the grammar G_1 in the latter part of the proof of Theorem 10.1.

6. Prove that every context-free grammar whose terminal alphabet consists of one letter only is of finite index.

7. Introduce the notion of index for the family $\mathscr{L}(2,3,0)$. Prove that for each language of finite index in the family $\mathscr{L}(2,3,0)$, there is a letter-equivalent regular language. Conclude by Exercise 5 to Chapter V that there are languages of infinite index in the family $\mathscr{L}(2,3,0)$.

8. Prove that the family of metalinear languages is properly included in the family of ultralinear languages.

9. For a context-free grammar $G = (V_N, V_T, X_0, F)$, let $w(a) = 0$ for $a \in V_T$, and let $w(X)$ be a natural number for $X \in V_N$. Extend the domain of w into $W(V_N \cup V_T)$ similarly as in Exercise 4 to Chapter III. A derivation $P_0 \Rightarrow \cdots \Rightarrow P_r$ according to G is k-*bounded* iff $w(P_j) \leq k$ for $0 \leq j \leq r$. Let

$L_k(G)$ be the subset of $L(G)$ consisting of all words for which there exists a k-bounded derivation from X_0. Prove that for every type-0 grammar G_1 such that $\text{ind}(G_1) = k$, there are a context-free grammar G and a function w such that $L(G_1) = L_k(G)$. [Cf. Ginsburg-Spanier (1968). This is a preliminary result needed in the proof of Proposition 10.3.]

10. Show (by Proposition 10.2 and Theorems 10.1 and 1.6) that $\mathscr{F}\mathscr{S}$ is a full AFL.

11. Prove that every context-free language over one letter is in the family $\mathscr{L}_2(1, 1)$.

12. Prove that the language

$$\{a^n b^n | n \geq 1\}\, d \cup (a \cup b)^* c$$

is LR(0).

13. Prove that the grammar determined by the productions

$$X_0 \to \lambda, \qquad X_0 \to aX_1 bX_0, \qquad X_0 \to bX_2 aX_0, \qquad X_1 \to \lambda,$$

$$X_1 \to aX_1 bX_1, \qquad X_2 \to \lambda, \qquad X_2 \to bX_2 aX_2$$

is an LR(1) grammar for the language of Example 1.2 in Part 1.

14. Prove that every LL(k) grammar is unambiguous.

15. Is the following "arithmetical expressions" grammar ($\{X_0, X, Y\}$, $\{a, b, (,), +, *\}, X_0, F)$, where F consists of the productions $X_0 \to X_0 + X$, $X_0 \to X$, $X \to X * Y$, $X \to Y$, $Y \to (X_0)$, $Y \to a$, and $Y \to b$, LR(k) or LL(k) for some k?

16. Let $\mathscr{L}$ be the family of languages L such that L is LL(k) for some $k \geq 0$. Prove that $\mathscr{L}$ is closed neither under left quotient with a finite language nor under mirror image. [Note that the language $\{a^n b^n | n \geq 1\} \cup \{a^n b^{2n} | n \geq 1\}$ is not LL(k) for any k.]

17. Prove that the family of s-languages is not closed under any of the operations of union, complementation, and intersection.

18. Prove that for any λ-free LL(k) grammar, there is an equivalent LL(k) grammar in the Greibach normal form. [Cf. Rosenkrantz-Stearns (1970).]

19. Prove that there is an algorithm for deciding whether or not the language accepted by a deterministic pushdown automaton is regular. [Cf. Stearns (1967).]

BIBLIOGRAPHICAL REMARKS

Formal power series in connection with formal languages were discussed by Chomsky and Schützenberger (1963). Proofs of Propositions 8.1 and 8.2 can be found in Schützenberger (1962). The Greibach normal form is due to Greibach (1965), our proof follows Rosenkrantz (1967). See also Wood

(1969). Theorem 9.1 is due to Gross (1964). The proof of Theorem 9.3 follows Maurer (1969a, b). For matters discussed in Note 9.1, see Maurer (1968) and, for Note 9.2, see Hibbard and Ullian (1966). Examples of languages of infinite index were given by Yntema (1967) and Nivat (1967). For proofs of Propositions 10.1 and 10.2, see Ginsburg and Spanier (1968). Various results concerning indices can be found also in Brainerd (1968), Stotskij (1969), Salomaa (1969), and Gruska (1971a, b.) Ultralinear languages have been characterized in terms of Szilard languages by Friant (1968). Theorem 10.2 is due to Ginsburg and Greibach (1966) and Theorem 10.3 to Matthews (1967). Various extensions have been given by Book (1971). Most of the material in Section 11 is due to Gruska (1971a) who also gives a proof of Proposition 11.1. Similar results have been obtained by Greibach (1969), Král (1970), Yntema (1971), and McWhirter (1971). LR(k) grammars were introduced by Knuth (1965). For a general discussion of this broad field and related problems concerning parsing, see Aho and Ullman (1972). Extensions to the context-sensitive case have been investigated by Walters (1970) and Révész (1971). The equivalence between deterministic pushdown automata and LR(k) grammars was established by Havel (1971). LL(k) grammars were introduced by Lewis and Stearns (1968) and Knuth (1971), and s-grammars by Korenjak and Hopcroft (1966). The fact that LL(k) languages form a proper hierarchy of language families was established by Kurki-Suonio (1969).

BIBLIOGRAPHY

A. Aho and J. Ullman. "The Theory of Parsing, Translation and Compiling." Prentice Hall, Englewood Cliffs, New Jersey, to be published.

R. V. Book. Terminal context in context-sensitive grammars. Center for Res. in Comput. Technol., Harvard Univ., Preprint no. 10 (1971).

B. Brainerd. An analog of a theorem about context-free languages. *Information Control* 11 (1968) 561–567.

N. Chomsky and M. P. Schützenberger. The algebraic theory of context-free languages. *In* P. Braffort and D. Hirschberg (eds.), "Computer Programming and Formal Systems." North Holland Publ., Amsterdam, 1963, pp. 118–161.

J. Friant. Langages Ultralineaires et Superlineaires, Nouvelles Caracterisations. Univ. de Montréal MA-102 (1968).

S. Ginsburg and S. Greibach. Mappings which preserve context-sensitive languages. *Information Control* 9 (1966) 563–582.

S. Ginsburg and E. Spanier. Derivation-bounded languages. *J. Comput. System Sci.* 2 (1968) 228–250.

S. Greibach. A new normal form theorem for context-free phrase structure grammars. *J. Assoc. Comput. Mach.* 12 (1965) 42–52.

S. Greibach. Full AFL's and nested iterated substitution. *IEEE Conf. Record 10th Ann. Symp. Switching Automata Theory* (1969) 222–230.

M. Gross. Inherent ambiguity of minimal linear grammars. *Information Control* 7 (1964) 366–368.

J. Gruska. A characterization of context-free languages. *J. Comput. System Sci.* **5** (1971a) 353–364.

J. Gruska. A few remarks on the index of context-free grammars and languages. *Information Control* **19** (1971b) 216–223.

I. M. Havel. Strict Deterministic Languages. Univ. of California (Berkeley), Comput. Sci. Dept. Tech. Rep. No. 1 (1971).

T. Hibbard and J. Ullian. The independence of inherent ambiguity from complementedness among context-free languages. *J. Assoc. Comput. Mach.* **13** (1966) 588–593.

D. E. Knuth. On the translation of languages from left to right. *Information Control* **8** (1965) 607–639.

D. E. Knuth. Top-down syntax analysis. *Acta Informatica* **1** (1971) 79–110.

A. Korenjak and J. Hopcroft. Simple deterministic languages. *IEEE Conf. Record 7th Ann. Symp. Switching Automata Theory* (1966) 36–46.

J. Král. A modification of a substitution theorem and some necessary and sufficient conditions for sets to be context-free. *Math. Systems Theory* **4** (1970) 129–139.

R. Kurki-Suonio. Notes on top-down languages. *BIT* **9** (1969) 225–238.

P. M. Lewis, II, and R. Stearns. Syntax-directed transduction. *J. Assoc. Comput. Mach.* **15** (1968) 464–488.

I. McWhirter. Substitution expressions. *J. Comput. System Sci.* **5** (1971) 629–637.

H. Maurer. A Context-Free Language which is Inherently Ambiguous of Degree 3. Univ. of Calgary. Dept. of Math. Res. Paper No. 63 (1968).

H. Maurer. A direct proof of the inherent ambiguity of a simple context-free language. *J. Assoc. Comput. Mach.* **16** (1969a) 256–260.

H. Maurer. "Theoretische Grundlagen der Programmiersprachen." Hochschultaschen-bücher 404, Bibliographisches Inst. (1969b).

G. Matthews. Two-way languages. *Information Control* **10** (1967) 111–119.

M. Nivat. Transductions des Langages de Chomsky. Doctoral dissertation, Chapter 6, Grenoble Univ. (1967).

G. Révész. Unilateral context sensitive grammars and left-to-right parsing. *J. Comput. System Sci.* **5** (1971) 337–352.

D. Rosenkrantz. Matrix equations and normal forms for context-free grammars. *J. Assoc. Comput. Mach.* **14** (1967) 501–507.

D. Rosenkrantz and R. Stearns. Properties of deterministic top-down grammars. *Information Control* **17** (1970) 226–256.

A. Salomaa. On the index of a context-free grammar and language. *Information Control* **14** (1969) 474–477.

M. P. Schützenberger. On a theorem of R. Jungen. *Proc. Amer. Math. Soc.* **13** (1962) 885–890.

R. Stearns. A regularity test for pushdown machines. *Information Control* **11** (1967) 323–340.

E. D. Stotskij. Ponjatie indeksa v obobshchennykh grammatikakh. *Akad. Nauk SSSR Nauchno-Tekhn. Inform. Ser.* **2** (1969) 16–17.

D. Walters. Deterministic context-sensitive languages, I and II. *Information Control* **17** (1970) 14–61.

D. Wood. The normal form theorem—another proof. *Comput. J.* **12** (1969) 139–147.

M. Yntema. Inclusion relations among families of context-free languages. *Information Control* **10** (1967) 572–597.

M. Yntema. Cap expressions for context-free languages. *Information Control* **18** (1971) 311–318.

Chapter VII

Some Further Classes of Generative Devices

The purpose of this chapter is to define some new generative devices for languages. They are either modifications of grammars, some of them resembling the devices considered in Chapter V, or else obtained from rewriting systems by an approach somewhat different from the one leading to the notion of a grammar.

13. LINDENMAYER SYSTEMS:
PARALLEL REWRITING WITHOUT TERMINALS

When we introduced the basic hierarchy of language families $\mathscr{L}_i$, $0 \leqq i \leqq 3$, we essentially divided the alphabet of a rewriting system into two parts: nonterminals and terminals. Such a division increases the generative capacity of the system because it gives an additional tool of distinguishing acceptable words. If $G = (V_N, V_T, X_0, F)$ is a grammar, we consider the language

$$L(G) = \{P \in W(V_T) | X_0 \Rightarrow^* P\}$$

rather than the language

$$L_S(G) = \{P | X_0 \Rightarrow^* P\}. \tag{13.1}$$

234

The linguistic motivation for introducing nonterminals is that nonterminals correspond to the syntactic classes of a language. With this picture in mind, (13.1) can be termed as the language of *sentential forms* of a grammar G.

Beginning with the notion of a rewriting system, we can develop the theory without partitioning the alphabet. In the *Lindenmayer systems* or, in short, *L-systems* considered in this section there are *no specified terminal letters*. All generated words are in the language of the system, not only those which consist entirely of terminal letters. The resulting loss in generative capacity is to some extent recovered by the requirement that rewriting happens *simultaneously* to all letters of the word under scan, and by allowing an *initial word* instead of an initial letter. L-systems were introduced in connection with a theory proposed for the development of filamentous organisms. Developmental stages of cellular arrays are represented by words, each letter being a cell. Productions correspond to developmental instructions with which known kinds of organisms can be generated. They are applied simultaneously to all letters (cells) because in a growing organism development proceeds simultaneously everywhere. There are no terminal letters because they would correspond to dead cells which remain permanently fixed in their place in the organism. (Disappearing cells can be represented by the empty word λ.)

The various parts of a developing organism may or may not be in communication with each other. We first define a model, called a *0L-system*, which is obtained by assuming no communication among the cells. Basically, a 0L-system corresponds to simultaneous context-free rewriting.

Definition. A *0L-system* is an ordered triple $0LS = (V, P_0, F)$ where V is an alphabet, P_0 is a nonempty word over V (called the *axiom* or the *initial word*), and F is a finite set of ordered pairs (a, P) with $a \in V$ and $P \in W(V)$. Furthermore, for each $a \in V$, there is at least one word $P \in W(V)$ such that $(a, P) \in F$. The elements (a, P) of F are called *productions* and written $a \to P$.

A binary relation $\Rightarrow_{0LS}$ or, in short, $\Rightarrow$ on the set $W(V)$ is defined as follows: $P \Rightarrow Q$ holds iff there is an $n \geqq 1$, letters a_i, and words Q_i, $1 \leqq i \leqq n$, such that

$$P = a_1 \cdots a_n, \qquad Q = Q_1 \cdots Q_n,$$

and $a_i \to Q_i$ is in F for $i = 1, \ldots, n$; $\Rightarrow^*$ is the reflexive transitive closure of $\Rightarrow$. The *language generated* by the 0L-system is defined by

$$L(0LS) = \{P \mid P_0 \Rightarrow^* P\}. \tag{13.2}$$

Our 0L-system is *deterministic* iff, for each $a \in V$, there is exactly one $P \in W(V)$ such that $(a, P) \in F$. It is *λ-free* or *propagating* iff, for all productions $a \to P$ in F, $P \neq \lambda$. Notations D0LS, P0LS, and DP0LS are used for these systems. (Thus, DP0LS is a 0L-system which is both deterministic and propagating.) Languages of the form (13.2) are referred to as *0L-languages*. D0L-, P0L-, and DP0L-languages are defined accordingly. It follows immediately by the definitions that the family of DP0L-languages is included in the intersection of the families of D0L- and P0L-languages, and both of the latter families are included in the family of 0L-languages. Two 0L-systems are termed *equivalent* iff they generate the same language.

Example 13.1. For $0LS = (\{a\}, a, \{a \rightarrow a^2\})$, we have

$$L(0LS) = \{a^{2^n} | n \geq 0\}. \tag{13.3}$$

Hence, (13.3) is a DP0L-language. For

$$0LS = (\{a, b\}, a, \{a \rightarrow b, b \rightarrow ab\}),$$

the words in $L(0LS)$ are

$$a, b, ab, bab, abbab, bababbab, \dots.$$

The lengths of these words are the Fibonacci numbers. For

$$0LS = (\{a, b, c\}, a, \{a \rightarrow abcc, b \rightarrow bcc, c \rightarrow c\}),$$

the words in $L(0LS)$ are

$$a, abcc, abccbcccc, abccbccccbcccccc, \dots.$$

The lengths of these words are the squares of natural numbers. For

$$0LS = (\{a, b, c\}, a, \{a \rightarrow abc, b \rightarrow bc, c \rightarrow c\}),$$

the words in $L(0LS)$ are

$$a, abc, abcbcc, abcbccbccc, abcbccbcccbcccc, \dots.$$

The lengths of these words are the triangular numbers. For

$$0LS = (\{a, b, c, d\}, a, \{a \rightarrow abcd^5, b \rightarrow bcd^5, c \rightarrow cd^6, d \rightarrow d\}),$$

the words in $L(0LS)$ are

$$a, abcd^5, abcd^5bcd^5cd^6d^5, \dots.$$

The lengths of these words are the cubes of natural numbers.

Example 13.1 should give an idea of the capacity of (deterministic and propagating) 0L-systems to generate various kinds of non-context-free languages. The next example, due to Lindenmayer, illustrates the developmental stages of a red alga.

Example 13.2. Consider the deterministic and propagating 0L-system, where the alphabet and the productions are given by the following table.

1	2	3	4	5	6	7	8	(	)	#	0
$2\#3$	2	$2\#4$	504	6	7	8(1)	8	(	)	#	0

(The right side of each production is in the second row.) Starting with the axiom $P_0 = 1$, we get the following words in the language $L(0LS)$:

$$P_0 = 1, \quad P_1 = 2\#3, \quad P_2 = 2\#2\#4, \quad P_3 = 2\#2\#504,$$

$$P_4 = 2\#2\#60504, \quad P_5 = 2\#2\#7060504, \quad P_6 = 2\#2\#8(1)07060504.$$

It can be verified inductively that for all $n \geq 0$,

$$P_{n+6} = 2\#2\#8(P_n)08(P_{n-1})0 \cdots 08(P_0)07060504.$$

The developmental stages P_6, P_8, and P_{13} are illustrated in Fig. 13. Parenthesized expressions are branches whose position is indicated by the 8's. The 0's are marked by oblique walls drawn alternately right and left inclined. The branches are shown as attached on alternate sides of the branch on which they are borne, and the #'s are marked by vertical walls. It is easy to verify that $L(0LS)$ is context-sensitive but not context-free.

The family of 0L-languages displays an extraordinary resistance to those operations for languages we have considered in connection with the basic hierarchy. We use the term *anti-AFL* to mean a family of languages which is closed under none of the operations of union, λ-free catenation closure, λ-free homomorphism, inverse homomorphism, and intersection with regular languages.

Theorem 13.1. The family of 0L-languages is an anti-AFL.

Proof. Nonclosure under union follows because $\{a\}$ and $\{a^2\}$ are 0L-languages (as is any language consisting of one nonempty word), whereas their union is not a 0L-language. Nonclosure under inverse homomorphism is seen by considering the homomorphism $h(a) = a^2$ and noting that $h^{-1}\{a\} = \emptyset$ is not a 0L-language. (Less trivial counterexamples can easily be given.)

Consider next the language

$$L_1 = \{aa\} \cup \{b^{2^n} | n \geq 2\}$$

generated by the system

$$(\{a, b\}, aa, \{a \rightarrow bb, b \rightarrow bb\}).$$

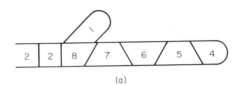

(a)

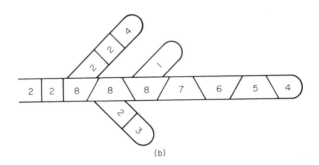

(b)

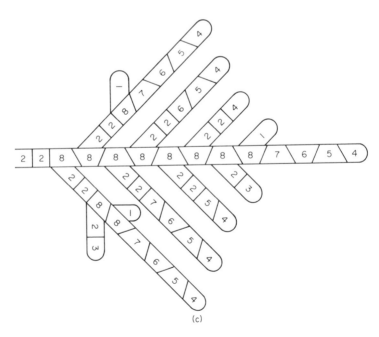

(c)

FIGURE 13

We claim that L_1^+ is not a 0L-language. In fact, since $\lambda \notin L_1^+$, any system generating L_1^+ must be propagating. This implies that aa has to be the axiom. Since $a^4 \in L_1^+$, $a \to a^2$ is one of the productions. (If we have $a \to a$ and $a \to a^3$, we obtain $ab^i \in L_1^+$ for some i, which is a contradiction. A similar contradiction arises if one tries to generate a^4 using an intermediate word containing an occurrence of b.) Since $b^4 \in L_1^+$, we have $a^2 \Rightarrow^* b^4$. Consequently, there is a production $a \to b^i$ for some i with $1 \leq i \leq 3$. Using productions $a \to a^2$ and $a \to b^i$, we obtain $a^2 b^i \in L_1^+$, $1 \leq i \leq 3$, which is impossible. Hence, nonclosure under $+$ follows.

The language $L_2 = \{\lambda, a, a^2\}$ is generated by the system with the axiom a^2 and productions $a \to a$ and $a \to \lambda$. For the λ-free homomorphism h defined by $h(a) = a^2$,

$$h(L_2) = \{\lambda, a^2, a^4\},$$

is not a 0L-language. The same holds true with respect to the intersection $L_2 \cap |(a^3)^*| = \{\lambda\}$. ∎

It is an immediate consequence of Theorem 13.1 that the family of 0L-languages is closed neither under gsm nor under inverse gsm mapping. Another consequence is that it is not closed under substitution. It is easy to prove that the family is closed under none of the operations of complementation, intersection, catenation, and catenation closure. The following theorem gives some positive closure results.

Theorem 13.2. The family of 0L-languages is closed under mirror image. If L is a 0L-language over one letter, then so is L^*.

Proof. The mirror image of a language generated by the system (V, P_0, F) is generated by the system $(V, \text{mi}(P_0), \text{mi}(F))$ where $\text{mi}(F)$ is obtained from F by replacing the right side of every production by its mirror image.

To prove the second sentence we assume that L is generated by the 0L-system $H = (\{a\}, a^\mu, F)$ where $\mu \geq 1$. We consider first the case that L is finite. If $L = \{a\}$ or $L = \{\lambda, a\}$, then L^* is generated by the system with the axiom a and productions $a \to \lambda$, $a \to a$, and $a \to a^2$. If $L = \{P_1, ..., P_k\}$ where $k \geq 1$ and $P_1 \neq a, \lambda$, then L^* is generated by the system

$$(\{a\}, P_1, \{a \to \lambda, a \to P_1, ..., a \to P_k\}).$$

Since $\varnothing$ and $\{\lambda\}$ are not 0L-languages, we have exhausted the cases of L being finite. Assume now that L is infinite. For each i, where $1 \leq i \leq \mu$, let Q_i be the shortest word in L whose length is of the form $k\mu + i$ for some $k \geq 0$. Then Q_i is undefined if there is no word in L whose length is of this form. Let M be the finite set consisting of a^μ and in addition of all words R

such that $a^\mu \Rightarrow_H R$ or $Q_i \Rightarrow_H R$ for some i. Consider the 0L-system

$$H_1 = (\{a\}, a^\mu, \{a \to \lambda\} \cup \{a \to R | R \in M\}).$$

We claim that

$$L(H_1) = L^*. \tag{13.4}$$

Assume that $P \in L(H_1)$. If $P = a^\mu$, we obviously have $P \in L^*$. Otherwise, there is a word $P_1 \in L(H_1)$ such that $P_1 \Rightarrow_{H_1} P$. This implies that P can be written as a catenation $P = R_1 \cdots R_k$ where $k \geq 1$ and each of the words R_j either equals λ or belongs to M. Since all the words in M belong to L, we obtain $P \in L^*$, from which the inclusion

$$L(H_1) \subseteq L^* \tag{13.5}$$

follows.

To establish the reverse inclusion, we show first that, for all words P and P_1, the relations

$$P_1 \Rightarrow_H P \quad \text{and} \quad P_1 \in L \tag{13.6}$$

imply the relation

$$P_1 \Rightarrow_{H_1} P. \tag{13.7}$$

Assuming (13.6), we see by the definition of the words Q_i that P_1 can be expressed as a catenation

$$P_1 = (a^\mu)^j Q_i \tag{13.8}$$

for some $j \geq 0$ and $1 \leq i \leq \mu$. By (13.8) and the fact that $P_1 \Rightarrow_H P$, the word P can be written as a catenation $P = R_1 \cdots R_{j+1}$ where the words R belong to M. By the definition of the production set of H_1 it is now obvious that (13.7) holds true. Since the axioms of H and H_1 coincide, we conclude by an inductive argument that whenever $P \in L$, then $P \in L(H_1)$ also.

Assume now that $P \in L^*$. If $P = \lambda$, then $P \in L(H_1)$. Otherwise, $P = P_1 \cdots P_k$ where $k \geq 1$ and each P_i satisfies the conditions $P_i \neq \lambda$ and $P_i \in L$. By what was shown above,

$$a^\mu \Rightarrow_{H_1}^* P_i, \qquad 1 \leq i \leq k. \tag{13.9}$$

Since L is an infinite language, we see by the definition of H_1 that $a^\mu \Rightarrow_{H_1}^* a^{j\mu}$ for all $j \geq 0$. If all the derivations (13.9) are of the same length, we obtain

$$a^\mu \Rightarrow_{H_1}^* a^{k\mu} \Rightarrow_{H_1}^* P_1 \cdots P_k = P \tag{13.10}$$

and consequently $P \in L(H_1)$. If all the derivations (13.9) are not of the same length originally, then we "synchronize" them by adding an appropriate number of steps

$$a^\mu \Rightarrow_{H_1} a^\mu. \tag{13.11}$$

The steps (13.11) are valid because the productions $a \to \lambda$ and $a \to a^\mu$ are in H_1. Consequently, (13.10) holds true also if the derivations (13.9) are not of the same length. This implies that $L^* \subseteq L(H_1)$. By (13.5), we see that (13.4) holds. ∎

Similarly, as in the proof of Theorem 13.2 we see that if L is a finite language over one letter containing a nonempty word, then L^* is a 0L-language. This result holds true also in case L itself is not a 0L-language, for example, $L = \{a^2, a^5\}$.

Using techniques similar to those applied in Theorem 13.2, one can characterize 0L-languages over one letter. For natural numbers $n, s, m_1, ..., m_s$, we use the notation

$$M(n, m_1, ..., m_s) = \{n\} \cup \{k_1 m_1 + \cdots + k_s m_s | k_i \geqq 0, 1 \leqq i \leqq s\}.$$

Sets of this form are referred to as M-sets.

Theorem 13.3. Let L be an infinite language over the alphabet $\{a\}$ such that $\lambda \in L$. Then L is a 0L-language iff there is an M-set M_L such that

$$L = \{a^i | i \in M_L\}. \tag{13.12}$$

Proof. Assume that there is an M-set

$$M_L = M(n, m_1, ..., m_s)$$

such that (13.12) holds. Without loss of generality we assume that it is not the case that $s = m_1 = 1$. Consider the 0L-system

$$H = (\{a\}, a^n, \{a \to \lambda, a \to a^{m_1}, ..., a \to a^{m_s}\}). \tag{13.13}$$

We claim that

$$L = L(H). \tag{13.14}$$

This proves that L is a 0L-language. But (13.14) will prove also the converse part of our theorem because any infinite 0L-language containing the empty word is generated by a system (13.13) from which the set M_L can be immediately formed.

We prove first that the left side of (13.14) is included in the right side. Consider a word a^i where $i \in M_L$. If $i = n$, then $a^i \in L(H)$, by the choice of the axiom. Otherwise, there exist nonnegative integers $k_1, ..., k_s$ such that

$$i = k_1 m_1 + \cdots + k_s m_s. \tag{13.15}$$

By our assumption, at least one of the m's is greater than 1. Consequently, H generates a word a^k with $k > k_1 + \cdots + k_s$. This implies that $a^i \in L(H)$. [For $i = 0$, this is obvious. Otherwise, $a^k \Rightarrow_H a^i$. This is seen by applying

$a \to a^{m_j}$ to k_j occurrences of a for $j = 1, ..., s$, and $a \to \lambda$ to the remaining $k - (k_1 + \cdots + k_s)$ occurrences of a.] Hence, the left side of (13.14) is included in the right side.

To prove the reverse inclusion, we assume that $a^i \in L(H)$. If $i = n$, then clearly $a^i \in L$. Otherwise, there exists a word $a^j \in L(H)$ with the property $a^j \Rightarrow_H a^i$. But this implies the existence of integers $k_1, ..., k_s$ satisfying (13.15). [The production $a \to a^{m_v}$ is applied to k_v occurrences of a for $1 \leq v \leq s$, and the production $a \to \lambda$ to the remaining $j - (k_1 + \cdots + k_s)$ occurrences of a.] Hence $a^i \in L$. We conclude that the right side of (13.14) is included in the left side, and thus (13.14) holds true. ∎

If $L \subseteq W\{a\}$ is a finite 0L-language, then the system generating L cannot contain any length-increasing productions. Consequently, L equals one of the following languages for some $m \geq 1$:

$$\{a^m\}, \{\lambda, a^m\}, \{\lambda, a, ..., a^{m-1}, a^m\}. \tag{13.16}$$

By Theorem 13.3, we obtain the following result.

Theorem 13.4. Assume that $L \subseteq W\{a\}$ contains the empty word λ. Then L is a 0L-language iff either (13.12) holds for some M-set M_L or else L is among the latter two languages (13.16). Consequently, all 0L-languages $L \subseteq W\{a\}$ containing the empty word are regular.

The characterization given in Theorem 13.4 can be extended to concern all 0L-languages over one letter.

Proposition 13.1. There is an algorithm which yields, for any 0L-system $H = (\{a\}, P_0, F)$, either a regular expression denoting the language $L(H)$ or an equivalent 0L-system H_1 containing one production only. Consequently, there is an algorithm for deciding whether or not two given 0L-systems over one letter are equivalent.

The second sentence of Proposition 13.1 cannot be extended to concern arbitrary 0L-systems. This follows from the fact that there is no algorithm to decide whether or not two context-free grammars generate the same sentential forms.

We are now in the position to compare the family $0\mathscr{L}$ of 0L-languages with the families $\mathscr{L}_i$, $0 \leq i \leq 3$, in our basic hierarchy.

Theorem 13.5. Each of the families $\mathscr{L}_3, \mathscr{L}_2 - \mathscr{L}_3$, and $\mathscr{L}_1 - \mathscr{L}_2$ has a nonempty intersection with both of the families $0\mathscr{L}$ and $0\mathscr{L}_1$, the family of languages which are not 0L-languages. Any language L generated by a 0L-system (V, P_0, F) such that F contains the production $a \to a$, for each $a \in V$, is context-free. For any context-free language L, there is a 0L-system H and an alphabet V_1 such that

$$L = L(H) \cap W(V_1). \tag{13.17}$$

Proof. Examples of 0L-languages in the families $\mathscr{L}_3, \mathscr{L}_2 - \mathscr{L}_3$, and $\mathscr{L}_1 - \mathscr{L}_2$ are $\{a\}$, $\{a^i b a^i | i \geq 0\}$, and L_1 in the proof of Theorem 13.1, respectively. [The second among these languages is generated by the system $(\{a, b\}, b, \{b \to aba, a \to a\})$.] Examples of languages in the intersections

$$\mathscr{L}_3 \cap 0\mathscr{L}_1, \quad (\mathscr{L}_2 - \mathscr{L}_3) \cap 0\mathscr{L}_1, \quad (\mathscr{L}_1 - \mathscr{L}_2) \cap 0\mathscr{L}_1$$

are

$$\{a, a^2\}, \quad \{a^i b^i | i \geq 0\}, \quad \{a^{2^n} | n \geq 0\} \cup \{a^3\},$$

respectively.

To prove the second sentence, we define

$$V_N = \{N_a | a \in V\}.$$

Let F_N be the set obtained from F by replacing in every production every letter a with N_a. The notation $(P_0)_N$ is defined similarly. Clearly, L is generated by the context-free grammar

$$(V_N \cup \{X_0\}, V, X_0, F_N \cup \{X_0 \to (P_0)_N\} \cup \{N_a \to a | a \in V\}).$$

To prove the last sentence, let L be generated by the context-free grammar (V_N, V_T, X_0, F). Consider the 0L-system

$$H = (V_N \cup V_T, X_0, F \cup \{a \to a | a \in V_N \cup V_T\}).$$

Clearly, $L = L(H) \cap W(V_T)$. ∎

Theorem 13.5 leaves open the question of whether there are 0L-languages which are not context-sensitive. The answer to this question is negative, as is shown in Theorem 13.7. We first prove a lemma to the effect that erasing is essentially linear in a 0L-system.

Theorem 13.6. For every 0L-system $H = (V, P_0, F)$, there is an integer $k(H)$ such that every nonempty $P \in L(H)$ possesses a derivation

$$P_0 \Rightarrow P_1 \Rightarrow \cdots \Rightarrow P_v = P \tag{13.18}$$

satisfying $lg(P_i) \leq k(H) lg(P)$ for $i = 0, \ldots, v$.

Proof. We first add a new letter X_0 and the production $X_0 \to P_0$ to the system H. Let the resulting system with the axiom X_0 be H_1. [Clearly,

$L(H_1) = L(H) \cup \{X_0\}$.] We now associate a generation tree with each derivation according to H_1. We say that a derivation is *reduced* iff the associated generation tree has the following property. There is no subtree T such that (i) all leaves of T are labeled by λ and (ii) T has a path where two nodes possess the same label. For any derivation of a word P, there is a reduced derivation of P. The latter is obtained by identifying the appropriate nodes in the derivation tree of the original derivation (cf. Fig. 14).

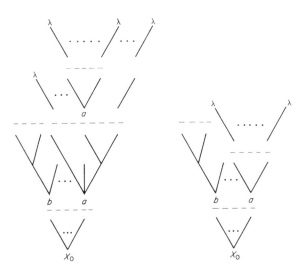

FIGURE 14

Let now m be the length of the longest word appearing on the right side of some production in H_1, and let n be the number of letters in the alphabet of H_1. We claim that we can choose

$$k(H) = 6m^n. \tag{13.19}$$

In fact, for any nonempty $P \in L(H)$, assume that (13.18), added with the initial step $P_{-1} = X_0 \Rightarrow P_0$, is a reduced derivation of P. An occurrence of a letter a in one of the words P_i is termed *improductive* iff this occurrence of a is the label of the root of a tree all of whose leaves are labeled by λ. Otherwise, the occurrence is termed *productive*. Since $P \neq \lambda$, each P_i contains at least one productive letter. Furthermore, the number of productive letters in P_i is less than or equal to $lg(P)$. Thus (13.19) follows if we can show that for all i, whenever Q is a subword of P_i satisfying $lg(Q) = 3m^n$, then Q contains at least one productive letter.

For $i < n$, no subword of P_i is of length $3m^n$. For $i = n+j$, $j \geq 0$, assume that Q is a subword of P_i of length $3m^n$. Write Q in the form

$$Q = Q_1 Q_2 Q_3, \qquad lg(Q_1) = lg(Q_2) = lg(Q_3) = m^n.$$

Assume that Q contains only improductive letters. Consider any occurrence of a letter a in Q_2. There is a unique (occurrence of a) letter b in P_{i-n} such that a is a label in the tree T whose root is labeled by b. Furthermore, by the choice of Q, m, and n, all leaves of T are labeled by λ. But this is a contradiction because clearly there is a path in T with two nodes labeled by the same letter. ∎

Theorem 13.7. Every 0L-language is context-sensitive.

Proof. Assume that L is generated by the 0L-system $H = (V, P_0, F)$. Consider the grammar

$$G = (\{X_i | 0 \leq i \leq 3\}, V, X_0, F_1)$$

where F_1 consists of all of the following productions:

(i) $X_0 \to X_1 P_0 X_1$, $X_1 \to \lambda$, $X_1 a \to X_1 X_2 a$ for all $a \in V$; $X_2 X_1 \to X_3 X_1$, $aX_3 \to X_3 a$ for all $a \in V$, $X_1 X_3 \to X_1$.
(ii) $X_2 a \to PX_2$ for all productions $a \to P$ in F.

Clearly, $L(G) = L(H)$; $L(G)$ is context-sensitive by Theorem 13.6 above and Theorem 10.1 in Part 1. ∎

We now introduce some generalizations of 0L-systems. We consider first the case where rewriting happens in a context-free manner.

In a T0L-system, the production set is divided into subsets, so-called *tables*. At each step of the rewriting process, only productions belonging to the same table can be used. The underlying biological motivation is that different sets of rules may be needed at different developmental stages.

Definition. A *T0L-system* is an ordered triple $H = (V, P_0, T)$ where V and P_0 are as in the definition of a 0L-system and T is a finite nonempty collection of finite subsets of $V \times W(V)$. Furthermore, each $t \in T$ satisfies the following *completeness* condition: For each $a \in V$, there is a $P \in W(V)$ such that t contains the pair (a, P).

A binary relation $\Rightarrow$ on the set $W(V)$ is defined as follows: $P \Rightarrow Q$ iff there exist an integer $k \geq 1$, letters $a_1, \ldots, a_k$, words $Q_1, \ldots, Q_k$, and an element $t \in T$ such that $P = a_1 \cdots a_k$, $Q = Q_1 \cdots Q_k$, and t contains the pair (a_i, Q_i) for each $i = 1, \ldots, k$. The *language generated* by the system is defined by

$$L(H) = \{P | P_0 \Rightarrow^* P\}$$

where $\Rightarrow^*$ is the reflexive transitive closure of $\Rightarrow$.

Example 13.3. Consider the T0L-system

$$H = (\{a\}, a, \{\{a \to a^2\}, \{a \to a^3\}\}).$$

Clearly, $L(H) = \{a^i | i = 2^m 3^n$ for some $m, n \geq 0\}$. Note that this is not a 0L-language. Note also that H is *deterministic* (each table is deterministic) and *propagating* (each table is propagating).

Clearly, 0L-systems are obtained from T0L-systems as the degenerate case where the set T contains exactly one element. Consequently, the family of 0L-languages is contained in the family of languages generated by T0L-systems. The previous example shows that this containment is proper. The same result holds true with respect to the corresponding deterministic families. It is easy to see that the families of 0L-languages and deterministic T0L-languages are incomparable. The nonclosure results we established for 0L-languages hold for T0L-languages as well.

One can extend Theorem 13.7 to concern T0L-languages. In fact, even the following stronger result can be obtained.

Proposition 13.2. Every λ-free language generated by a T0L-system is generated by a context-free λ-free programmed grammar.

One can still take a step further and introduce control devices for the use of tables, similar to the ones considered in Chapter V. For instance, an application of a table may determine which tables can be applied at the next step of the derivation. If the completeness of the tables is not assumed, a particular table need not be applicable to the word under scan. Thus we get *success* and *failure fields* as in Chapter V. Failure fields do not contribute anything to the generative capacity: Appearance checking can always be eliminated. The corresponding problem for grammars is open, as was pointed out in Chapter V.

We finally consider the case where rewriting is not context-free. From the biological point of view, this corresponds to the case where neighboring cells may communicate with each other.

Definition. A *2L-system* is an ordered quadruple $H = (V, P_0, a_0, F)$ where V and P_0 are as in the definition of a 0L-system, $a_0 \in V$ (so-called *input from the environment*), and F is a finite subset of $V \times V \times V \times W(V)$. Furthermore, for all letters $a, b, c \in V$ (not necessarily distinct), there is a word $P \in W(V)$ such that F contains the quadruple (a, b, c, P).

A binary relation $\Rightarrow$ on the set $W(V)$ is defined as follows: $P \Rightarrow Q$ holds iff there exist an integer $n \geq 1$, letters $a_1, \ldots, a_n$, and words $Q_1, \ldots, Q_n$ such that F contains the quadruples

$$(a_0, a_1, a_2, Q_1), \qquad (a_{n-1}, a_n, a_0, Q_n), \qquad (a_{i-1}, a_i, a_{i+1}, Q_i)$$

for $i = 2, ..., n-1$ and $P = a_1 \cdots a_n$, $Q = Q_1 \cdots Q_n$. [For $n = 1$, F contains the quadruple (a_0, a_1, a_0, Q_1).] The *language generated* by H is defined by

$$L(H) = \{P | P_0 \Rightarrow^* P\}$$

where $\Rightarrow^*$ is the reflexive transitive closure of $\Rightarrow$.

A 2L-system is a *1L-system* iff one of the following conditions holds: (i) for all a, b, c, d, P, the set F contains the quadruple (a, b, c, P) iff it contains the quadruple (a, b, d, P); or (ii) for all a, b, c, d, P, the set F contains the quadruple (a, b, c, P) iff it contains the quadruple (d, b, c, P).

A language is a *2L-language* (resp. *1L-language*) iff it is generated by a 2L-system (resp. 1L-system).

Thus, in a 0L-system the rewriting of a letter does not depend on its neighbors. In a 1L-system, it depends on one of the neighbors, and either always on the left one or always on the right one. In a 2L-system, the rewriting of a letter depends on both neighbors. The input from the environment serves the purpose of providing a neighbor for the first and the last letter.

By definition, every 0L-language is 1L, and every 1L-language is 2L. The following theorem shows that these inclusions are proper.

Theorem 13.8. There is a 1L-language which is not 0L. There is a 2L-language which is not 1L.

Proof. The language $L_1 = \{a, a^2\}$ is generated by the 1L-system

$$(\{a_0, a\}, a^2, a_0, F),$$

where F consists of the quadruples (a, a, x, λ), for $x = a, a_0$, and (x, y, z, y) for all x, y, z. Clearly, L_1 is not 0L. The language

$$L_2 = |a \cup a^2 \cup a^3 b^* \cup b^* a^3|$$

is generated by the 2L-system

$$(\{a_0, a, b\}, a, a_0, F),$$

where F is defined by the schema

$$(a_0, a, a_0) \rightarrow \{a^2, a^3, a^3 b, ba^3\},$$

$$(a_0, a, a) \rightarrow a^3,$$

$$(b, a, a) \rightarrow a^3,$$

$$(a, a, x) \rightarrow \lambda,$$

$$(x, b, y) \rightarrow \{b, b^2\}.$$

We have given the first three members of the quadruples to the left of the arrow, and the corresponding fourth members to the right of the arrow. Here x and y range over all letters of the alphabet. If a triple (x, y, z) has not been listed, F contains the quadruple (x, y, z, y).

We now prove that L_2 is not 1L. Assume the contrary. Since $\mathrm{mi}(L_2) = L_2$, we assume without loss of generality that the 1L-system H generating L_2 satisfies condition (i) of the definition. We denote the productions of H by

$$(x, y) \to P,$$

meaning that an occurrence of the letter y may be rewritten as the word P, provided the left neighbor of y (possibly the input a_0 from the environment) is x. We now claim that the following assertions (i)–(iv) are satisfied:

(i)   For some $k \geq 1$, $(b, b) \to b^k$ is one of the productions.

(ii)   For any production $(a_0, a) \to P$, the word P is of the form $P = aP_1$. Consequently, the axiom of H is of the form $b^u a^3$ where $u \geq 1$.

(iii)   For any production $(a, a) \to P$, we have $P = \lambda$, $P = a$, or $P = b^i$, $i \geq 1$.

(iv)   It is not the case that both $(a, a) \to \lambda$ and $(a, a) \to a$ are productions of H.

In the proof of these assertions, we apply the argument that whenever $P \in L_2$ and $P \Rightarrow_H P_1$, then also $P_1 \in L_2$.

To prove (i), we note first that if $(b, b) \to P$ is one of the productions in H, then $P = b^i$ for some $i \geq 0$. Otherwise, the word $a^3 b^5 \in L_2$ would yield directly a word with at least four occurrences of the letter a. But if $(b, b) \to \lambda$ is the only production with (b, b) on the left side, then H generates only a finite subset of L_2. Consequently, (i) follows.

The production $(a_0, a) \to \lambda$ does not belong to H because $a \in L_2$ and $\lambda \notin L_2$. If $(a_0, a) \to bP_1$ is one of the productions, then by (i) the word $a^3 b^2 \in L_2$ yields directly a word beginning and ending with b, and no such word belongs to L_2. Thus if $(a_0, a) \to P$ is one of the productions, then P begins with the letter a. This implies that no word beginning with b is generated by a word beginning with a, which proves (ii).

Assertion (iii) follows because if P is of any other form, then a^3 yields directly a word which is not in L_2. To prove (iv), assume the contrary. Then by (i), the word $b^2 a^3 \in L_2$ yields directly both of the words $P_1 b^k P_2$ and $P_1 b^k P_2 a^2$ for some words P_1, P_2 and $k \geq 1$. [Thus $(a_0, b) \to P_1$ and $(b, a) \to P_2$ are productions in H.] But there are no P_1 and P_2 such that both of these words belong to L_2.

We now consider productions with (a, a) on the left side, and show that a contradiction arises in each case. Assume first that $(a, a) \to b^i$, $i \geq 1$, is one of the productions. By (i), the word $b^2 a^3 \in L_2$ yields directly the word

$P_1 b^k P_2 b^{2i}$ for some words P_1, P_2 and $k \geq 1$; $P_1 b^k P_2 b^{2i} \in L_2$ only if $P_1 = a^3 b^j$ where $j \geq 0$. By (ii), no word which begins with b and is not the axiom belongs to $L(H)$. Thus H does not generate L_2. This contradiction shows that $(a, a) \to b^i$, $i \geq 1$, is not among the productions.

Assume next that $(a, a) \to a$ is one of the productions. By (iii), (iv), and the previous paragraph, it is the only production with (a, a) on the left side. Since now $a^3 b^2 \in L_2$ yields directly the word $P_1 a^2 P_2 b^k$, for some words P_1, P_2 and $k \geq 1$, we conclude by (ii) that $(a_0, a) \to a$ is the only production with (a_0, a) on the left side. Clearly, any word of the form $b^i a^3$, $i \geq 1$, yields directly only words of the same form or powers of a. By (ii), $L(H)$ contains no words of the form $a^3 b^i$, $i \geq 1$, which is a contradiction.

By (iii), we may now assume that $(a, a) \to \lambda$ is the only production with (a, a) on the left side. Since the word $b^2 a^3$ yields directly the word $P_1 b^k P_2$, for some words P_1, P_2 and $k \geq 1$, we conclude that one of the following alternatives (v) and (vi) must hold.

(v) All productions with (a_0, b) on the left side are of the form $(a_0, b) \to a^3 b^i$, $i \geq 0$, and all productions with (b, a) on the left side are of the form $(b, a) \to b^i$, $i \geq 0$.

(vi) All productions with (a_0, b) on the left side are of the form $(a_0, b) \to b^i$, $i \geq 0$, and all productions with (b, a) on the left side are of the form $(b, a) \to b^i a^3$, $i \geq 0$.

By (ii) we conclude that if (v) holds, then $L(H)$ contains only one word of the form $b^i a^3$, $i \geq 1$, which is impossible. Hence, (vi) holds. This implies that every word of the form $b^i a^3$, $i \geq 1$, yields directly a word of the form $b^j a^3$, $j \geq 0$. Furthermore, by (ii), some $b^i a^3$ yields a^3 directly. Since both $a \in L_2$ and $a^3 b \in L_2$, the system H must contain by (ii) both the production $(a_0, a) \to a$ and the production $(a_0, a) \to a^3 b^i$ for some $i \geq 1$. Using the latter production and (i), we see that $a^3 b^2$ yields directly the word $a^3 b^i P_1 b^k$ for some P_1 and $k \geq 1$. This implies that all productions with (a, b) on the left side are of the form $(a, b) \to b^j$, $j \geq 0$. But using the production $(a_0, a) \to a$, we see that $a^3 b^2$ generates the word ab^{j+k} for some $k \geq 1$. Thus we have derived a contradiction also in this case and conclude that L_2 is not 1L. ∎

If only languages over one letter are considered, then the families of 0L-, 1L-, and 2L-languages are almost identical, the only addition to generative capacity being due to the input from the environment. One can give an exact characterization for these language families and prove that there is an algorithm for deciding whether or not two 2L-systems generate the same language.

Note 13.1. Interesting aspects in the study of deterministic Lindenmayer systems are the *growth functions*, that is, functions showing the successive sizes of the organism throughout the development. The growth function $f(n)$ of a D0L-system (V, P_0, F) is defined by

$$f(n) = lg\big(h^n(P_0)\big), \qquad n \geq 0,$$

where h is the homomorphism defining the set F and $h^0(P_0) = P_0$. For instance, for the first D0L-system in Example 13.1, we have

$$f(n) = 2^n,$$

and for the last system,

$$f(n) = (n+1)^3.$$

For D1L- and D2L-systems, growth functions are defined accordingly. [Thus, $f(n)$ is always the length of the nth word generated from the axiom.] Two systems are *growth-equivalent* iff they have the same growth function.

If t is the length of the axiom and u the length of the longest right side among the productions, then $f(n) \leq tu^n$ for all n. This bound is valid for any deterministic Lindenmayer systems. The growth is termed *malignant* iff there is no polynomial $p(n)$ such that $f(n) \leq p(n)$ for all n.

Growth functions of D0L-systems are special cases of *sequential word functions*. If V_1 is an alphabet, then any function mapping $V_1{}^*$ into the set of real numbers is termed a *word function*. A word function f is termed *sequential* iff there is an integer $k \geq 1$, k-dimensional row and column vectors π and η, and k-dimensional square matrices $M(a)$, for each $a \in V_1$, such that for any $P \in V_1{}^*$,

$$f(P) = \pi M(P) \eta. \tag{13.20}$$

Here, by definition, $M(\lambda)$ is the identity matrix and $M(a_1 \cdots a_i) = M(a_1) \cdots M(a_i)$ if each $a_j \in V_1$. (Sequential word functions occupy a central position in the theory of probabilistic automata.) If V_1 consists of only one letter a, there is only one matrix M and (13.20) can be written in the form

$$f(n) = \pi M^n \eta. \tag{13.21}$$

[We have replaced in (13.21) a^n by n, which gives us a function from non-negative integers into reals.] Many classical results are applicable to functions of the form (13.21). In particular, each of the following three conditions is equivalent to a function f being representable in the form (13.21).

(i) There is an integer q and constants $\alpha_1, \ldots, \alpha_q$ such that for all $n > q$,

$$f(n) = \alpha_1 f(n-1) + \cdots + \alpha_q f(n-q). \tag{13.22}$$

(ii) The generating function of $f(n)$ is a rational function.
(iii) The infinite matrix whose jth row, $j \geq 1$, consists of the elements

$$f(1+j-1), f(2+j-1), f(3+j-1), \ldots$$

is of finite rank.

The growth function of a D0L-system (V, P_0, F) can be represented in the form (13.21) as follows. Let k be the number of letters in the alphabet V. The letters are assumed to be ordered so that we can speak of the ith letter, $i = 1, \ldots, k$. Let π be the k-dimensional row vector whose ith component equals the number of occurrences of the ith letter in the axiom P_0 for $i = 1, \ldots, k$. Let η be the k-dimensional column vector whose every component equals 1. Finally, let M be the k-dimensional square matrix whose (i, j)th entry equals the number of occurrences of the jth letter on the right side of the production whose left side equals the ith letter. For instance, for the last of the systems considered in Example 13.1, we obtain

$$
\pi = (1,0,0,0), \qquad M = \begin{pmatrix} 1 & 1 & 1 & 5 \\ 0 & 1 & 1 & 5 \\ 0 & 0 & 1 & 6 \\ 0 & 0 & 0 & 1 \end{pmatrix}, \qquad \eta = \begin{pmatrix} 1 \\ 1 \\ 1 \\ 1 \end{pmatrix}.
$$

It is easy to verify that (13.21) holds for π, M, and η thus defined. Consequently, the equivalent formulations (i)–(iii) become applicable. This gives algorithms for the solution of the growth-equivalence problem of two D0L-systems, as well as methods of transition from a D0L-system to its growth function, and vice versa.

It is easy to see (cf. Exercise 10) that there are D1L growth functions which are not D0L growth functions. It is an open problem whether or not the family of D2L growth functions properly includes the family of D1L growth functions. (Examples are known which show that proper inclusions among language families are not always preserved as regards the corresponding families of growth functions.) It is also not known whether or not the growth-equivalence of D1L-systems (or DP1L-systems) is decidable.

Note 13.2. The differences between Lindenmayer systems and grammars were pointed out at the beginning of Section 13: In Lindenmayer systems (i) rewriting happens in a parallel manner, (ii) there is only one alphabet, and (iii) there is an axiom instead of an initial letter. Here point (iii) is of minor importance. (Cf. Exercise 11 to Chapter I.) On the other hand, it is interesting to know what special properties of Lindenmayer systems are a consequence of (i) [resp. (ii)] only. If (ii) is not required (i.e., a special terminal alphabet is introduced), then we are dealing with the so-called *canonical extensions* of Lindenmayer systems. Of course, the generative capacity increases in this change. Any type-0 language is generated by a canonical extension of a 1L-system. However, canonical extensions of 0L-systems resist many closure operations.

Conversely, if (i) is not required but (ii) is required, then we are dealing with so-called *pure grammars*. Thus, a pure grammar (V, S_0, F) is defined exactly as a grammar except that there is only one alphabet V and the initial letter is replaced by a finite set S_0 of axioms, that is, words over V. The language *generated* by a pure grammar consists of all words P over V such that $X_0 \Rightarrow^* P$ where $X_0 \in S_0$. A language is *pure* iff it is generated by a pure grammar. Restrictions on the form of productions can be introduced also now and thus one can speak of context-free pure grammars.

For instance, the language $\{a^n b^n | n \geq 1\}$ is generated by the pure grammar $(\{a, b\}, \{ab\}, \{ab \rightarrow aabb\})$. A language over one letter is pure iff it is regular. Consequently, there are context-sensitive languages that are not pure. All regular languages are pure but there is a deterministic language which is not pure. Also the language $\{a^n b^n c^n | n \geq 1\}$ is not pure. The family of pure languages has similar nonclosure properties as L-systems.

14. TRANSFORMATIONAL, CATEGORIAL, INDEXED, SCATTERED CONTEXT, AND PROBABILISTIC GRAMMARS

We give in this section an overview of some classes of grammars without trying to develop the details of the formal theory.

Context-free grammars are in general too weak for the description of natural language and thus have to be replaced by a stronger concept like that of a *transformational grammar*. Indeed, transformational grammars have received considerable attention from linguists. Unfortunately, there is a lack of unanimity among linguists as regards many aspects of the theory. Basically, transformational grammars operate on derivation trees, and thus sets of trees are of prime importance as opposed to sets of words.

Consider the following two English sentences:

(i) The cat ate the mouse.
(ii) The mouse was eaten by the cat.

Using certain morphophonemic rules (of no concern to us in this context), sentences (i) and (ii) can be derived from the following forms, where $\#$ acts as a boundary marker:

(iii) $\#$ The cat P_{ast} eat the mouse $\#$
(iv) $\#$ The mouse P_{ast} be E_n eat by the cat $\#$

It is easy to construct a context-free grammar generating (iii). We could then choose additional productions to generate (iv) also. However, this would complicate the grammar considerably and would not indicate that (iii) is related to (iv). The additional productions could also produce sentences we do not want. Therefore, we introduce an operational rule of a different kind than a production, a so-called *transformation rule*. It operates on "structured" sentences to produce other structured sentences or, equivalently, it operates on trees to produce other trees.

Returning back to our example, we can say that a sentence of the form

$$\# \, N_p^1 T_{ns} \, V \, N_p^2 \, \# \tag{14.1}$$

is converted to the sentence

$$\# \, N_p^2 \, (T_{ns} \text{ be } E_n) \, V \text{ (by } N_p^1) \, \# \tag{14.2}$$

(Here N_p, T_{ns}, and V stand for "noun phrase," "tense," and "verb," respectively. The upper indices indicate that two, not necessarily distinct, noun phrases are involved.) In order to convert (14.1) to (14.2), we now introduce the following transformation rule. The rule consists of two parts, the *domain statement* and the *structural change statement*. The domain statement is (14.1) and the structural change statement,

$$1 - 5 - 3 \text{ be } E_n - 4 - \text{by } 2 - 6. \tag{14.3}$$

The number i, $1 \leq i \leq 6$, indicates the ith letter in (14.1). According to (14.3), the ith letter in (14.1) is replaced with the ith word separated by the dashes. Thus we obtain 14.2 (where the structure is indicated by parentheses). It is understood that (14.1) may be a part of a longer sentence. The scope of the application of the transformation rule is indicated by the boundary markers $\#$. The rule leaves the other parts of the (structured) sentence unchanged. The application of the rule is illustrated in Fig. 15. There A_{ux} stands for "verb auxiliary." The reader is encouraged to consider the corresponding context-free productions.

We have described a transformation rule of converting a sentence into a passive one. The general definition of a transformation rule is similar: The

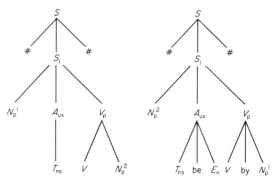

FIGURE 15

rule consists of two parts, the domain statement and the structural change statement. However, domain statements can be more complicated than in our example. In particular, a domain statement can be a Boolean combination of several words, one of which is designated as the object of the structural change statement. The structural change can be made iff the given tree "satisfies" the domain statement. For example, the tree in Fig. 16 satisfies the domain statement

$$(AB \wedge ACBB \wedge \sim ACB) \vee BB, \qquad (14.4)$$

because there is a "frontier" with nodes labeled by A and B, another frontier with nodes labeled by A, C, B, B, and no frontier with nodes labeled by A, C, B. The words in a domain statement may also contain empty spaces which may carry numbers, meaning that the empty spaces carrying the same number must be filled with identical structures. For example, the tree in Fig. 16 satisfies the domain statement

$$AC(\ )_1 C(\ )_2 \wedge ABC(\ )_2$$

but does not satisfy the statement

$$AC(\ )_1 C(\ )_1.$$

Finally, also the letters of the alphabet may be provided with indices. If two occurrences of a letter have the same index, then the trees whose roots are labeled by these occurrences must be identical. With this convention, our tree in Fig. 16 satisfies the domain statement

$$A_1 C_1 B_1 B_2 \wedge A_1 C_1 B_1 B_1 C_1 B_1 \qquad (14.5)$$

but does not satisfy the statement $A_1 C_1 B_1 B_1$.

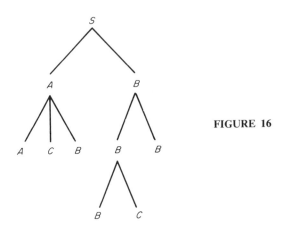

FIGURE 16

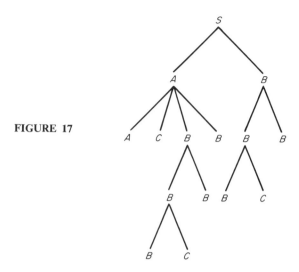

FIGURE 17

By definition, a transformational grammar consists of the following items: (i) a base of trees, (ii) a finite set of transformation rules, and (iii) a control device for the application of the transformation rules. The base of trees is simply a set of labeled trees, usually the set of generation trees of a context-free grammar. Transformation rules have been described above. We repeat that the structural change is made in the tree corresponding to the specified part of the domain statement. [For example, assume that in (14.5) this specified part is $A_1 C_1 B_1 B_2$, and that the structural change statement is $1-24-3-4$. Then the resulting tree is in Fig. 17.] The control device may be a partial order in the set of transformation rules, or a finite automaton guiding their application, or both.

When one considers the family of languages generated by transformational grammars, one can use results established in Section 11 of Part 1 according to which every type-0 language can be expressed in terms of regular and Dyck languages, and homomorphisms and intersections. This implies that every type-0 language L is generated by a transformational grammar whose base of trees is generated by a type-3 grammar and which does not even have any control device. (Furthermore, the transformation rules depend on the alphabet of L alone.) This assertion follows because Dyck languages and intersections are easily described in terms of domain statements, whereas homomorphisms are taken care of by structural change statements. (Note that the latter statements make erasing possible.) However, since transformational grammars operate on trees rather than words, their generative capacity is by no means the most important issue.

Another grammar of considerable linguistic importance is *categorial grammar*. It has two disjoint alphabets: terminal alphabet and the alphabet of *categories*. One or more words $\varphi(P)$ over the latter alphabet are assigned to each word P over the terminal alphabet. There are certain reduction rules for the words over the alphabet of categories. The word P is accepted iff one of the words $\varphi(P)$ can be reduced by these rules to a specified initial category X_0. Intuitively, these categories correspond to grammatical categories such as "noun phrase" or "article." The initial category corresponds to the grammatical category "sentence." Categorial grammars are recognition devices rather than generative devices.

Returning to our example sentence (i), we assign categories to the different items as follows:

$$\varphi(\text{the}) = A, \qquad \varphi(\text{cat}) = \varphi(\text{mouse}) = [A\backslash N_p], \qquad \varphi(\text{ate}) = [N_p\backslash[X_0/N_p]].$$

Thus, the whole sentence (i) is assigned the category

$$A[A\backslash N_p][N_p\backslash[X_0/N_p]]\, A[A\backslash N_p]. \tag{14.6}$$

We now introduce the following reduction rules which are valid for any α and β:

$$\alpha[\alpha\backslash\beta] \to \beta, \qquad [\alpha/\beta]\beta \to \alpha. \tag{14.7}$$

Using these rules, (14.6) is immediately reduced to X_0, and thus (i) is accepted.

Formally, a *categorial grammar* is an ordered quadruple $G = (C, V_T, X_0, \varphi)$ where the different items are defined as follows: C and V_T are disjoint alphabets, referred to as the set of *fundamental categories* and the *terminal* alphabet, respectively. Let $[,],\backslash,/$ be letters not in the alphabet $V_T \cup C$. A word P over the alphabet $C \cup \{[,],\backslash,/\}$ is a *category* iff one of the following conditions is satisfied:

(i) P is an element of C.
(ii) $P = [Q\backslash R]$ or $P = [Q/R]$ where Q and R are categories.

Returning to the definition of the remaining items of G, we require X_0 to be a category and φ a mapping of V_T into the collection of finite subsets of the set of categories. For $a \in V_T$, any element in $\varphi(a)$ is termed a *category assigned* to a. For a nonempty word P over V_T, any juxtaposition of categories assigned to the letters of P (without changing the order) is termed a category assigned to P. The word P is *accepted* by the grammar G iff there is a category $\varphi(P)$ assigned to P such that $\varphi(P) \Rightarrow^* X_0$. Here $\Rightarrow$ is the yield-relation of the rewriting system determined by the productions (14.7) where α and β are fundamental categories. All accepted words constitute the language accepted by G.

As an example consider the categorial grammar

$$G = (\{X_0, A\}, \{a, b\}, X_0, \varphi),$$

where

$$\varphi(a) = \{A, [A/X_0]\}, \qquad \varphi(b) = \{[A\backslash X_0]\}.$$

It is easy to verify that the language accepted by G equals $\{a^n b^n | n \geq 1\}$.

The productions (14.7) can be considered as productions in an analytic context-free grammar. Thus it is obvious that every language accepted by a categorial grammar is context-free. One can also prove the converse: Every λ-free context-free language is accepted by a categorial grammar.

The categorial grammars considered above are *bidirectional* in the sense that both left and right "quotients" (i.e., both $\backslash$ and $/$) are allowed in (14.7) and in (ii) of the definition. One can consider also *unidirectional* categorial grammars, that is, only one of the quotients is allowed. The family of acceptable languages still equals the family of λ-free context-free languages.

In the remaining types of grammars considered in this section, the core productions are context-free, but there are some restrictions on the use of productions. However, the restrictions are somewhat different from those considered in Chapter V, and cannot be conveniently expressed in terms of a control language. Consequently, very little is known about the size of the resulting language families and inclusion relations, for instance, with the families $\mathcal{M}$ and $\mathcal{M}_{ac}$.

An *indexed grammar* is an ordered quintuple $G = (V_N, V_T, X_0, F, E)$, where V_N, V_T, and X_0 are as in an ordinary grammar and F and E are finite sets of *productions* and *indices* or *flags*, respectively. The flags in E are finite sets of *index productions* of the form $X \to P$ where $X \in V_N$ and $P \in W(V)$, $V = V_N \cup V_T$. The productions in F are of the form

$$X \to P, \qquad X \in V_N, \quad P \in (V_N E^* \cup V_T)^*.$$

Thus, nonterminals in a word can be followed by arbitrary lists of flags. If a nonterminal, with flags following, is replaced in a derivation by one or more nonterminals, the flags follow each of the new nonterminals. If a nonterminal is replaced by terminals, the flags disappear. If a nonterminal X is followed by the sequence of flags $e_1 e_2 \cdots e_n$, and e_1 includes an index production of the form $X \to P$ we can replace X by P and follow each nonterminal of P by the sequence $e_2 \cdots e_n$. In this way, the flags can be "consumed."

Formally, a binary yield-relation $\Rightarrow$ on the set $(V_N E^* \cup V_T)^*$ is defined as follows: $P \Rightarrow Q$ iff either

(i) $P = P_1 X \alpha P_2$, where $P_1, P_2 \in (V_N E^* \cup V_T)^*$, $X \in V_N$, and $\alpha \in E^*$; $X \to X_1 \beta_1 \cdots X_n \beta_n$, $X_i \in V$, $\beta_i \in E^*$, is a production in F; and $Q = P_1 X_1 \gamma_1 \cdots X_n \gamma_n P_2$, where $\gamma_i = \beta_i \alpha$ if $X_i \in V_N$, and $\gamma_i = \lambda$ if $X_i \in V_T$ for $i = 1, \ldots, n$ (or $X \to \lambda$ is in F and $Q = P_1 P_2$); or else

(ii) $P = P_1 X e \alpha P_2$, where P_1, P_2, X, α are as in (i) and $e \in E$; $X \to X_1 \cdots X_n$ is an index production in the index e; and $Q = P_1 X_1 \gamma_1 \cdots X_n \gamma_n P_2$, where $\gamma_i = \alpha$ if $X_i \in V_N$, and $\gamma_i = \lambda$ if $X_i \in V_T$ for $i = 1, \ldots, n$.

Let $\Rightarrow^*$ be the reflexive transitive closure of the relation $\Rightarrow$. The *language generated* by the indexed grammar G is defined by

$$L(G) = \{P \in W(V_T) | X_0 \Rightarrow^* P\}.$$

As illustrations, consider the indexed grammars

$$G_1 = (\{X_0, X, Y\}, \{a, b, c\}, X_0, F_1, \{e_1, e_2\}),$$

$$G_2 = (\{X_0, X_1, X, Y, Z\}, \{a, b\}, X_0, F_2, \{e_3, e_4\}),$$

where F_1 consists of the productions $X_0 \to a X e_1 c$, $X \to a X e_2 c$, and $X \to Y$; F_2 consists of the productions $X_0 \to X_1 e_3$, $X_1 \to X_1 e_4$, and $X_1 \to XYX$; and

$$e_1 = \{Y \to b\}, \qquad\qquad e_2 = \{Y \to bY\},$$

$$e_3 = \{X \to a, \; Y \to b, \; Z \to b\}, \qquad e_4 = \{X \to aX, \; Y \to bYZZ, \; Z \to bZ\}.$$

It is easy to verify that

$$L(G_1) = \{a^n b^n c^n | n \geq 1\}, \qquad L(G_2) = \{a^n b^{n^2} a^n | n \geq 1\}.$$

Just as in the case of ordinary context-free grammars, generation trees can be used to describe derivations according to an indexed grammar. The node labels are of the form $X\alpha$ where $X \in V_N \cup V_T \cup \{\lambda\}$ and $\alpha \in E^*$. The derivation of $a^2 b^2 c^2$ according to the grammar G_1 is illustrated in Fig. 18.

Every indexed grammar can be reduced to an equivalent grammar in a "normal form," that is, an indexed grammar where all index productions are of the form $X \to Y$, and all productions in F are of one of the forms

$$X \to YZ, \qquad X \to Ye, \qquad X \to a,$$

where $X, Y, Z \in V_N$, $e \in E$, and $a \in V_T \cup \{\lambda\}$. Furthermore, the productions $X \to \lambda$ can be eliminated similarly as from context-free grammars, after which λ does not appear on the right side of any production other than (possibly) $X_0 \to \lambda$. If $X_0 \to \lambda$ is among the productions, then X_0 does not appear on the right side of any production.

The family $\mathcal{K}$ of languages generated by indexed grammars is a full AFL which is closed under substitution and mirror image but not under inter-

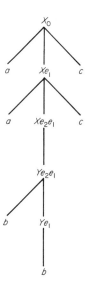

FIGURE 18

section or complement. By definition, the family $\mathcal{K}$ contains the family $\mathcal{L}_2$ of context-free languages. The examples given above show that the containment is proper. It can also be shown that $\mathcal{K}$ is included in $\mathcal{L}_1$. Since $\mathcal{K}$ is closed under homomorphism, this inclusion must also be a proper one. There is an algorithm for deciding whether or not the language generated by a given indexed grammar is empty. Certain subfamilies of $\mathcal{K}$ are also of interest. The family obtained by considering only right-linear productions and index productions equals the family $\mathcal{L}_2$.

In a context-sensitive grammar, there usually are "messengers" to transmit information back and forth through the word. In a *scattered context grammar*, it is possible to transmit information between widely separated parts of a word without sending nonterminals back and forth. Rewriting depends on context but a letter can be rewritten even if the context is not adjacent to the letter.

Formally, a *scattered context grammar* is an ordered quadruple $G = (V_N, V_T, X_0, F)$ where V_N, V_T, and X_0 are as in an ordinary grammar but the productions in F are of the form

$$(X_1, ..., X_n) \rightarrow (Q_1, ..., Q_n), \qquad n \geqq 1, \quad X_i \in V_N, \quad Q_i \in V^+. \qquad (14.8)$$

The binary yield-relation $\Rightarrow$ on $W(V)$ is now defined as follows: $P \Rightarrow Q$ holds iff there is a production (14.8) such that for some words $P_1, ..., P_{n+1}$,

$$P = P_1 X_1 P_2 \cdots P_n X_n P_{n+1}, \qquad Q = P_1 Q_1 P_2 \cdots P_n Q_n P_{n+1}. \qquad (14.9)$$

The *language generated* by G is defined by

$$L(G) = \{P \in W(V_T) | X_0 \Rightarrow^* P\} \qquad (14.10)$$

where again $\Rightarrow^*$ is the reflexive transitive closure of $\Rightarrow$. Languages of the form (14.10) are referred to as *scattered context languages*.

It is an immediate consequence of the definition that the family $\mathscr{SCL}$ of scattered context languages contains all λ-free context-free languages. The scattered context grammar determined by the productions

$$(X_0) \to (ABC), \qquad (A, B, C) \to (aA, bB, cC), \qquad (A, B, C) \to (a, b, c)$$

generates the language $\{a^n b^n c^n | n \geq 1\}$. Hence, there are non-context-free languages in $\mathscr{SCL}$. On the other hand, it is easy to prove by the workspace theorem that every language in $\mathscr{SCL}$ is context-sensitive. It is an open problem whether or not there are λ-free context-sensitive languages which are not scattered context.

Every scattered context grammar can be reduced to a "2-limited" form such that each production (14.8) satisfies the conditions $n \geq 2$ and $lg(Q_i) \leq 2$ for all Q_i. The family $\mathscr{SCL}$ is an AFL which is closed under mirror image, intersection, λ-free substitution, and linear erasing. It is not closed under arbitrary homomorphism. (Otherwise, Section 11 in Part 1 would imply the equation $\mathscr{SCL} = \mathscr{L}_0$.)

In an *unordered scattered context grammar*, the production (14.8) can be applied by simultaneously rewriting X_i as Q_i, $i = 1, ..., n$, no matter in what order the nonterminals X_i appear in the word under scan. [Thus, in the definition of the yield-relation, (14.9) is replaced by

$$P = P_1 X_{p(1)} P_2 \cdots P_n X_{p(n)} P_{n+1}, \qquad Q = P_1 Q_{p(1)} P_2 \cdots P_n Q_{p(n)} P_{n+1},$$

where p is an arbitrary permutation of the numbers $1, ..., n$.] The family $\mathscr{USCL}$ of languages generated by unordered scattered context grammars is included in the family $\mathscr{SCL}$. This follows because, for any unordered scattered context grammar G, there is an equivalent scattered context grammar G_1. This G_1 is obtained from G by replacing every production (14.8) with the set of productions

$$(X_{p(1)}, ..., X_{p(n)}) \to (Q_{p(1)}, ..., Q_{p(n)}),$$

where p runs through all permutations of the numbers $1, ..., n$. It is an open problem whether or not the inclusion $\mathscr{USCL} \subseteq \mathscr{SCL}$ is proper. On the other hand, it is easy to prove, using the techniques developed in Section 6, that

$$\mathscr{USCL} = \mathscr{M} = \mathscr{L}(2 - \lambda, 3, 0).$$

Hence, the family $\mathscr{USCL}$ properly includes the family of λ-free context-free languages and is properly included in the family of λ-free context-sensitive languages.

In a *probabilistic grammar*, each production is assigned a probability. This can be done in two essentially different ways. One may require that the sum of the probabilities, assigned for productions with the same left side, equals 1. Another possibility is to consider the core grammar to be a programmed one, and assign each production f a stochastic vector $v(f)$. The components of $v(f)$ indicate the probabilities of the different productions being applied *after* an application of f.

When probabilities have been assigned to the productions of a grammar G (in one of the ways described briefly above), one may compute for each word $P \in L(G)$ the probability $p(P)$ of P being generated by G. This is done by summing up the probabilities of different derivations of P. The *language generated* by G can now be defined in three different ways. One may simply consider pairs $(P, p(P))$ with $P \in L(G)$, and study grammar transformations (such as the transition to Chomsky or Greibach normal form) which leave the set of such pairs invariant. Another possibility is to choose a *cut-point η* satisfying $0 \leq \eta < 1$ and consider the language $L(G, \eta)$ consisting of words $P \in L(G)$ with $p(P) > \eta$.

As an illustration, consider the (context-free) probabilistic grammar G defined by the schema

$$f_1 : X_0 \rightarrow XZ \qquad (0, \tfrac{1}{2}, 0, \tfrac{1}{2}, 0),$$
$$f_2 : X \ \ \rightarrow aXb \qquad (0, 0, 1, 0, 0),$$
$$f_3 : Z \ \ \rightarrow cZ \qquad (0, \tfrac{1}{2}, 0, \tfrac{1}{2}, 0),$$
$$f_4 : X \ \ \rightarrow ab \qquad (0, 0, 0, 0, 1),$$
$$f_5 : Z \ \ \rightarrow c \qquad (0, 0, 0, 0, 1).$$

The stochastic vectors indicating the probabilities are given together with each production. Thus the probability of f_2 being applied after an application of f_3 equals $\tfrac{1}{2}$. Clearly, $L(G, 0) = \{a^n b^n c^n | n \geq 1\}$.

The third possibility of defining the language generated by G is to choose a cut-point and consider the collection of all words $P \in L(G)$ possessing at least one derivation whose probability is greater than the cut-point. For both of these cut-point interpretations, as well as the interpretation dealing with pairs $(P, p(P))$, one can obtain similar interrelations between probabilistic grammars and probabilistic automata as were obtained in Chapter I between ordinary grammars and automata.

EXERCISES

1. Prove that the language denoted by the regular expression $a^3 \cup a^2(a^2)^*$ is not 0L.

2. Give an algorithm for determining the set M in the proof of Theorem 13.2.

3. Prove that the languages denoted by the regular expressions $b^*a^3 \cup a^3b^*$ and $a \cup a^2 \cup b^*a^3$ are 1L.

4. Prove that the family of (i) D0L-languages, (ii) DP0L-languages is an anti-AFL.

5. Define $L = \{a^{2^i}|i \geqq 0\}$ and the homomorphism h by $h(a) = a$, $h(b) = \lambda$. Show that $h^{-1}(L)$ is not of the form $L_1 \cap W(V_T)$ where L_1 is a 0L-language. [This fact has been used by Herman (1971) to exhibit 2^8 families of languages, none of which is an AFL.]

6. Prove that there is a pure grammar which generates a nonrecursive language. Use this fact to prove that there are 1L-languages which are not recursive. Prove also that the family of languages generated by propagating (i.e., λ-free) 2L-systems is properly included in the family of context-sensitive languages.

7. Determine the growth function of the DP0L-system with the axiom a and productions $a \to b^2$, $b \to a^5$. Is the growth malignant?

8. Show that the two DP0L-systems with the axiom a and productions

   (i) $a \to acde$, $b \to cde$, $c \to bbdd$, $d \to ddd$, $e \to bd$;
   (ii) $a \to abbb$, $b \to bbb$

are growth-equivalent.

9. Construct a DP0L-system with the growth function $(n+1)^4$.

10. Use the characterization (13.22) to give an example of a D1L-growth function which is not the growth function of any D0L-system. [Use the context-sensitivity in such a way that growth can only take place after a messenger has traveled through the word. Then the longer the word grows, the longer it takes the messenger to get through. Consequently, the growth function will have arbitrarily long constant intervals without becoming ultimately constant. No function of the form (13.22) can have these two properties.]

11. Using the workspace theorem, prove that the family of languages generated by indexed grammars is proeprly included in the family of context-sensitive languages.

12. Construct a categorial grammar for the language of arithmetical expressions defined in Exercise 15 of Chapter VI.

BIBLIOGRAPHICAL REMARKS

Lindenmayer systems were introduced by Lindenmayer (1968). Example 13.2 is also due to him. Herman (1971) shows the resistance of L-systems against closure operations. The results concerning languages over one letter are due to Herman *et al.* (1972). Theorem 13.7 was established (by a different method) by Rozenberg and Doucet (1971), whereas van Leeuwen (1972) is a general study concerning 0L-languages. Systems with tables are due to Rozenberg (1971a). Restricted use of productions was considered by Rozenberg (1971b) and context-dependent systems by Rozenberg (1971c). For growth functions, see Szilard (1971) and Paz and Salomaa (1972) and, for pure grammars, Gabrielian (1970). The computing capacity of canonical extensions was established by Herman (1969). For transformational grammars, see Ginsburg and Partee (1969). They also give references to the broad underlying field of linguistical problems. The generative capacity was discussed by Salomaa (1971). A more recent paper is by Peters and Ritchie (1971). Categorial grammars were introduced by Bar-Hillel *et al.* (1960). Beletskij (1969) shows an interconnection with another type of grammar. Scattered context grammars are due to Greibach and Hopcroft (1969). See also Král (1969). Indexed grammars belong to Aho (1968). For probabilistic grammars, see Fu and Huang (1971) and Salomaa (1969).

BIBLIOGRAPHY

A. Aho. Indexed grammars—An extension of context-free grammars. *J. Assoc. Comput. Mach.* **15** (1968) 647–671.

Y. Bar-Hillel, C. Gaifman, and **E. Shamir.** On categorial and phrase-structure grammars. *Bull. Res. Council Israel* **9F** (1960) 1–16.

M. Beletskij. O svjazi mezhdu kategorialnymi i dominatsionnymi grammatikami. *Kibernetika* **4** (1969) 129–135.

K. S. Fu and **T. Huang.** Stochastic grammars and languages. Purdue Univ., School of Elec. Eng. Rep. TR-EE 71–23 (1971).

A. Gabrielian. Pure grammars and pure languages. Univ. of Waterloo, Dept. of Appl. Anal. and Comput. Sci. Res. Rep. CSRR 2027 (1970).

S. Ginsburg and **B. Partee.** A mathematical model of transformational grammars. *Information Control* **15** (1969) 297–334.

S. Greibach and **J. Hopcroft.** Scattered context grammars. *J. Comput. System Sci.* **3** (1969) 233–247.

G. Herman. The computing ability of a developmental model for filamentous organisms. *J. Theoret. Biol.* **25** (1969) 421–424.

G. Herman. Closure properties of some families of languages associated with biological systems. State Univ. of New York at Buffalo, Dept. of Comput. Sci. Rep. 7-71 (1971).

G. Herman, K. Lee, J. van Leeuwen, and **G. Rozenberg.** Unary Developmental Systems and Languages. Manuscript (1972).

J. Král. On multiple grammars. *Kybernetika* **1** (1969) 60–85.

A. Lindenmayer. Mathematical models for cellular interactions in development, parts I–II. *J. Theoret. Biol.* **18** (1968) 280–315.

A. Paz and **A. Salomaa.** Integral sequential word functions and growth equivalence of Lindenmayer systems. *Information Control* (1972) (to appear).

P. S. Peters, Jr. and **R. Ritchie.** On restricting the base component of transformational grammars. *Information Control* **18** (1971) 483–501.

G. Rozenberg. T0L-systems and languages. ERCU Publicaties (Utrecht) no. 103 (1971a).

G. Rozenberg. On 0L-systems with restricted use of productions. ERCU Publicaties (Utrecht) no. 116 (1971b).

G. Rozenberg. L-systems with interactions. ERCU Publicaties (Utrecht) no. 120 (1971c).

G. Rozenberg and **P. Doucet.** On 0L-languages. *Information Control* **19** (1971) 302–318.

A. Salomaa. Probabilistic and weighted grammars. *Information Control* **15** (1969) 529–544.

A. Salomaa. The generative capacity of transformational grammars of Ginsburg and Partee. *Information Control* **18** (1971) 227–232.

A. Szilard. Growth Functions of Lindenmayer Systems. Manuscript (1971).

J. van Leeuwen. 0L-Languages. Manuscript (1972).

PART THREE

Chapter VIII

Solvability and Unsolvability

The final part of this book is devoted to the study of two problems. What questions concerning languages and language families can be solved mechanically? Are some questions intrinsically more difficult to solve than some others? The present chapter deals with the former problem. We first summarize some results about the existence of algorithms which we have obtained in earlier chapters, and establish some simple unsolvability results. Then a more sophisticated tool, the unsolvability of the Post correspondence problem, is introduced and consequently a variety of unsolvability results is obtained. Finally, the attention is focused on context-free languages and an important solvability result is established.

1. EXISTENCE OF ALGORITHMS

We have in this book considered many times a certain specific problem dealing with languages and given an effective procedure for the solution of the problem. A typical example is the problem: Is a given context-free language infinite? ("Given" is of course understood in terms of a grammar.) A solution to this problem is obtained by Theorem 6.5 in Part 1. This theorem gives an effective procedure which is applicable for any context-free grammar G and whose output is "yes" if $L(G)$ is infinite, and "no" if $L(G)$ is finite. (The notion of an effective procedure was discussed in Part 1, Section 9. Some authors make a distinction between an algorithm and an effective procedure: An algorithm is an effective procedure which always terminates. Thus an effective procedure for listing the words in an infinite language is not an algorithm. We do not make this distinction but use the words as synonyms. Similarly, we use the words "decidability" and "solvability" synonymously.)

In this chapter we intend to make a systematic study of the existence of algorithms for solving problems dealing with languages. We are not going to formalize the notion of a problem. In fact, such a formalization is not necessary because we do not prove any results about solvability of problems in general. The problems such as the one mentioned above consist of an infinity of instances, to each of which the answer is either yes or no. A problem is *solvable* iff there is an algorithm which for any instance of the problem outputs the answer for that instance. The solvability can be shown without formalizing the notion of an effective procedure, whereas such a formalization is necessary for establishing unsolvability results.

Consider a class M of devices for defining languages. Such an M might consist of all grammars of some type, or of all automata of some kind, or, finally, of all property-specifying devices of some specific nature, such as regular expressions. By the *equivalence problem* for M we understand the problem of determining of any two devices m_1 and m_2 in M whether or not they define the same language. In the *inclusion problem* for M one has to determine of arbitrary m_1 and m_2 in M whether or not the language defined by m_1 is included in the language defined by m_2. Clearly, a solution for the inclusion problem yields a solution for the equivalence problem. By the *emptiness* (resp. *infinity*) *problem* for M we understand the problem of determining for an arbitrary device $m \in M$ whether or not the language defined by m is empty (resp. infinite). The *membership problem* for M consists of deciding for an arbitrary $m \in M$ and for an arbitrary word P whether or not P belongs to the language defined by m. (In all cases we have considered, m determines an alphabet V. It may be assumed that P is a word over V.)

Using the terminology now introduced, Theorem 6.5 in Part 1 shows that the infinity problem for context-free grammars is solvable. The problems mentioned above are the most important ones among the problems we are going to consider. However, some other problems are discussed also. Assume that the family $\mathscr{L}(M)$ of languages definable by the devices in M is not closed under some operation ω. Then we may consider the problem of whether ω applied to some languages in $\mathscr{L}(M)$ yields a language in $\mathscr{L}(M)$. The devices in M may also give syntactic descriptions for words in the languages in $\mathscr{L}(M)$, and thus the notion of ambiguity may be introduced. Then another problem is to decide whether or not a given $m \in M$ is ambiguous. The problem of deciding inherent ambiguity is derived from this problem in an obvious fashion. One may also consider special cases of all of these problems. A special case of the equivalence problem is to choose some language L from $\mathscr{L}(M)$ and ask regarding an arbitrary device $m \in M$ whether or not m defines the language L. In what follows, we often speak of problems for $\mathscr{L}(M)$ rather than problems for M.

Many solvability results have already been presented in this book. (In fact, since the proofs are constructive, almost every theorem can be viewed as a solvability result.) Considering the basic hierarchy, it is obvious that if a problem is solvable for $\mathscr{L}_i$, it is also solvable for $\mathscr{L}_j$ with $j > i$, and if a problem is unsolvable for $\mathscr{L}_i$, it is also unsolvable for $\mathscr{L}_j$ with $j < i$. Obviously, an analogous statement can be made about any hierarchy of language families.

Membership problem for type-1 grammars is solvable according to Theorem 9.1 in Part 1. So are the emptiness and infinity problems for type-2 grammars as shown in Part 1, Section 6. Also the equivalence problem is solvable for type-3 grammars, as is obvious by the basic results concerning type-3 grammars. [In fact, $L_1 = L_2$ iff $(L_1 - L_2) \cup (L_2 - L_1) = L_3$ is empty. Given type-3 grammars for L_1 and L_2, a type-3 grammar G_3 for L_3 can be constructed. The emptiness of $L(G_3)$ can be decided since G_3 is context-free.] The algorithm for the solution of the infinity problem is simpler for type-3 than for type-2 grammars (cf. Exercise 1). As an example of a solvability result of a different nature we would like to mention Theorem 12.2 in Part 2.

Loosely speaking, one can say that all problems for type-3 grammars are solvable. By this we mean that no unsolvability results are known for type-3 grammars, although there are some unsettled questions like the star height problem. As we will see, many problems for type-2 grammars are unsolvable and so are most problems for type-1 grammars. All problems for type-0 grammars are unsolvable. (This statement can be expressed as a formal theorem.)

After giving an overview of some simple solvability results, we now turn to the discussion of unsolvability. For this discussion, the notion of an effective procedure has to be formalized. The natural formalization is a Turing machine. Thus, unsolvability of a problem means that there is no Turing machine which "solves" the problem. (Roughly speaking, this means that the machine, when given an instance of the problem in a suitably encoded form, prints out the answer to that instance.) This definition is in accordance with Church's thesis. Also the subsequent proofs of unsolvability make use of Church's thesis which is often, in the sequel, understood in the wider sense: Every effective procedure can be carried out by a Turing machine.

By definition, the family of recursive languages is the largest family of languages for which the membership problem is solvable. Thus, by Theorem 9.6 in Part 1 and by the fact that the family of recursively enumerable languages equals the family of type-0 languages, we obtain our first result.

Theorem 1.1. Membership problem is unsolvable for type-0 grammars.

It follows by the proof of Theorem 9.6 in Part 1 that Theorem 1.1 is valid, even if the membership problem is restricted for type-0 grammars with a fixed terminal alphabet V_T, that is, there is no algorithm for deciding for a given type-0 grammar G with the terminal alphabet V_T and a word P over V_T whether or not P belongs to $L(G)$. It is to be emphasized that Theorem 1.1 excludes the existence of one Turing machine which would solve all instances of the problem. Of course, for many instances (even for infinite collections of them) a machine can be constructed.

Theorem 1.2. The emptiness problem is unsolvable for type-0 grammars.

Proof. Assume the contrary. We will indicate an algorithm for solving the membership problem of type-0 grammars which contradicts Theorem 1.1. Let $G = (V_N, V_T, X_0, F)$ be an arbitrary type-0 grammar and $P \in W(V_T)$ an arbitrary word. Consider the grammar

$$G_1 = (V_N \cup \{Y_0, \#\}, V_T, Y_0, F \cup \{Y_0 \to \#X_0\#, \#P\# \to \lambda\}).$$

By our assumption, we may decide whether or not $L(G_1)$ is empty. [Note that $L(G_1)$ either is empty or consists of the empty word.] But $L(G_1)$ is nonempty exactly in case $P \in L(G)$. ∎

Using Theorem 1.2, problems can be shown unsolvable for type-0 grammars. Since the empty language is type 0, the equivalence problem for type-0 grammars is unsolvable. So is the infinity problem: For any grammar G, it is easy to construct a grammar G_1 such that $L(G)$ is nonempty iff $L(G_1)$ is infinite. Thus a solution for the infinity problem would give a solution for the emptiness problem. By a similar argument, the following problem is also unsolvable for any word P: deciding for a given type-0 grammar G whether or not P occurs as a subword of some word in $L(G)$. In fact, all problems can be reduced in this fashion to the emptiness problem. Consider any nontrivial property T of type-0 languages. (T being nontrivial means that there is a type-0 language with the property T and there is a type-0 language which does not possess T.) Then it is unsolvable for type-0 grammars G whether or not $L(G)$ possesses T.

Theorem 1.2 can be used to obtain unsolvability results also in a different way. Consider Theorem 9.9 in Part 1. Clearly, the type-1 language L_1 constructed in the theorem is empty iff the given type-0 language L is empty. Hence, a solution for the emptiness problem of type-1 grammars would give a solution for the emptiness problem of type-0 grammars. Thus we obtain our next result.

Theorem 1.3. The emptiness problem is unsolvable for type-1 grammars.

The emptiness problem remains unsolvable even if only type-1 grammars with a fixed terminal alphabet are considered. The reason for this was pointed out above: The essential tool, Theorem 9.6 in Part 1, holds for languages over one letter.

Since the homomorphic image of a language L is empty iff L is empty, Theorems 11.1 and 11.4 in Part 1 and Theorem 1.2 above yield the following.

Theorem 1.4. There is no algorithm of deciding whether or not the intersection of two context-free languages is empty. There are two context-free languages L_1' and L_2' such that there is no algorithm for deciding for an arbitrary regular language K whether or not the intersection $L_1' \cap L_2' \cap K$ is empty.

In some sense, the second sentence of Theorem 1.4 can be considered as an unsolvability result for type-3 languages since K is the only variable. However, one can say that it is not a problem dealing "properly" with type-3 languages.

Note 1.1. Theorem 1.1 is the basic tool in establishing unsolvability results. Our proof of Theorem 1.1 was based on Theorem 9.6 in Part 1 and on Church's thesis. Another proof is briefly outlined in this note. As pointed out in Note 12.1 of Part 1, a Turing machine TM is completely determined by a word P_{TM} obtained by writing the productions one after the other, separated by some boundary marker. Let us call a Turing machine TM *self-applicable* iff TM halts with the word P_{TM}. By the *self-applicability problem* we mean the problem of deciding whether or not an arbitrary Turing machine is self-applicable. We claim that the self-applicability problem is unsolvable. Assume the contrary: There is a Turing machine TM_0 which halts in the state s^+ (resp. s^-) for all inputs P_{TM} where TM is a Turing machine which is (resp. is not) self-applicable. The following modified machine TM_1 can easily be obtained from TM_0. If TM is self-applicable, then TM_1 does not halt with P_{TM}. If TM is not self-applicable, then TM_1 behaves with the input P_{TM} exactly as TM_0, that is, halts in the state s^-. (Thus, in the transition from TM_0 to TM_1, one has to add a loop starting from s^+.) Then TM_1 halts with P_{TM_1} iff TM_1 does not halt with P_{TM_1}. This contradiction shows that our claim is correct.

The *halting problem* consists of deciding for an arbitrary Turing machine TM and a word P whether or not TM halts with the input P. Since the self-applicability problem is a special case, we conclude that the halting problem is unsolvable. Given a Turing machine TM, it is easy to construct a Turing machine TM_1 such that TM_1 accepts exactly those words for which TM halts. By Theorem 4.4 in Part 1, we may construct a type-0 grammar G for the language $L(\text{TM}_1)$. Hence, $P \in L(G)$ iff TM halts with P. This implies that if we can solve the membership problem for type-0 grammars, we can also solve the halting problem, which in fact we cannot do. Thus, we have a proof of Theorem 1.1 which does not use Church's thesis.

Note 1.2. Among the classical mathematical problems, the unsolvability of *Hilbert's tenth problem* has been recently established. Since the problem is also of some interest from the point of view of formal languages, we discuss it briefly here.

Consider equations of the form

$$U(x_1, \ldots, x_n) = 0 \tag{1.1}$$

where U is a polynomial in the variables $x_1, \ldots, x_n$ with integer coefficients. Hilbert's tenth problem consists of deciding whether or not an arbitrary equation (1.1) has a solution in nonnegative integers. [In the original formulation of the problem, arbitrary integer solutions were considered. Because every nonnegative integer is a sum of four squares, the equation (1.1) has a solution in nonnegative integers iff the equation

$$U(p_1{}^2 + q_1{}^2 + r_1{}^2 + s_1{}^2, \ldots, p_n{}^2 + q_n{}^2 + r_n{}^2 + s_n{}^2) = 0$$

has an integral solution. On the other hand, (1.1) has a solution in integers iff the equation

$$U(p_1 - q_1, \ldots, p_n - q_n) = 0$$

has a solution in nonnegative integers. Thus a solution of the problem in the original formulation gives a solution of the problem in our formulation, and vice versa.]

Consider predicates $T(x_1, \ldots, x_n)$ with variables ranging over nonnegative integers. Such a predicate is termed *diophantine* iff there exists a polynomial $U_T(x_1, \ldots, x_n, y_1, \ldots, y_k)$ with integer coefficients such that, for any $x_1, \ldots, x_n$, $T(x_1, \ldots, x_n)$ is true exactly in case

$$U_T(x_1, \ldots, x_n, y_1, \ldots, y_k) = 0$$

for some nonnegative integers $y_1, \ldots, y_k$.

It can be shown that every recursively enumerable predicate is diophantine. This implies (when the universal Turing machine is considered) the existence of a polynomial $U_0(z, x_1, \ldots, x_n, y)$ with integer coefficients such that the following condition is satisfied. For every recursively enumerable set S of nonnegative integers, one can determine a nonnegative integer z_S such that S equals the set of numbers y_0 that satisfy

$$U_0(z_S, x_1, \ldots, x_n, y_0) = 0 \tag{1.2}$$

for some nonnegative integers $x_1, ..., x_n$. One can interpret this result as follows from the point of view of formal languages by considering the m-adic encoding φ. For any type-0 language S, one can determine a nonnegative integer z_S such that $\varphi(S)$ (i.e., the set of codes of the words in S) equals the set of numbers y_0 for which the equation (1.2) has a solution in nonnegative integers $x_1, ..., x_n$. Consequently, there is no algorithm for deciding whether or not the equation

$$U_0(z, x_1, ..., x_n, y) = 0, \qquad (1.3)$$

where z is an arbitrary but fixed nonnegative integer, has a solution in nonnegative integers $x_1, ..., x_n, y$. This follows because such an algorithm would give a solution of the emptiness problem for type-0 languages, contradicting Theorem 1.2. But the deciding of the solutions of (1.3) is a special case of Hilbert's tenth problem which, thus, must be unsolvable.

Thus every recursively enumerable set can be characterized as the set of numbers for which a certain polynomial equation has a solution in nonnegative integers. It is easy to see (cf. Exercise 3) that the polynomial can always be replaced by a polynomial with degree ≤ 5. On the other hand, if the degree is reduced, then the number n of variables increases. It is also easy to prove (cf. Exercise 2) that every recursively enumerable set can be characterized as the set of positive values of a certain polynomial. More specifically, there exists a polynomial $U_1(z, x_1, ..., x_p)$ with integer coefficients such that the following condition is satisfied. For every recursively enumerable set S, one can determine a nonnegative integer z_S such that S equals the set of positive values of the polynomial $U_1(z_S, x_1, ..., x_p)$ when the variables $x_1, ..., x_p$ range over nonnegative integers. (Furthermore, one can show that U_1 assumes only nonnegative values and is of degree ≤ 4.) For instance, S might be the set of quadruples (x, y, z, n) which satisfy the conditions $x^n + y^n = z^n$ and $n \geq 3$. Then Fermat's last theorem reduces to the statement that the polynomial $U_1(z_S, x_1, ..., x_p)$ assumes no positive values. Similarly, the collection of m-adic codes of the words in any type-0 language L can be represented as the set of positive values of a polynomial U_L. One can ask whether the polynomials U_L, where L ranges over some language family like the context-free languages, have any common properties. No results are known in this direction.

2. POST CORRESPONDENCE PROBLEM AND UNSOLVABLE PROBLEMS FOR LANGUAGES

So far our proofs of unsolvability have been based directly on Theorem 1.1. We now introduce a more sophisticated tool which enables us to prove various unsolvability results, especially for context-free languages.

Definition. A *Post correspondence problem* is an ordered quadruple $PCP = (V, n, \alpha, \beta)$ where V is an alphabet, $n \geq 1$, and

$$\alpha = (\alpha_1, \ldots, \alpha_n), \qquad \beta = (\beta_1, \ldots, \beta_n)$$

are ordered n-tuples of nonempty words over V. A *solution* to PCP is a non-empty finite sequence of indices $i_1, \ldots, i_k$ such that

$$\alpha_{i_1} \cdots \alpha_{i_k} = \beta_{i_1} \cdots \beta_{i_k}.$$

Example 2.1. The Post correspondence problem

$$(\{a, b\}, 3, \alpha, \beta), \qquad \alpha = (a^2, b^2, ab^2), \qquad \beta = (a^2b, ba, b)$$

possesses the solution $1, 2, 1, 3$ because

$$a^2b^2a^2ab^2 = a^2bbaa^2bb.$$

The Post correspondence problem

$$(\{a\}, 2, \alpha, \beta), \qquad \alpha = (a^3, a^4), \qquad \beta = (a^2, a^3)$$

does not possess any solutions because for any nonempty sequence of indices the α-word is longer than the corresponding β-word. In general, if the alphabet consists of one letter only, then it is easy to decide whether or not any given PCP possesses a solution (cf. Exercise 4). The requirement of the words α_i and β_i being nonempty is added to the definition of a PCP for a technical reason which becomes apparent in the proof of Theorem 2.4.

Theorem 2.1. There is no algorithm for deciding whether or not an arbitrary Post correspondence problem possesses a solution.

Proof. We assume the contrary and show how to solve the membership problem for type-0 grammars. From this Theorem 2.1 follows by Theorem 1.1.

Consider an arbitrary type-0 grammar $G = (V_N, V_T, a_1, F)$ where

$$V = V_N \cup V_T = \{a_1, \ldots, a_r\}, \qquad F = \{P_i \to Q_i | 1 \leq i \leq n\}.$$

Let $P \in W(V_T)$ be arbitrary. We construct a Post correspondence problem PCP which possesses a solution iff $P \in L(G)$. This would give a method of solving the membership problem for type-0 grammars.

Without loss of generality, we assume that $a_1 \to a_1$ is one of the productions in F because if necessary, we can add it to F without changing $L(G)$. Moreover, we may assume that G is λ-free; that is, each Q_i is nonempty. For if this is not the case originally, we then replace every production $R \to \lambda$ by all productions $aR \to a$ and $Ra \to a$ where $a \in V$. (The same construction was carried out in the proof of Theorem 3.2 in Part 1.) On the other hand, our proof of Theorem 1.1 shows that the theorem remains valid if only membership of nonempty words is considered.

Denote

$$V' = \{a' | a \in V\}, \qquad V_1 = V \cup V' \cup \{B, E, c, c'\}.$$

For any word $Q \in W(V)$, we denote by Q' the word over V', obtained from Q by replacing every letter a_i with a_i'. By definition, $\lambda' = \lambda$. Consider the Post correspondence problem

$$PCP = (V_1, 2r + 2n + 4, \alpha, \beta),$$

with

$$\alpha = (\alpha_1, ..., \alpha_{2r+2n+4}), \qquad \beta = (\beta_1, ..., \beta_{2r+2n+4}),$$

where

$$\alpha_1 = Ba_1 c, \qquad \qquad \beta_1 = B,$$

$$\alpha_2 = c', \qquad \qquad \beta_2 = c,$$

$$\alpha_3 = c, \qquad \qquad \beta_3 = c',$$

$$\alpha_4 = E, \qquad \qquad \beta_4 = c'PE,$$

$$\alpha_{4+i} = a_i', \qquad \qquad \beta_{4+i} = a_i, \qquad 1 \leq i \leq r,$$

$$\alpha_{4+r+i} = a_i, \qquad \qquad \beta_{4+r+i} = a_i', \qquad 1 \leq i \leq r,$$

$$\alpha_{4+2r+i} = Q_i', \qquad \qquad \beta_{4+2r+i} = P_i, \qquad 1 \leq i \leq n,$$

$$\alpha_{4+2r+n+i} = Q_i, \qquad \qquad \beta_{4+2r+n+i} = P_i', \qquad 1 \leq i \leq n.$$

Note that all of the words α_j and β_j are nonempty. We have to prove that PCP possesses a solution iff $P \in L(G)$.

I. Assume first that $P \in L(G)$. We prove that PCP possesses a solution. Since $P \in L(G)$, there is an integer m, words $R_{j1}, R_{j2} \in W(V)$, and indices $g(j)$ with $1 \leq g(j) \leq n$, defined for all $j = 0, ..., m$, such that the following conditions are satisfied. For every $j = 0, ..., m-1$,

$$R_{j1} Q_{g(j)} R_{j2} = R_{(j+1)1} P_{g(j+1)} R_{(j+1)2}. \tag{2.1}$$

Furthermore,

$$R_{m1} Q_{g(m)} R_{m2} = P. \tag{2.2}$$

Thus we consider the following derivation according to G:

$$a_1 = R_{01} P_{g(0)} R_{02} \Rightarrow R_{01} Q_{g(0)} R_{02} = R_{11} P_{g(1)} R_{12} \Rightarrow R_{11} Q_{g(1)} R_{12}$$

$$= R_{21} P_{g(2)} R_{22} \Rightarrow \cdots \Rightarrow R_{(m-1)1} Q_{g(m-1)} R_{(m-1)2}$$

$$= R_{m1} P_{g(m)} R_{m2} \Rightarrow R_{m1} Q_{g(m)} R_{m2} = P.$$

Without loss of generality, we assume that m is odd:

$$m = 2m_1 - 1. \tag{2.3}$$

(If this is not the case originally, we add one step to the derivation, consisting of an application of the production $a_1 \to a_1$.)

We now give a solution of PCP. By definition, a solution is a finite sequence of indices i_j with $1 \le i_j \le 2r + 2n + 4$ for which the α- and β-words coincide. In what follows, for two sequences T and U of indices, we mean by TU the sequence obtained by writing U after T. We define next two mappings, φ and φ', of the set $W(V)$ into the set of sequences of indices by

$$\varphi(\lambda) = \varphi'(\lambda) = \varnothing \quad \text{(the empty sequence)},$$

$$\varphi(a_{i_1} \cdots a_{i_k}) = (4 + r + i_1, \ldots, 4 + r + i_k),$$

$$\varphi'(a_{i_1} \cdots a_{i_k}) = (4 + i_1, \ldots, 4 + i_k),$$

where $k \ge 1$. For a sequence $U = (i_1, \ldots, i_k)$, we denote

$$\alpha(U) = \alpha_{i_1} \cdots \alpha_{i_k}, \qquad \beta(U) = \beta_{i_1} \cdots \beta_{i_k}.$$

Consider now the following sequences of indices

$$U_{2i} = \varphi'(R_{(2i)1})(4 + 2r + g(2i))\varphi'(R_{(2i)2}),$$

$$U_{2i+1} = \varphi(R_{(2i+1)1})(4 + 2r + n + g(2i + 1))\varphi(R_{(2i+1)2}),$$

for $0 \le i < m_1$. By (2.3), U_i has been defined for $0 \le i \le m$. Furthermore, for all i,

$$\alpha(U_{2i}) = R'_{(2i)1} Q'_{g(2i)} R'_{(2i)2},$$

$$\beta(U_{2i}) = R_{(2i)1} P_{g(2i)} R_{(2i)2},$$

$$\alpha(U_{2i+1}) = R_{(2i+1)1} Q_{g(2i+1)} R_{(2i+1)2},$$

$$\beta(U_{2i+1}) = R'_{(2i+1)1} P'_{g(2i+1)} R'_{(2i+1)2}.$$

The sequence

$$U = (1) U_0(2) U_1(3) U_2(2) U_3(3) U_4(2) \cdots U_{m-1}(2) U_m(4)$$

is a solution of PCP. [Recall that $m - 1$ is even. Hence the alternation between (2) and (3) comes out correctly.] In fact,

$$\alpha(U) = Ba_1 cR'_{01} Q'_{g(0)} R'_{02} c' R_{11} Q_{g(1)} R_{12} c R'_{21} Q'_{g(2)} R'_{22} c'$$

$$\cdots R'_{(m-1)1} Q'_{g(m-1)} R'_{(m-1)2} c' R_{m1} Q_{g(m)} R_{m2} E,$$

$$\beta(U) = BR_{01} P_{g(0)} R_{02} cR'_{11} P'_{g(1)} R'_{12} c' R_{21} P_{g(2)} R_{22} c$$

$$\cdots R_{(m-1)1} P_{g(m-1)} R_{(m-1)2} cR'_{m1} P'_{g(m)} R'_{m2} c'PE.$$

By (2.1) and (2.2), it is immediately verified that

$$\alpha(U) = \beta(U).$$

(Note that the first part of the proof of Theorem 2.1, which we have just presented, bears a resemblance to the proof of Theorem 11.1 in Part 1. However, now it is not necessary to switch between words and their mirror images. The assumption of m being odd is needed because c', and not c, occurs in β_4.)

II. We now assume, conversely, that PCP possesses a solution U_1. We prove that $P \in L(G)$.

The index 1 is the only index j for which α_j and β_j begin with the same letter. This follows because all of the words P_i and Q_i are nonempty. Similarly, the index 4 is the only index j for which α_j and β_j end with the same letter. Consequently, U_1 must be of the form

$$U_1 = (1)\, U(4) \tag{2.4}$$

for some sequence U. We may assume, without loss of generality, that U contains neither the index 1 nor the index 4. For if this is not the case originally, then we consider the first occurrence of 4 in U_1, that is, $U_1 = (1)\, U_2(4)\, U_3(4)$, where 4 does not occur in U_2. Since E occurs only in α_4 and β_4, $(1)\, U_2(4)$ is also a solution of PCP. We next consider the last occurrence of 1 in $(1)\, U_2(4)$, obtaining

$$U_1 = (1)\, U_4(1)\, U_5(4)\, U_3(4)$$

where neither 1 nor 4 occurs in U_5. Since B occurs only in α_1 and β_1, the sequence $(1)\, U_5(4)$ is a solution of PCP.

We thus assume that in (2.4) U contains neither 1 nor 4. Let h be the homomorphism of $W(V \cup V')$ onto $W(V)$, defined by

$$h(a') = h(a) = a \quad \text{for} \quad a \in V.$$

We now claim that the following assertion holds true.

ASSERTION (A). For any decomposition $U = T_1 T_2$, there are words R_1, R_2, R_3, R_4 with the properties

$$\alpha((1)\, T_1) = R_1 R_2 R_3 R_4, \qquad \beta((1)\, T_1) = R_1,$$
$$R_3 \in \{c, c'\}, \qquad a_1 \Rightarrow_G^* h(R_4 R_2). \tag{2.5}$$

Before proving Assertion (A), we note that the assertion implies the membership $P \in L(G)$. This is seen by applying the assertion to the case where T_2 is the empty sequence. First (2.5) gives

$$\alpha((1)\, U(4)) = R_1 R_2 R_3 R_4 E, \qquad \beta((1)\, U(4)) = R_1 c' PE,$$
$$a_1 \Rightarrow_G^* h(R_4 R_2). \tag{2.6}$$

Since $\alpha((1) U(4)) = \beta((1) U(4))$ (recall that U_1 is a solution of PCP), since R_3 equals either c or c', and since $R_2 R_4$ contains neither c nor c' [otherwise, the last of the conditions (2.6) could not be satisfied], we conclude that

$$R_2 = \lambda, \qquad R_3 = c', \qquad R_4 = P, \qquad a_1 \Rightarrow_G^* h(P) = P.$$

This shows that $P \in L(G)$.

Hence, to complete the proof of Theorem 2.1, it suffices to establish Assertion (A). This is done by induction on the length of the sequence T_1. Assume first that the length equals zero; that is, T_1 is the empty sequence. Then

$$\alpha((1) T_1) = Ba_1 c, \qquad \beta((1) T_1) = B.$$

We may choose

$$R_1 = B, \qquad R_2 = a_1, \qquad R_3 = c, \qquad R_4 = \lambda.$$

We now make the following inductive hypothesis: Assertion (A) holds for $U = T_1 T_2$; that is, (2.5) is satisfied. Consider the decomposition

$$U = T_1^+ T_2^+, \qquad T_1^+ = T_1(q),$$

where $1 \leq q \leq 4+2r+2n$. We have to prove that there are words R_1^+, R_2^+, R_3^+, R_4^+ with the properties

$$\alpha((1) T_1^+) = R_1^+ R_2^+ R_3^+ R_4^+, \qquad \beta((1) T_1^+) = R_1^+,$$
$$R_3^+ \in \{c, c'\}, \qquad a_1 \Rightarrow_G^* h(R_4^+ R_2^+). \tag{2.7}$$

This is shown by considering the possible values of q separately. Since U contains neither 1 nor 4, we conclude that $q \neq 1, 4$.

(i) Assume that $q = 2$. Then

$$\alpha((1) T_1^+) = R_1 R_2 R_3 R_4 c', \qquad \beta((1) T_1^+) = R_1 c.$$

Since one of these two words has to be an initial subword of the other, we obtain $R_2 = \lambda$ and $R_3 = c$. We may now choose

$$R_1^+ = R_1 c, \qquad R_2^+ = R_4, \qquad R_3^+ = c', \qquad R_4^+ = \lambda.$$

Then (2.7) is satisfied. In particular, the last condition in (2.7) follows by (2.5) because $h(R_4 R_2) = h(R_4) = h(R_4^+ R_2^+)$.

(ii) Assume that $q = 3$. Then

$$\alpha((1) T_1^+) = R_1 R_2 R_3 R_4 c, \qquad \beta((1) T_1^+) = R_1 c'.$$

Consequently, $R_2 = \lambda$ and $R_3 = c'$. We now choose

$$R_1^+ = R_1 c', \qquad R_2^+ = R_4, \qquad R_3^+ = c, \qquad R_4^+ = \lambda.$$

(iii)   Assume that $q = 4 + i$ where $1 \leq i \leq r$. Then

$$\alpha((1) T_1^+) = R_1 R_2 R_3 R_4 a_i', \qquad \beta((1) T_1^+) = R_1 a_i.$$

This implies that $R_2 = a_i Q$ for some word Q. We now choose

$$R_1^+ = R_1 a_i, \qquad R_2^+ = Q, \qquad R_3^+ = R_3, \qquad R_4^+ = R_4 a_i'.$$

Then (2.7) is satisfied because

$$h(R_4^+ R_2^+) = h(R_4 a_i' Q) = h(R_4 a_i Q) = h(R_4 R_2).$$

(iv)   Assume that $q = 4 + r + i$ where $1 \leq i \leq r$. Then

$$\alpha((1) T_1^+) = R_1 R_2 R_3 R_4 a_i, \qquad \beta((1) T_1^+) = R_1 a_i'.$$

Consequently, $R_2 = a_i' Q$ for some Q. We choose

$$R_1^+ = R_1 a_i', \qquad R_2^+ = Q, \qquad R_3^+ = R_3, \qquad R_4^+ = R_4 a_i.$$

Also now $h(R_4^+ R_2^+) = h(R_4 R_2)$.

(v)   Assume that $q = 4 + 2r + i$ where $1 \leq i \leq n$. Then

$$\alpha((1) T_1^+) = R_1 R_2 R_3 R_4 Q_i', \qquad \beta((1) T_1^+) = R_1 P_i.$$

We now obtain $R_2 = P_i Q$ for some word Q. In this case we choose

$$R_1^+ = R_1 P_i, \qquad R_2^+ = Q, \qquad R_3^+ = R_3, \qquad R_4^+ = R_4 Q_i'.$$

By (2.5), $a_1 \Rightarrow^* h(R_4 P_i Q)$. Since $h(Q_i') = Q_i$ and $P_i \to Q_i$ is one of the productions of G, we obtain

$$a_1 \Rightarrow^* h(R_4 Q_i' Q) = h(R_4^+ R_2^+).$$

(vi)   Assume finally that $q = 4 + 2r + n + i$ where $1 \leq i \leq n$. Then

$$\alpha((1) T_1^+) = R_1 R_2 R_3 R_4 Q_i, \qquad \beta((1) T_1^+) = R_1 P_i'.$$

Consequently, there is a word Q such that $R_2 = P_i' Q$. We choose

$$R_1^+ = R_1 P_i', \qquad R_2^+ = Q, \qquad R_3^+ = R_3, \qquad R_4^+ = R_4 Q_i.$$

Then (2.7) is satisfied because $h(P_i') = P_i$ and $P_i \to Q_i$ is one of the productions of G.

This completes the inductive step since the possible values of q have been exhausted. We conclude that Assertion (A) holds true. ∎

The following stronger version of Theorem 2.1 can now be established easily.

Theorem 2.2. Let V_2 be an alphabet consisting of two letters. There is no algorithm for deciding whether or not an arbitrary Post correspondence problem

$$\text{PCP} = (V_2, n, \alpha, \beta), \qquad \alpha = (\alpha_1, ..., \alpha_n), \qquad \beta = (\beta_1, ..., \beta_n) \qquad (2.8)$$

possesses a solution.

Proof. Let $V_2 = \{a, b\}$. Assume the contrary. We prove that there is an algorithm for deciding whether or not an arbitrary Post correspondence problem

$$\text{PCP}' = (V, n, \alpha', \beta'), \qquad V = \{a_1, ..., a_r\},$$

possesses a solution, which contradicts Theorem 2.1. In fact, define a homomorphism h of $W(V)$ into $W(V_2)$ by

$$h(a_i) = ba^i b, \qquad 1 \leqq i \leqq r.$$

Let α and β be n-tuples obtained from α' and β' by replacing every word with its homomorphic image. Then PCP possesses a solution iff PCP' possesses a solution. ∎

We are now in the position to establish the unsolvability of several problems concerning context-free languages. Denote

$$V_2 = \{a, b\}, \qquad V_3 = \{a, b, c\}.$$

Some special languages are considered in the sequel. Define

$$L_{mi} = \{P_1 c P_2 c \, \text{mi}(P_2) c \, \text{mi}(P_1) | P_1, P_2 \in W(V_2)\}.$$

Consider a Post correspondence problem (2.8). Introduce the language

$$L(\alpha) = \{ba^{i_k}b \cdots ba^{i_1} c \alpha_{i_1} \cdots \alpha_{i_k} | k \geqq 1; 1 \leqq i_j \leqq n\}.$$

The language $L(\beta)$ is defined similarly. Finally, let

$$L(\text{PCP}) = L(\alpha) c \, \text{mi}(L(\beta)).$$

Thus, both L_{mi} and all languages $L(\text{PCP})$ are languages over V_3. Our next theorem is a lemma which is used in subsequent unsolvability proofs.

Theorem 2.3. The language L_{mi}, all languages $L(\text{PCP})$, as well as their complements

$$W(V_3) - L_{mi}, \qquad W(V_3) - L(\text{PCP})$$

are context-free languages.

Proof. As regards L_{mi} and $L(\text{PCP})$, the theorem is obvious. The complements can be expressed as a union of context-free languages. In fact

$$W(V_3) - L_{mi} = L_1 \cup L_2 \cup L_3,$$

where (i) L_1 consists of all words over V_3 where the number of c's is different from 3, (ii) L_2 consists of all words over V_3 of the form

$$P_1 c P_2 c P_3 c P_4, \qquad P_4 \neq \text{mi}(P_1),$$

and (iii) L_3 consists of all words of the form

$$P_1 c P_2 c P_3 c P_4, \qquad P_3 \neq \text{mi}(P_2).$$

A context-free grammar can be immediately constructed for each of the languages L_i. The details of this construction, as well as the proof for the complement of $L(\text{PCP})$, are left to the reader. In this regard Ginsburg (1966, pp. 123–125) may be consulted. ∎

In the statement of the following theorem, the unsolvability of a problem means that there is no algorithm which solves the problem for all context-free grammars G_1 and G_2.

Theorem 2.4. Each of the following problems is unsolvable for context-free grammars G_1 and G_2 where we denote $L_1 = L(G_1)$ and $L_2 = L(G_2)$:

(i)   Is $L_1 \cap L_2$ empty?

(ii) Is $L_1 \cap L_2$ infinite?

(iii) Is $L_1 \cap L_2$ regular?

(iv) Is $L_1 \cap L_2$ context-free?

(v)   Is $\sim L_1$ empty?

(vi) Is $\sim L_1$ infinite?

(vii) Is $\sim L_1$ regular?

(viii) Is $\sim L_1$ context-free?

(ix) Is L_1 regular?

(x)   Is L_1 contained in L_2?

(xi) Is L_1 equal to L_2?

(xii) Is G_1 unambiguous?

(xiii) Is $L(G_1)$ unambiguous?

Proof. We prove that an algorithm for any of the problems (i)–(xiii) gives an algorithm for solving all Post correspondence problems (2.8), which contradicts Theorem 2.2. To achieve this goal, we make use of the languages L_{mi} and $L(\text{PCP})$.

For any PCP, the intersection

$$L(\text{PCP}) \cap L_{mi} \tag{2.9}$$

is nonempty iff PCP possesses a solution. This follows because (2.9) consists of all words of the form

$$ba^{i_k} \cdots ba^{i_1} c \alpha_{i_1} \cdots \alpha_{i_k} c \, \text{mi}(\beta_{i_1} \cdots \beta_{i_k}) c a^{i_1} b \cdots a^{i_k} b, \tag{2.10}$$

where $k \geq 1$, $1 \leq i_j \leq n$, and $\alpha_{i_1} \cdots \alpha_{i_k} = \beta_{i_1} \cdots \beta_{i_k}$. Clearly, if $(i_1, \ldots, i_k)$ is a solution of PCP, then also $(i_1, \ldots, i_k, i_1, \ldots, i_k)$ is a solution of PCP. This implies that (2.9) is nonempty iff it is infinite. Hence the unsolvability of

(i) and (ii) follows. [In fact, the unsolvability of (i) was already shown in Theorem 1.4.]

We now claim that (2.9) contains no infinite context-free language, no matter how PCP is chosen. Assume the contrary: For some PCP, (2.9) contains an infinite context-free language L. By Theorem 6.4 in Part 1, every word in L of sufficient length can be written in the form

$$R_1 Q_1 RQ_2 R_2, \qquad Q_1 Q_2 \neq \lambda, \qquad R_1 Q_1{}^i RQ_2{}^i R_2 \in L, \qquad (2.11)$$

for each $i \geq 0$. Since L is infinite, it contains such words. Let (2.10) be a word in L which can be written also in the form (2.11). We abbreviate by P_j, $j = 1, 2, 3, 4$, the words in (2.10) which are separated by the c's. Thus

$$P_1 cP_2 cP_3 cP_4 = R_1 Q_1 RQ_2 R_2.$$

If $Q_1 Q_2$ contains an occurrence of c, then the word $R_1 Q_1{}^4 RQ_2{}^4 R_2$ contains at least four occurrences of c and consequently does not belong to (2.9), which contradicts (2.11). Hence $Q_1 Q_2$ does not contain any occurrences of c. Therefore the word $R_1 Q_1{}^2 RQ_2{}^2 R_2$ is obtained from the word $R_1 Q_1 RQ_2 R_2$ by making at least one and at most two of the words P_j, $1 \leq j \leq 4$, longer. This implies that the word $R_1 Q_1{}^2 RQ_2{}^2 R_2$ does not belong to (2.9) because otherwise all of the words P_j would have been changed. (To be able to make this conclusion, we required in the definition of a PCP that the words be non-empty.) This contradiction shows that (2.9) contains no infinite context-free language.

Consequently, (2.9) itself is either empty or else infinite and not context-free. It is empty exactly in case PCP possesses no solution. The unsolvability of (iii) and (iv) now follows.

To establish the unsolvability of (v)–(ix), we consider the language

$$L' = W(V_3) - (L(\text{PCP}) \cap L_{mi}) = (W(V_3) - L(\text{PCP})) \cup (W(V_3) - L_{mi}).$$

By Theorem 2.3, L' is context-free. The complement of L' equals (2.9). By the unsolvability of (i)–(iv), the unsolvability of (v)–(viii) follows. Since (2.9) is either empty or else infinite and nonregular, L' is regular iff (2.9) is empty. Consequently, (ix) is unsolvable.

Assume that (xi) is solvable. Hence there is an algorithm for deciding whether or not $L' = W(V_3)$. But $L' = W(V_3)$ iff (2.9) is empty and, as we have seen, (2.9) is empty iff PCP possesses no solutions. Therefore such an algorithm is not possible and (xi) is unsolvable. This implies that (x) is unsolvable.

For a Post correspondence problem (2.8), consider the grammar $G(\text{PCP})$ determined by the productions

$$X_0 \to X_\alpha, \qquad X_0 \to X_\beta, \qquad X_\alpha \to ba^i c\alpha_i, \qquad X_\alpha \to ba^i X_\alpha \alpha_i,$$

$$X_\beta \to ba^i c\beta_i, \qquad X_\beta \to ba^i X_\beta \beta_i, \qquad i = 1, \ldots, n.$$

The grammar $G(\mathrm{PCP})$ generates the union of the languages $L(\alpha)$ and $L(\beta)$ considered in the definition of $L(\mathrm{PCP})$. The grammar $G(\mathrm{PCP})$ is ambiguous iff PCP possesses a solution. Hence the unsolvability of (xii) follows.

Finally, consider the context-free language

$$L_1(\mathrm{PCP}) = \{a^m b^m c^n | m, n \geqq 1\} \{d\} L(\mathrm{PCP})$$

$$\cup \ \{a^m b^n c^n | m, n \geqq 1\} \{d\} L_{mi}$$

over the alphabet $\{a, b, c, d\}$. Clearly, each of the languages

$$\{a^m b^m c^n | m, n \geqq 1\}, \quad \{a^m b^n c^n | m, n \geqq 1\}, \quad \{d\}, \quad L(\mathrm{PCP}), \quad L_{mi}$$

is unambiguous. Consequently, $L_1(\mathrm{PCP})$ is unambiguous if (2.9) is empty. On the other hand, it is easy to verify using Theorem 9.3 in Part 2 that $L_1(\mathrm{PCP})$ is inherently ambiguous if (2.9) is not empty. Thus, the unsolvability of (xiii) follows also. ∎

Using our standard coding techniques, we may extend Theorem 2.4 to the case where it is assumed that G_1 and G_2 possess the same terminal alphabet of two letters. (Such an extension to the one-letter case is not possible because,

TABLE 5

Problem	Type			
	3	2	1	0
Membership	S	S	S	U
Inclusion	S	U	U	U
Equivalence	S	U	U	U
Emptiness	S	S	U	U
Infinity	S	S	U	U
Is $L(G) = W(V_{\mathrm{T}})$?	S	U	U	U
Is $L(G)$ regular?	T	U	U	U
Is $L(G)$ context-free?	T	T	U	U
Is G unambiguous?	S	U	—	—
Is $L(G)$ unambiguous?	T	U	—	—
Is $\sim L(G)$ empty?	S	U	U	U
Is $\sim L(G)$ infinite?	S	U	U	U
Is $\sim L(G)$ regular?	T	U	U	U
Is $\sim L(G)$ context-free?	T	U	U	U
Is $\sim L(G)$ of the same type as G?	T	U	?	U
Is $L(G_1) \cap L(G_2)$ empty?	S	U	U	U
Is $L(G_1) \cap L(G_2)$ infinite?	S	U	U	U
Is $L(G_1) \cap L(G_2)$ regular?	T	U	U	U
Is $L(G_1) \cap L(G_2)$ context-free?	T	U	U	U
Is $L(G_1) \cap L(G_2)$ of the same type as G_1 and G_2?	T	U	T	T

by Theorem 7.3 in Part 1, all of the problems mentioned are solvable in this case.) Our proof of Theorem 2.4 shows also that (i)–(iv) remain valid if G_2 is fixed to be a grammar for L_{mi}.

Table 5 summarizes some solvability and unsolvability results we have established for grammars in our basic hierarchy. [Note that some results for type-1 grammars follow by (i)–(iv) of Theorem 2.4.] In the table S means "solvable," U "unsolvable," T "true for the whole class," question mark "unsettled," and dash "not applicable."

We now derive an unsolvability result of a somewhat different nature. One can consider the number of nonterminals or the number of productions in a context-free grammar as a measure of complexity for the grammar. Given a context-free grammar, we may want to find an equivalent context-free grammar with fewest nonterminals. This is referred to as the *nonterminal minimization problem*. Similarly, the *production minimization problem* is to find for a given context-free grammar an equivalent context-free grammar with fewest productions. As above, the unsolvability of each of these problems means that there is no algorithm which solves all instances of the problem.

Theorem 2.5. Both the nonterminal minimization problem and the production minimization problem are unsolvable.

Proof. We prove first three assertions from which the theorem easily follows.

ASSERTION (A). The problem of deciding whether an arbitrary context-free language equals $W(V_3)\{d\}$, where $V_3 = \{a, b, c\}$, is unsolvable.

In the proof of Theorem 2.4, it was seen that the problem of deciding whether an arbitrary context-free language equals $W(V_3)$ is unsolvable. For a grammar G with initial letter X_0, we denote by G_d the grammar obtained from G by adding a new initial letter X_0' and the production $X_0' \to X_0 d$. Then

$$L(G) = W(V_3) \quad \text{iff} \quad L(G_d) = W(V_3)\{d\},$$

and Assertion (A) follows.

ASSERTION (B). A context-free grammar with fewest productions that generates $W(V_3)\{d\}$ is

$$G_1 = (\{X_0\}, \{a, b, c, d\}, X_0, \{X_0 \to aX_0, X_0 \to bX_0, X_0 \to cX_0, X_0 \to d\}).$$

Furthermore, G_1 is the only context-free grammar (apart from renaming X_0) with four productions which generates $W(V_3)\{d\}$.

Let G be an arbitrary (context-free) grammar generating $W(V_3)\{d\}$. Consider derivations of the words ad, bd, cd, and d. An application of a production with the right side $P_1 aQ_1$, $P_2 bQ_2$, $P_3 cQ_3$, and $P_4 dP_5$ (respectively), where each $P_i \in W(V_N)$ and each $Q_i \in W(V_N) \cup \{d\}$, must take place in these derivations. Hence G has at least four productions. Assume now that G has exactly four productions. Consequently, G has no production with λ on the right side. This implies that each P_i equals λ, and each Q_i is d, λ, or a non-terminal. Furthermore, $X_0 \rightarrow d$ is one of the productions. If $Q_1 = d$, then G does not generate the word $a^2 d$. If $Q_1 = \lambda$ or a nonterminal other than X_0, then the word ad is not generated. Consequently, $Q_1 = X_0$. Similarly it is seen that $Q_2 = Q_3 = X_0$. Since it is now obvious that the left side of each of the four productions we are considering must be X_0, we conclude that Assertion (B) holds.

ASSERTION (C). Assume that G generates $W(V_3)\{d\}$ and that X_0 is the only nonterminal in G. Then all productions of G are of one of the two forms $X_0 \rightarrow PX_0$ and $X_0 \rightarrow Pd$ where $P \in W(V_3)$.

In fact, we note first that $X_0 \rightarrow \lambda$ is not among the productions because $\lambda \notin W(V_3)\{d\}$. On the other hand, $X_0 \rightarrow d$ must be among the productions. (Otherwise, d would not be generated.) This implies that every production with only terminals on the right side must be of the form $X_0 \rightarrow Pd$, and the remaining productions of the form $X_0 \rightarrow PX_0$, where in both cases $P \in W(V_3)$.

We now prove Theorem 2.5. Assume the contrary: We can solve either the nonterminal minimization problem or the production minimization problem. Considering the former alternative first, we denote by G_{nt} a grammar with fewest nonterminals which is equivalent to a given grammar G. Thus we can determine G_{nt} for an arbitrary G. By inspecting G_{nt}, we can decide whether

$$L(G) = W(V_3)\{d\}, \tag{2.12}$$

which contradicts Assertion (A). In fact, if G_{nt} has at least two nonterminals, then (2.12) does not hold. If G_{nt} has only one nonterminal and the productions are not of the forms mentioned in Assertion (C), then (2.12) does not hold. If the productions are of these forms, then G_{nt} is right-linear and consequently we can decide whether G_{nt} generates the regular language $W(V_3)\{d\}$.

Assume, secondly, that we can for any (context-free) grammar G determine a grammar G_{pr} with fewest productions which is equivalent to G. If the number of productions in G_{pr} does not equal 4, then (2.12) does not hold, by Assertion (B). If the number of productions equals 4, then, by Assertion (B), we can decide whether (2.12) holds. Hence, a contradiction with Assertion (A) results also in this case. ∎

Note 2.1. It is possible to develop a theory which shows that some un-solvable problems are "more unsolvable" than others. Such a theory was originated by Post, who defined five different ways of reducing problems to others. By the decision problem for the set S, we mean the problem of deciding whether an arbitrary element x belongs to S. (Clearly, the problems we have considered are of this form. For example, for the ambiguity problem of context-free grammars, the set S is the set of unambiguous grammars.) The most restrictive type of reducibility introduced by Post is the so-called one-to-one reducibility. The decision problem for the set S_1 is one-to-one reducible to the decision problem for the set S_2 iff there exists a one-to-one (total) recursive function f such that $x \in S_1$ exactly in case $f(x) \in S_2$. The least restrictive type of reducibility is called Turing reducibility. It requires the existence of a procedure which at certain times raises a question as to whether some y belongs to S_2. If the correct answer is provided to each such question, then the whole procedure will eventually terminate with the correct answer to the question as to whether the given x belongs to S_1. Under these circumstances, we say the decision problem for S_1 is Turing reducible to the decision problem for S_2. (The described procedure may be formalized using the notion of a Turing machine with an "oracle.")

Both of these types of reducibility are reflexive and transitive. Hence an equivalence relation among decision problems can be introduced: T_1 is equivalent to T_2 iff T_1 is reducible to T_2, and vice versa. The resulting equivalence classes are called *degrees*. Depending on what type of reducibility we are considering, we may speak of *one-to-one degrees* and *Turing degrees*.

Two Turing degrees may be incomparable, that is, neither one of them is reducible to the other in the sense that problems in the former are reducible to problems in the latter. However, one can delineate a totally ordered subset of Turing degrees which consists of useful reference points. It is customary to denote Turing degrees in this subset by nonnegative integers. Then the degree 0 consists of solvable problems. Degree 1 consists of problems (Turing) equivalent to the halting problem. Examples of such problems are the membership problem for type-0 grammars, the emptiness problem for type-1 and type-0 grammars, and the equivalence problem for type-2 and type-1 grammars. A more general example of a degree-1 problem is the following. Let $\mathscr{L}$ be any family of recursive languages which includes the smallest AFL containing the language $\{a^n b^n | n \geq 1\}$. Then the inclusion and equivalence problems of $\mathscr{L}$ are unsolvable of Turing degree 1. In general, a problem of degree 1 is defined by a predicate T such that exactly one of T and $\sim T$ is recursively enumerable. For degrees higher than 1, neither T nor $\sim T$ is recursively enumerable. Examples of problems of degree 2 are the infinity problem for type-1 and type-0 grammars, the inclusion and equivalence problems for type-0 grammars, and the infinity problem for the intersection of two context-free languages. Another example is the problem of determining whether a context-free or context-sensitive language is regular. Examples of problems of degree 3 are the problem of determining whether a type-0 grammar G generates a regular, context-free, or context-sensitive language and whether the complement of $L(G)$ is type 0.

3. SOLVABILITY OF STRUCTURAL EQUIVALENCE OF CONTEXT-FREE GRAMMARS

We have seen that context-free grammars possess the undesirable feature that their equivalence problem is unsolvable. However, we prove in this section that there is an algorithm for deciding whether two context-free grammars are *structurally equivalent*, that is, generate the same words and assign similar generation trees (differing only in the labeling of the nodes) to each. (Many authors refer to structural equivalence as "strong" equivalence and to ordinary equivalence as "weak" equivalence.) Thus two structurally equivalent grammars not only generate the same words but also structure these words in the same manner. If grammars are intended for use in a situation entailing the translation or interpretation of words (as in a compiler), then from the practical point of view structural equivalence is more important than ordinary equivalence. In what follows, structural equivalence is defined in terms of a *parenthesis grammar* since the latter notion is very convenient to work with.

Definition. A context-free grammar

$$G_1 = (V_N, V_T \cup \{(,)\}, X_0, F_1), \qquad V = V_N \cup V_T, \qquad (3.1)$$

is a *parenthesis grammar* iff the right side of every production is of the form (P) where $P \in W(V)$. For a context-free grammar $G = (V_N, V_T, X_0, F)$, (3.1) is termed the *parenthesized version* of G, in symbols, $G_1 = (G)$, iff F_1 consists of all productions $X \to (P)$ such that $X \to P$ is in F. Two grammars G and G' are *structurally equivalent* iff their parenthesized versions (G) and (G') generate the same language.

It is an immediate consequence of the definition that if two grammars are structurally equivalent, then they are also equivalent. It is also easy to see that the definition of structural equivalence corresponds to the intuitive description given above. This is due to the fact that a nested bracketing defines a tree, and vice versa. Two grammars G and G' generate a word P with the same form of generation tree iff (G) and (G') generate the same "parenthesized version" of P. For example, the parenthesized version of the tree in Fig. 17 is

$$((AC((BC)B)B)((BC)B)). \qquad (3.2)$$

If (3.2) is known, the tree can be reconstructed, apart from the labels of the nodes other than leaves. (If one considers the structural grammars of Note 6.2 in Part 1, then also the labels of the nodes are determined by the indexed parentheses.) Thus, if (G) and (G') are equivalent, then G and G' generate the same words with the same generation trees, provided the labels of the nodes other than leaves are disregarded.

We prove in this section that there is an algorithm for deciding whether two arbitrary context-free grammars are structurally equivalent. This is done by showing that the equivalence problem is solvable for parenthesis grammars. First some auxiliary concepts are introduced. Then some lemmas are established. From them the main result follows easily.

A context-free grammar is *invertible* iff no two productions have the same right side. Clearly, in an invertible parenthesis grammar any word can be parsed starting from an innermost parenthesized part, and at every step in the process the context may be disregarded.

In the following proofs it is convenient to allow parenthesis grammars several initial letters. A *parenthesis grammar in the wider sense* or, in short, a wsp grammar, is an ordered quadruple

$$G = (V_N, V_T \cup \{(,)\}, S_0, F) \qquad (3.3)$$

where S_0 is a nonempty subset of V_N and the other items are as in the definition of a parenthesis grammar. The set S_0 is referred to as the set of initial letters, and $V_T \cup \{(,)\}$ is referred to as the terminal alphabet. A word P is *derivable* according to G iff $s_0 \Rightarrow^* P$ for some $s_0 \in S_0$. The language generated by (3.3) consists of all derivable terminal words. The notions of equivalence and invertibility are extended to concern wsp grammars.

Theorem 3.1. For every wsp grammar, one may construct an equivalent invertible wsp grammar.

Proof. Let (3.3) be a given wsp grammar. Consider the wsp grammar

$$G' = (V_N', V_T \cup \{(,)\}, S_0', F')$$

where the different items are defined as follows. The elements of V_N' are the nonempty subsets of V_N. The set S_0' consists of those subsets (i.e., elements of V_N') which contain at least one element of S_0. (From a logical point of view, it would be better to define the elements of V_N' as $[S]$ where S is a nonempty subset of V_N. However, we do not make this distinction since there is no danger of confusion.)

Consider a word P' over $V_N' \cup V_T \cup \{(,)\}$. A word P over $V_N \cup V_T \cup \{(,)\}$ *corresponds* to P' iff P is obtained from P' by replacing every occurrence of a letter S of V_N' with a letter X of V_N such that $X \in S$. (Different occurrences of the same letter S may be replaced by different letters X.) A production $S \rightarrow (P')$ belongs to F' iff S is exactly the set of nonterminals $Y \in V_N$ such that $Y \rightarrow (P)$ is a production in F for some word P corresponding to P'. [For instance, if P' is a word over V_T, then $S \rightarrow (P')$ belongs to F' iff S is exactly the set of nonterminals $Y \in V_N$ such that $Y \rightarrow (P')$ is a production in F.] Because the set S is always unique, this definition of F' guarantees that G' is invertible.

It is obvious that every word in $L(G)$ is also in $L(G')$. In fact, any derivation according to G is immediately converted to a derivation of the same length according to G' by working through the generation tree from the leaves to the root. Conversely, consider a derivation D' according to G'. It begins with a letter $s_0' \in S_0'$. By the definition of S_0', there is a letter $s_0 \in S_0$ corresponding to s_0'. ("Corresponding" is understood in the sense defined above.) As an inductive hypothesis, suppose that we have found, for the first k steps in D', a derivation D according to G which consists of words corresponding to those in D'. Assume that the $(k+1)$st step in D' is $Q_k' \Rightarrow Q_{k+1}'$ where Q_{k+1}' is obtained from Q_k' by applying the production $S \to (P')$ to the mth letter of Q_k'. By the inductive hypothesis, there is a word Q_k corresponding to Q_k' and derivable according to G. Hence the mth letter Y of Q_k belongs to S. By the definition of F', there is a production $Y \to (P)$ in F where P corresponds to P'. By applying this production to the mth letter of Q_k, the inductive step is completed. Hence every word in $L(G')$ is in $L(G)$. Consequently, G and G' are equivalent. ∎

In our following considerations, we mean by a *context* α a word with one blank. [Formally, a context over an alphabet V is a word in $W(V)\{—\}W(V)$, where the letter $—$ is called a blank.] We denote by $\alpha[P]$ the context α with its blank replaced by the word P. Two nonterminals X and Y of a wsp grammar G are termed *equivalent* iff, for every context α, $\alpha[X]$ is derivable according to G exactly in case $\alpha[Y]$ is derivable according to G. (Clearly, this is an equivalence relation.) A nonterminal X is *useless* iff there is no context α such that $\alpha[X]$ is derivable or X generates no terminal word. (These conditions were considered already in Section 9 of Part 2.) A terminal a is *useless* iff it does not appear in any word of $L(G)$. A wsp grammar is *reduced* iff it has no useless terminals or nonterminals and no two nonterminals are equivalent.

We are going to prove that, for any given wsp grammar (generating a nonempty language), one may construct an equivalent reduced invertible wsp grammar. The next theorem is a lemma needed in this proof.

Theorem 3.2. There is an algorithm to determine the equivalence classes of the nonterminals in an invertible wsp grammar G.

Proof. We introduce some auxiliary terminology. A nonempty set V_1 of nonterminals in G is *n-distinguishable* ($n \geq 0$) iff there is a context α with at most n parenthesis pairs such that $\alpha[X]$ is derivable exactly in case $X \in V_1$. (Note that the length of the derivation in question equals the number of parenthesis pairs in α.) A set V_1 is *distinguishable* iff it is n-distinguishable for some n. Clearly, two nonterminals are equivalent iff there is no distinguishable set having one of them without the other. Hence, to prove our theorem, it suffices to give an algorithm for listing all distinguishable sets. Such an algorithm results if we can decide whether or not an arbitrary set is distinguishable. Again, the required decision method exists if we can show that an arbitrary V_1 is distinguishable iff it is 2^r-distinguishable where r is the number of nonterminals of G.

Let us call a set V_1 *strictly n-distinguishable* iff it is n-distinguishable but not $(n-1)$-distinguishable. We establish the following Assertion (A).

ASSERTION (A).   For any strictly n-distinguishable set, where $n \geq 2$, there is a strictly $(n-1)$-distinguishable set.

This assertion implies that no set can be strictly n-distinguishable with $n > 2^r$. Hence a set V_1 is distinguishable iff it is 2^r-distinguishable, which proves the theorem.

To prove Assertion (A), we assume that V_n is strictly n-distinguishable with $n \geq 2$. Hence there is a context α_n with n parenthesis pairs such that V_n is precisely the set of nonterminals X for which $\alpha_n[X]$ is derivable. The blank in α_n must be inside a parenthesis phrase that does not have another parenthesis phrase within it, that is, α_n is of neither of the forms

$$(P_1(P_2)P_3{-}P_4), \qquad (P_1{-}P_3(P_2)P_4),$$

where the dash denotes the blank. Otherwise, V_n would be $(n-1)$-distinguishable, as can be seen by replacing (P_2) with a suitable nonterminal. Since G is invertible, there cannot be several nonterminals Y satisfying $Y \Rightarrow^* (P_2)$.

Thus the blank in α_n is inside a parenthesis phrase $Q = (P_1{-}P_2)$ where P_1 and P_2 are words over $V_N \cup V_T$. Let α_{n-1} be a context obtained from α_n by replacing Q with a single blank. Hence, α_{n-1} has $n-1$ parenthesis pairs. Let V_{n-1} be the set of all nonterminals X such that $\alpha_{n-1}[X]$ is derivable. By definition, V_{n-1} is $(n-1)$-distinguishable.

To complete the proof of Assertion (A), we have to show that V_{n-1} is not $(n-2)$-distinguishable. Assume the contrary. Then there is a context α_{n-2} with $n-2$ or fewer parenthesis pairs such that V_{n-1} equals the set of nonterminals Y for which $\alpha_{n-2}[Y]$ is derivable. Replace the blank in α_{n-2} by Q, and denote the resulting context by β_{n-1}. Clearly, β_{n-1} has $n-1$ or fewer parenthesis pairs. Moreover, V_n equals the set of nonterminals X for which $\beta_{n-1}[X]$ is derivable. [Recall that V_n equals the set of all nonterminals X for which $Y \to (P_1 X P_2)$ is a production of G for some $Y \in V_{n-1}$.] Consequently, V_n is $(n-1)$-distinguishable. This contradicts the assumption that V_n is strictly n-distinguishable. Hence our assumption is wrong and V_{n-1} is strictly $(n-1)$-distinguishable. ∎

Theorem 3.3. For every wsp grammar generating a nonempty language, one may construct an equivalent wsp grammar which is both invertible and reduced.

Proof. By Theorem 3.1, we may assume that the given wsp grammar G is invertible. Since useless terminals and nonterminals can be found effectively, we also assume without loss of generality that G has no useless terminals or nonterminals. [The assumption of $L(G)$ being nonempty is needed because otherwise all nonterminals would be useless.] We determine, using the algorithm of Theorem 3.2, the equivalence classes of nonterminals; assume that they are $S_1, ..., S_m$.

A wsp grammar G' is now defined. The nonterminal alphabet of G' is $\{S_1, ..., S_m\}$, and S_i is an initial letter iff it contains some initial letter of G. (Note that if $X \in S_i$ is initial in G, then every letter in S_i is initial in G. This is seen by considering the empty context.) As in the proof of Theorem 3.1, we say that a word Q' over the union of the alphabets of G' *corresponds* to a word Q over the union of the alphabets of G iff Q is obtained from Q' by replacing every occurrence of a letter S_i with a letter $X \in S_i$. (Different occurrences of the same S_i may be replaced by different letters X.) By definition, $X' \to (P')$ is a production of G' iff G has a production $X \to (P)$ such that X' (resp. P') corresponds to X (resp. P).

Clearly, G' is a wsp grammar. Moreover, if a word Q is derivable according to G and Q' corresponds to Q, then Q' is derivable according to G'. Also the converse holds true: If Q' is derivable according to G' and Q is any word such that Q' corresponds to Q, then Q is derivable according to G. This is immediately seen by an induction on the length of the derivation of Q': An application of a production $X' \to (P')$ can be converted to an application of a production $X \to (P)$. Moreover, if Q is replaced by any Q_1 such that Q' also corresponds to Q_1, then also Q_1 is derivable according to G by the definition of equivalence classes. Hence G and G' are equivalent.

We prove next that G' is reduced. Clearly, G' has no useless terminals or nonterminals since G has none. Assume that G' has two equivalent nonterminals S_i and S_j, $i \ne j$. Then for every context α', $\alpha'[S_i]$ is derivable according to G' iff $\alpha'[S_j]$ is derivable according to G'. Choose elements $X_i \in S_i$ and $X_j \in S_j$. Then $\alpha'[S_i]$ corresponds to $\alpha[X_i]$ and $\alpha'[S_j]$ corresponds to $\alpha[X_j]$ where α is obtained from α' by replacing every nonterminal with a corresponding one. By what was shown above, $\alpha'[S_i]$ is derivable according to G' iff $\alpha[X_i]$ is derivable according to G, and $\alpha'[S_j]$ is derivable according to G' iff $\alpha[X_j]$ is derivable according to G. This implies that X_i and X_j are equivalent, which contradicts the fact that S_i and S_j are different equivalence classes. Hence G' is reduced.

Finally we prove that G' is invertible. Assume the contrary: G' has two productions

$$S_i \to (P'), \qquad S_j \to (P'), \qquad i \ne j.$$

This implies that G has two productions

$$X_i \to (P_1), \qquad X_j \to (P_2), \qquad X_i \in S_i, \quad X_j \in S_j, \qquad (3.4)$$

where P' corresponds to both P_1 and P_2. Thus, for any context β, $\beta[(P_1)]$ is derivable according to G iff $\beta[(P_2)]$ is derivable according to G. Since G is invertible, we infer by (3.4) that $\beta[X_i]$ is derivable according to G iff $\beta[X_j]$ is derivable according to G. Since the context β was arbitrary, this implies that X_i and X_j are equivalent, which again contradicts the fact that S_i and S_j are different equivalence classes. Consequently, G' is invertible. ∎

We say that two wsp grammars G_1 and G_2 *differ only by the names of non-terminals* iff each of the following conditions is satisfied: (i) G_1 and G_2 have the same terminal alphabet; (ii) there is a one-to-one correspondence between the nonterminal alphabets of G_1 and G_2 such that the initial letters of G_1 correspond to the initial letters of G_2; and (iii) there is a one-to-one correspondence between the production sets F_i of G_i, $i = 1, 2$, such that any production in one set is obtained from the corresponding production in the other set by replacing each nonterminal in the latter production with the corresponding [according to (ii)] nonterminal in the former.

Theorem 3.4. Two equivalent reduced invertible wsp grammars differ only by the names of nonterminals.

Proof. Assume that G and G' are wsp grammars which are equivalent, reduced, and invertible. Since G and G' are equivalent and reduced, they have the same terminal alphabet. (Note that a reduced grammar always generates a nonempty language.) We define a one-to-one correspondence between the nonterminals of G and G'.

Consider an arbitrary nonterminal X of G. Denote by $T(X)$ the set of terminal words derivable from X. Since X is not useless, $T(X)$ is nonempty. Choose an arbitrary $P \in T(X)$. Because no nonterminal of G is useless, P must be a subword of a word in $L(G)$. Moreover, P begins and ends with a pair of mated parentheses. Since $L(G) = L(G')$, P must be derivable from some nonterminal X' according to G'. Denote by $T(X')$ the set of terminal words derivable from X' according to G'. We claim that

$$T(X) = T(X'). \qquad (3.5)$$

Assume the contrary. Suppose first there is a word Q in $T(X) - T(X')$. As above, we conclude that Q is derivable from some nonterminal Y' according to G'. Since $Q \notin T(X')$, we have $Y' \neq X'$. According to an invertible grammar, any word is derivable from at most one nonterminal. Hence, for any terminal context α, $\alpha[P]$ is in $L(G)$ iff $\alpha[Q]$ is in $L(G)$. But this implies, since G' has no useless nonterminals, that for any context β, $\beta[X']$ is derivable according to G' iff $\beta[Y']$ is derivable according to G'. Consequently, X' and Y' are equivalent. Since $X' \neq Y'$, this contradicts the fact that G' is reduced. Supposing that there is a word $Q' \in T(X') - T(X)$, we obtain similarly a contradiction with the fact that G is reduced. Hence, (3.5) holds.

Thus, for any nonterminal X of G, there corresponds a nonterminal X' of G' such that (3.5) is satisfied. Denote this correspondence by $\varphi : X' = \varphi(X)$. Since the roles of G and G' are symmetric, φ is one-to-one and onto the set of nonterminals of G'. Moreover, since the two grammars are equivalent, initial letters correspond to initial letters. [Recall that the sets $T(X)$, where X ranges over all nonterminals, are pairwise disjoint.] Consider now an arbitrary production $X \to (P)$ of G. Let P_1 be a word obtained from P by replacing every nonterminal Y_i with a terminal word (Q_i) derivable from Y_i (according to G). Hence, (P_1) is derivable from X according to G. Consequently, (P_1) is derivable from $\varphi(X)$ and each (Q_i) is derivable from $\varphi(Y_i)$ according to G'. Since G' is invertible, this is possible only if the production

$$\varphi(X) \to (\varphi(P))$$

is in the production set of G'. [Here $\varphi(P)$ is the word obtained from P by replacing every nonterminal Y_i with $\varphi(Y_i)$.] Again, because the roles of G and G' are symmetric, we reach the same conclusion if we start with an arbitrary production of G'. Consequently, the correspondence φ satisfies all of the requirements, and G and G' differ only by the names of nonterminals. ∎

We are now in the position to establish the main result.

Theorem 3.5. The equivalence problem for parenthesis grammars is solvable. Consequently, there is an algorithm for deciding whether two context-free grammars are structurally equivalent.

Proof. Since the emptiness problem is solvable for context-free grammars, we may assume that the given parenthesis grammars G and G' both generate a nonempty language. By Theorem 3.3, we may construct a reduced and invertible wsp grammar G_1 (resp. G_1') which is equivalent to G (resp. to G'). By Theorem 3.4, G and G' are equivalent iff G_1 and G_1' differ only by the names of nonterminals. We can immediately decide whether or not this latter condition is satisfied. ∎

EXERCISES

1. Describe algorithms, as simple as possible, for the solution of the emptiness and infinity problems for type-3 languages. (Cf. Exercise 15 to Chapter II.)

2. Prove that every diophantine set (i.e., a diophantine predicate of one variable) equals the set of positive values of a polynomial (with variables ranging over nonnegative integers).

3. Prove that every diophantine predicate can be expressed in terms of a polynomial with degree ≤ 5. Prove also that every diophantine set can be expressed as the set of positive values of a polynomial with degree ≤ 4.

4. Solve the Post correspondence problem in the case where the alphabet consists of one letter only.

5. Consider the following modification of the Post correspondence problem. Given an alphabet V, an integer $n \geq 1$, and two n-tuples

$$(\alpha_1, ..., \alpha_n), \qquad (\beta_1, ..., \beta_n)$$

of words over V, one has to decide whether or not some catenation of α-words equals some catenation of β-words. Describe an algorithm to solve this problem.

6. Show that it is unsolvable to decide for arbitrary context-free languages L_1 and L_2 whether or not there is a generalized sequential machine GSM such that $GSM(L_1) = L_2$.

7. Show that it is unsolvable to decide whether or not an arbitrary context-free language contains an infinite regular language.

8. Show that emptiness and infinity problems are solvable for Szilard languages of type-2 grammars.

9. Consider Table 5 given in Section 2 concerning solvability and unsolvability results. Give reasons for the appearance of each entry in the table.

10. Add the following problems to the statement of Theorem 2.4 and prove their unsolvability: (a) Is $L_1 \cap L_2$ linear? (b) Is $\sim L_1$ linear?

11. State and prove the unsolvability results of Theorem 2.4 as much as possible in terms of linear and metalinear grammars.

12. Assume that V is an alphabet with at least two letters, $a \in V$, and h is a homomorphism such that $h(a) = \lambda$, $h(b) = b$ for $b \neq a$. Consider the following problem: Given a regular language L and two Mealy machines M_1 and M_2, decide whether there is a word $P \in L$ such that $h(M_1(P)) = h(M_2(P))$. Using Post correspondence problem, show that this problem is unsolvable. (In a sense, this is an unsolvable problem dealing with type-3 languages.)

13. Study closure properties of parenthesis languages.

14. Show that the inclusion problem is solvable for parenthesis grammars.

15. Assume that $\mathscr{L}$ is an AFL such that $L = W(V_T)$ is unsolvable for languages $L \in \mathscr{L}$ and that $\mathscr{L}_1$ is a proper subfamily of $\mathscr{L}$, closed under union with $\{\lambda\}$, inverse gsm mappings, homomorphism, and intersection with regular languages. Show that it is unsolvable to determine whether an arbitrary $L \in \mathscr{L}$ belongs to $\mathscr{L}_1$. (Cf. Greibach, 1968.)

BIBLIOGRAPHICAL REMARKS

Rogers (1967) is a general introduction to unsolvability as well as to degrees of unsolvability. The latter have been studied from the point of view of languages by Cudia and Singletary (1968). For Hilbert's tenth problem, see Robinson (1971) and the references given therein. The final solution is due to Matijasevich (1971). Post correspondence problem was defined by Post (1946). Our proof of Theorem 2.1 follows Floyd (1964) and Maurer (1969). Theorem 2.5 is due to Taniguchi and Kasami (1970). For some interesting aspects of unsolvability concerning languages (not discussed in Chapter VIII), the reader is referred to Hartmanis (1967), Kaminger (1970), and Hartmanis and Hopcroft (1970). The material in Section 3 is due to McNaughton (1967). The same result was established by a different method by Paull and Unger (1968). The corresponding result for bracketed grammars (i.e., parentheses are numbered according to the productions) is due to Ginsburg and Harrison (1967).

BIBLIOGRAPHY

D. Cudia and **W. Singletary.** Degrees of unsolvability in formal grammars. *J. Assoc. Comput. Mach.* **15** (1968) 680–692.

R. Floyd. New Proofs of Old Theorems in Logic and Formal Linguistics. Computer Assoc., Wakefield, Massachusetts (1964).

S. Ginsburg. "The Mathematical Theory of Context-Free Languages." McGraw-Hill, New York, 1966.

S. Ginsburg and **M. Harrison.** Bracketed context-free languages. *J. Comput. System Sci.* **1** (1967) 1–23.

S. Greibach. A note on undecidable properties of formal languages. *Math. Systems Theory* **2** (1968) 1–6.

J. Hartmanis. Context-free languages and Turing machine computations. *Proc. Symp. Appl. Math.* (Amer. Math. Soc., Providence, Rhode Island) **19** (1967) 42–51.

J. Hartmanis and **J. Hopcroft.** What makes some language theory problems undecidable. *J. Comput. System Sci.* **4** (1970) 368–376.

F. Kaminger. The noncomputability of the channel capacity of context-sensitive languages. *Information Control* **17** (1970) 175–182.

R. McNaughton. Parenthesis grammars. *J. Assoc. Comput. Mach.* **14** (1967) 490–500.

Ju. Matijasevich. Diofantovo predstavlenie perechislimykh predikatov. *Izv. Akad. Nauk SSSR, Ser. Matem.* **35** (1971) 3–30.

H. Maurer. "Theoretische Grundlagen der Programmiersprachen." Hochschultaschenbücher 404, Bibliographisches Inst., 1969.

M. Paull and S. Unger. Structural equivalence of context-free grammars. *J. Comput. System Sci.* **2** (1968) 427–463.

E. Post. A variant of a recursively unsolvable problem. *Bull. Amer. Math. Soc.* **52** (1946) 264–268.

J. Robinson. Hilbert's tenth problem. *Proc. Symp. Pure Math.* (Amer. Math. Soc., Providence, Rhode Island) **20** (1971) 191–194.

H. Rogers, Jr. "Theory of Recursive Functions and Effective Computability." McGraw-Hill, New York, 1967.

K. Taniguchi and T. Kasami. Reduction of context-free grammars. *Information Control* **17** (1970) 92–108.

Chapter IX

Complexity

In the previous chapter, problems were classified as solvable and unsolvable. The understanding of the concept of solvability gives rise to a new question, namely, "how difficult to solve is a given problem," for example, in terms of time or memory space required. Thus we might consider the time (i.e., the number of steps in a computation) or space (i.e., the number of squares used in a computation) needed by a Turing machine. Conversely, we might require that when processing an input of length n, a Turing machine may use $\varphi(n)$ squares only where φ is a previously given function. This gives rise to a *complexity class* consisting of problems which can be solved in such a way that this requirement is satisfied. Analogous complexity measures can be introduced for grammars, too. For reasons that become apparent later, the complexity measures are associated with the algorithms and not directly with the problems. Thus a complexity class is obtained by introducing a bound (which usually is a function of the length of the input) on the amount of a particular resource (such as time or space) that an algorithm may use. A problem is in a given class iff there is an algorithm for solving it in which the amount of resource does not exceed the bound.

The theory of computational complexity has emerged as a very comprehensive theory during recent years. Most problems in this field lie beyond the scope of this book. We have investigated formal languages mostly from the point of view of grammars. On the other hand, the existing theory of computational complexity deals mostly with machine computations. The analogous problems for grammars are not yet satisfactorily understood.

We discuss in this chapter two topics in complexity theory. In Section 4, a time bound is introduced for grammars and a speedup result is developed in these terms. The last section (Section 5) deals with some aspects of an axiomatic (model independent) complexity theory.

4. TIME-BOUNDED GRAMMARS. SPEEDUP THEOREM

We now introduce the notion of the *time function* of a grammar. By placing bounds on time functions, we obtain families of languages (which can be considered as complexity classes). We make the convention that all grammars considered in this section are λ-free. This is assumed without any further mention.

For a grammar $G = (V_N, V_T, X_0, F)$, $V = V_N \cup V_T$, consider the language $L_S(G)$ of sentential forms of G. [Cf. (13.1) in Part 2.] For $P \in L_S(G)$, let $t_G(P)$ be the least integer $m \geq 1$ such that there is a derivation of P from X_0 according to G which is of length m. (We require $m \geq 1$ because we want to exclude the derivation of length 0 consisting of X_0 alone.) The *time function* for G is defined by

$$T_G(n) = \max\{t_G(P) | P \in L_S(G) \cap V^n\},$$

provided the intersection is nonempty; $T_G(n)$ is undefined for values of n such that $L_S(G) \cap V^n$ is empty.

Thus $T_G(n)$ is a partial function. Since G was assumed λ-free, $T_G(0)$ is undefined. In what follows, we consider computable or, equivalently, recursive functions. Here computability may be understood either in the informal sense meaning that there is an effective procedure for computing the values of the function (which procedure does not halt for those inputs for which the function is undefined), or in the formal sense explained in Part 1, Note 9.1.

Assume that T_G is both total and computable. Then both of the languages $L(G)$ and $L_S(G)$ are recursive. This follows because the membership $P \in L_S(G)$ can be decided by first computing the value $m = T_G(lg(P))$, and then checking through all of the finitely many derivations whose length does not exceed m. It is obvious that, conversely, if $L_S(G)$ is recursive, then T_G is a partial computable function. On the other hand, there exists a grammar G such that T_G is not even partial computable. To prove this, we consider a grammar G' such that $L(G')$ is not recursive. We can easily construct an equivalent grammar G such that T_G is total. This is done by adding a new (useless) nonterminal Y and productions $X_0 \to Y$, $Y \to Y^2$. If T_G were computable, $L(G)$ would be recursive, which is impossible.

For any G generating an infinite language, the growth of T_G is at least linear. In fact, if k is the greatest among the numbers $lg(Q) - lg(P) + 1$, where $P \to Q$ ranges over the productions of G, then

$$n/k \leq T_G(n) \qquad (4.1)$$

for all values of n such that $T_G(n)$ is defined. (Excluding the trivial cases, we may assume that $k \geq 2$.)

Motivated by (4.1) and the desire for effective constructions, we call a function f a *bounding function* iff it is a monotonically increasing total computable function with the property that there is a natural number k such that, for all n, $n/k \leq f(n)$. A bounding function f *bounds* a grammar G iff one may determine a number $k > 0$ such that any integer $n \geq k$, for which $T_G(n)$ is defined, satisfies

$$T_G(n) \leq f(n).$$

The next theorem is an immediate consequence of the definitions.

Theorem 4.1. If f is a bounding function which bounds a grammar G, then both $L(G)$ and $L_S(G)$ are recursive.

For a bounding function f, we denote by $\mathcal{L}_0(f)$ [resp. $\mathcal{L}_1(f)$] the family of languages that are generated by a type-0 [resp. length-increasing] grammar bounded by f. (Recall that all grammars in this section were assumed to be λ-free.) By Theorem 4.1, for any bounding function f, both of the families $\mathcal{L}_0(f)$ and $\mathcal{L}_1(f)$ are families of recursive languages. If two bounding functions f and g satisfy $f(n) \leq g(n)$, for all sufficiently large n, then

$$\mathcal{L}_1(f) \subseteq \mathcal{L}_1(g) \qquad \text{and} \qquad \mathcal{L}_0(f) \subseteq \mathcal{L}_0(g).$$

Clearly, if f is a bounding function and c is a positive (computable) number, then cf is also a bounding function. We prove that

$$\mathcal{L}_0(cf) = \mathcal{L}_0(f) \qquad \text{and} \qquad \mathcal{L}_1(cf) = \mathcal{L}_1(f). \qquad (4.2)$$

Equations (4.2) can be interpreted as follows. A bounding function induces a complexity measure for grammars. Suppose we have constructed for a language L a grammar which we think is "good" because it has a bounding function f with reasonably small values. Then we can always construct a "better" grammar with bounding function cf for any (arbitrarily small) positive c. The new grammar is length-increasing if the original was. In this speedup construction, the set of exceptional words whose derivations are not bounded by the bounding function usually becomes larger.

Comparing the families $\mathcal{L}_0(f)$ and $\mathcal{L}_1(f)$, it is immediately seen that

$$\mathcal{L}_1(f) \subseteq \mathcal{L}_0(f). \qquad (4.3)$$

Very little is known about the problem of finding those functions f for which the inclusion (4.3) is strict. In particular, call a grammar *linear-time* iff it is bounded by a linear bounding function. Denote by $\mathscr{L}_0(lin)$ [resp. $\mathscr{L}_1(lin)$] the family of languages which are generated by a type-0 [resp. length-increasing] linear-time grammar. It is not known whether

$$\mathscr{L}_1(lin) = \mathscr{L}_0(lin).$$

We now introduce the notion of connectivity, which is a very useful tool for proving results about time bounds. Consider a derivation

$$\alpha_0 \Rightarrow \alpha_1 \Rightarrow \cdots \Rightarrow \alpha_{m+1} \tag{4.4}$$

according to a grammar

$$G = (V_N, V_T, X_0, F), \qquad F = \{P_i \rightarrow Q_i | 1 \leq i \leq n\}.$$

Thus there are words R_{i1}, R_{i2} and indices $g(i)$, where $i = 0, \ldots, m$, such that for every $i = 0, \ldots, m-1$,

$$R_{i1} Q_{g(i)} R_{i2} = R_{(i+1)1} P_{g(i+1)} R_{(i+1)2} \tag{4.5}$$

and

$$\alpha_0 = R_{01} P_{g(0)} R_{02}, \qquad \alpha_{m+1} = R_{m1} Q_{g(m)} R_{m2}.$$

We refer to $\alpha_{i-1} \Rightarrow \alpha_i$ as the *ith step* of the derivation (4.4), for $i = 1, \ldots, m+1$.

We say that the $(i+1)$th step *occurs to the left* of the ith step iff $lg(R_{(i+1)1} P_{g(i+1)}) \leq lg(R_{i1})$. The $(i+1)$th step *occurs to the right* of the ith step iff $lg(R_{(i+1)1}) \geq lg(R_{i1} Q_{g(i)})$. If neither one of these conditions is satisfied, that is, if

$$lg(R_{(i+1)1} P_{g(i+1)}) > lg(R_{i1}) \quad \text{and} \quad lg(R_{(i+1)1}) < lg(R_{i1} Q_{g(i)})$$

then we say that the $(i+1)$th step is *connected* to the ith step.

It follows from the definition that these three alternatives are mutually exclusive and exhaust the possibilities. There are equivalent ways of defining these alternatives. For example, the first alternative holds iff $R_{(i+1)1} P_{g(i+1)}$ is an initial subword of R_{i1} iff $lg(R_{(i+1)2}) \geq lg(Q_{g(i)} R_{i2})$ iff $Q_{g(i)} R_{i2}$ is a final subword of $R_{(i+1)2}$. The last alternative holds iff

$$R_{i1} a_1 \cdots a_j = R_{(i+1)1} b_1 \cdots b_k,$$

for some $j, k > 0$ and letters a, b (terminals or nonterminals) such that $a_1 \cdots a_j$ [resp. $b_1 \cdots b_k$] is an initial subword of $Q_{g(i)}$ [resp. of $P_{g(i+1)}$]. The equivalence of these conditions is immediate by (4.5).

A derivation (4.4) is *connected* iff the words R_{ij} can be chosen in such a way that for every $i = 1, \ldots, m+1$, the ith step of the derivation is connected. [Note that the words R_{ij} are not in general uniquely determined by the derivation

(4.4).] A grammar is *connected* iff each derivation from the initial letter is connected.

Clearly, any (λ-free) linear grammar is connected, whereas metalinear grammars are not in general connected. For context-free grammars, we can establish the following result.

Theorem 4.2. Assume that all productions of a context-free grammar $G = (V_N, V_T, X_0, F)$ are of the form

$$X \to aP, \quad X \in V_N, \quad a \in V_T, \quad P \in W(V_N), \quad 0 \leq lg(P) \leq 2.$$
$$(4.6)$$

(By Theorem 8.5 in Part 2, any λ-free context-free language is generated by such a grammar G.) Then there is an equivalent connected length-increasing grammar G' such that $T_G(n)$ and $T_{G'}(n)$ are defined for the same values n, and always

$$T_G(n) = T_{G'}(n). \tag{4.7}$$

Proof. Define

$V_T' = \{a' | a \in V_T\},$

$G' = (V_N \cup V_T' \cup \{X_0'\}, V_T, X_0', F'),$

$F' = \{X_0' \to a | X_0 \to a \text{ in } F\} \cup \{X_0' \to a'P | X_0 \to aP \text{ in } F, P \neq \lambda\}$

$\quad \cup \{b'X \to ba'P | b \in V_T \text{ and } (4.6) \text{ in } F\}$

$\quad \cup \{b'X \to ba | b \in V_T \text{ and } X \to a \text{ in } F\}.$

In derivations according to G' from X_0', each word has at most one primed letter. From a word with no primed letters nothing can be derived. Thus the primed letters act as "connectors," and we conclude that G' is connected and (4.7) holds. Clearly, G' is equivalent to G. ∎

In the previous proof, the transition from a grammar to an equivalent connected grammar could be made without any increase in the time function. However, this was due to a property unique to context-free grammars: A derivation can be transformed into a leftmost one.

In general it is fairly obvious that for each type-1 or type-0 grammar, an equivalent connected grammar of the same type can be constructed. This follows by considering the equivalence of grammars of these two types to linear bounded automata and Turing machines, respectively. Clearly, a grammar obtained from an automaton is connected. However, this construction (begin with a grammar, construct a Turing machine which simulates it, and then a connected grammar equivalent to the machine) does not in general preserve the order of the time function of the grammar. We need the result in this form, and indeed the order is preserved in the proof of the following connectivity lemma.

Theorem 4.3. For a grammar G, one can construct an equivalent connected grammar G_1 and find a constant k_1 (which depends on G) such that, for any $n > 0$, if $T_G(n)$ is defined, then so is $T_{G_1}(n)$ and, furthermore,

$$T_{G_1}(n) \leq k_1 T_G(n). \tag{4.8}$$

If G is length-increasing, then so is G_1.

Proof. We show first that it is no loss of generality to consider only such derivations where no step occurs to the left of the previous one. More specifically, let us call a derivation (4.4) an *ordered* derivation iff the words R_{ij} can be chosen in such a way that no step occurs to the left of the preceding one. We now establish the following Assertion (A).

ASSERTION (A). For any grammar G and any derivation (4.4) according to G, one can find an ordered derivation according to G with the same length $(m+1)$ and the same initial and final words (α_0 and α_{m+1}).

In fact, assume that (4.4) is not ordered and let $i \geq 1$ be the least number such that the $(i+1)$th step occurs to the left of the ith step. Thus, if we follow the notation introduced after (4.4), there is a word R (may be empty) such that

$$\alpha_{i-1} = R_{(i-1)1} P_{g(i-1)} R_{(i-1)2} = R_{i1} P_{g(i)} RP_{g(i-1)} R_{(i-1)2},$$

$$\alpha_i = R_{(i-1)1} Q_{g(i-1)} R_{(i-1)2} = R_{i1} P_{g(i)} RQ_{g(i-1)} R_{(i-1)2},$$

$$\alpha_{i+1} = R_{i1} Q_{g(i)} R_{i2} = R_{i1} Q_{g(i)} RQ_{g(i-1)} R_{(i-1)2}.$$

Consequently, if we denote

$$\alpha_i' = R_{i1} Q_{g(i)} RP_{g(i-1)} R_{(i-1)2},$$

the derivation $\alpha_{i-1} \Rightarrow \alpha_i' \Rightarrow \alpha_{i+1}$ is an ordered one. Hence we have been able to eliminate the first step which occurs to the left of the preceding step. Continuing in the same way, all such steps can be eliminated. The length of the derivation, as well as the initial and final word, remains unaltered. This proves Assertion (A).

Returning to the proof of Theorem 4.3, we denote

$$G = (V_N, V_T, X_0, F), \qquad V = V_N \cup V_T,$$

$$V' = \{a' | a \in V\}, \qquad V'' = \{a'' | a \in V\}, \qquad V_1 = V_N \cup V' \cup V''.$$

Let P be a nonempty word over V. By definition, $U(P)$ is the set of cardinality $lg(P)$ consisting of those words over $V' \cup V''$ which are obtained from P by marking one letter with a double prime, and the remaining letters with a prime. [Thus, for $P = aXb$, we have $U(P) = \{a''X'b', a'X''b', a'X'b''\}$.] We now introduce the grammar G_1 by

$$G_1 = (V_1, V_T, X_0'', F_1),$$

$$F_1 = \{P_1 \to Q_1 | P \to Q \text{ in } F, P_1 \in U(P), Q_1 \in U(Q)\}$$

$$\cup \{a''b' \to a'b''|a, b \in V\} \cup \{a'' \to a|a \in V\} \cup \{a'b \to ab|a, b \in V\}.$$

The four classes in the union defining F_1 are referred to as the first, second, third, and fourth class. We may assume without loss of generality that every production in F_1 belongs to exactly one of the four classes. (The omission of productions $ab \to ab$ from F affects neither the time function nor the language generated.)

The grammar G_1 is connected. This follows because when productions in the first and second classes are used, then each word in the derivation contains exactly one letter marked with a double prime, and this letter acts as a connector. Productions in the third class can be used in any derivation from the initial letter at most once, after which only productions in the fourth class are applicable. The latter must be applied to the left of the position where the third class production was applied, and now the boundary between primed and unprimed letters acts as a connector.

By the definition of the set F_1, the grammar G_1 generates only "primed versions" of words generated by G. Thus, $L(G_1) \subseteq L(G)$. But also the reverse inclusion, $L(G) \subseteq L(G_1)$, is true. This follows because by Assertion (A) any word in $L(G)$ possesses a derivation where no step occurs to the left of the preceding one. Thus, we may first simulate the derivation by productions in the first and second classes, after which the rightmost letter is marked by the double prime. The primes are then eliminated using productions in the third and fourth classes. Consequently, G and G_1 are equivalent. Clearly, if G is length-increasing, then so is G_1.

It follows by the definition of F_1 that if $T_G(n)$ is defined, then so is $T_{G_1}(n)$. We still have to prove (4.8). Consider a derivation

$$D: X_0'' = P_0 \Rightarrow P_1 \Rightarrow \cdots \Rightarrow P_m, \qquad t_{G_1}(P_m) = m, \qquad lg(P_m) = n \geqq 1 \tag{4.9}$$

according to G_1. For $i = 1, 2, 3, 4$, let u_i be the number of applications of productions in D belonging to the ith class. Hence,

$$u_1 + u_2 + u_3 + u_4 = m. \tag{4.10}$$

By (4.9) and the definition of F_1, we obtain

$$u_1 \leqq T_G(n). \tag{4.11}$$

Clearly,

$$u_3 \leqq 1. \tag{4.12}$$

Since $u_4 \leqq lg(P_m) = n$, we conclude by (4.1) that there is a constant k such that always $n/k \leqq T_G(n)$ and hence

$$u_4 \leqq kT_G(n). \tag{4.13}$$

We now determine an upper bound for u_2. For $i = 0, ..., m$, the word P_i contains at least one letter which is not in V'. Assume that the leftmost such letter in P_i is the h_ith letter of P_i. Thus, $1 \leqq h_i \leqq lg(P_i)$. For $i = 1, ..., m$, define

$$g_i = h_i - h_{i-1}, \qquad g = \sum_{i=1}^{m} g_i = h_m - h_0.$$

Furthermore, let h be the length of the longest word appearing on either side of the productions in F. Assume that at the ith step $P_{i-1} \Rightarrow P_i$ of the derivation D a production in the jth class has been applied. Clearly,

(i)   if $j = 1$, then $|g_i| \leqq h$ and thus $-h \leqq g_i$;
(ii) if $j = 2$, then $g_i = 1$;
(iii) if $j = 3$, then $g_i = 0$;
(iv) if $j = 4$, then $g_i = -1$.

Consequently, we obtain the following estimates

$$-hu_1 + u_2 - u_4 \leqq g = h_m - h_0 < h_m \leqq lg(P_m) = n \leqq kT_G(n).$$

Hence, by (4.11) and (4.13),

$$u_2 \leqq hu_1 + u_4 + kT_G(n) \leqq (2k+h) T_G(n). \tag{4.14}$$

Since (4.10)–(4.14) hold for all derivations (4.9), we obtain

$$T_{G_1}(n) = m \leqq T_G(n) + (2k+h) T_G(n) + 1 + kT_G(n) \leqq (3k+h+2) T_G(n).$$

Thus, (4.8) holds for $k_1 = 3k+h+2$. ∎

Theorem 4.4 (The Speedup Theorem). Let G be a grammar, f a bounding function that bounds G, and $c > 0$. Then there is a connected grammar G' equivalent to G such that the function cf bounds G'. Moreover, if G is length-increasing, then so is G'.

Proof. We construct first a connected G_1 and k_1 as in the previous theorem such that (4.8) is satisfied. Assume that $G_1 = (V_N, V_T, X_0, F)$. Clearly, the function $k_1 f$ bounds G_1. Thus we may determine a constant $h_0 > 0$ such that if $n \geqq h_0$ and $T_{G_1}(n)$ is defined, then

$$T_{G_1}(n) \leqq k_1 f(n). \tag{4.15}$$

If $c/k_1 \geq 1$, we may choose $G' = G_1$. Assume that $0 < c/k_1 < 1$. Let m be a natural number such that

$$3/m \leq c/k_1. \tag{4.16}$$

Let L_0 be the finite subset of $L_S(G_1)$ consisting of words shorter than mh_0. Thus, $X_0 \in L_0$. Denote

$$F_0 = \{Y_0 \to P | P \in L_0\}.$$

We are now going to define a connected grammar G' equivalent to G such that if $n \geq mh_0$ and $T_{G'}(n)$ is defined, then

$$T_{G'}(n) \leq cf(n). \tag{4.17}$$

Basically, this is accomplished by combining m steps of a derivation according to G_1 into a single step in a derivation according to G'. This is possible because G_1 is connected and thus any m consecutive steps in a derivation must be performed not much apart.

Let k be the greatest among the numbers $lg(Q) - lg(P) + 1$ where $P \to Q$ ranges over the productions in F. (We may assume that $k \geq 2$.) Similarly, let k_0 be the greatest among the nonnegative differences $lg(P) - lg(Q)$. By definition, $k_0 = 0$ if all the differences $lg(P) - lg(Q)$ are negative. Finally, let k_2 be the length of the longest left side of the productions in F.

Let now F_1 be the set of all productions $P \to Q$ over $V_N \cup V_T$ such that (i) $lg(P) \leq m(k_0 + k_2 + k)$ and (ii) there is a connected derivation of Q from P according to G_1 that consists of i steps with $1 \leq i \leq m$. Clearly, F_1 is a finite set and can be determined effectively. Define

$$G' = (V_N \cup \{Y_0\}, V_T, Y_0, F_0 \cup F_1).$$

Since $F \subseteq F_1$ and F_0 contains the production $Y_0 \to X_0$, we conclude that $L(G_1) \subseteq L(G')$. Also the reverse inclusion holds since each step in a derivation according to G' can be simulated by a sequence of steps in a derivation according to G_1. Thus, G' is equivalent to G. The connectedness of G' follows by the connectedness of G_1. Clearly, G' satisfies the last sentence in the statement of the theorem. We still have to establish (4.17).

Consider a derivation

$$X_0 = P_0 \Rightarrow P_1 \Rightarrow \cdots \Rightarrow P_v, \quad v = t_{G_1}(P_v), \quad lg(P_v) \geq mh_0 \tag{4.18}$$

according to G_1. Now $t_{G_1}(P_v) \geq lg(P_v)/k$, which implies that $v \geq mh_0/k$. There is no loss of generality in assuming that $h_0 \geq k$. (Otherwise, we replace h_0 by a greater number satisfying this condition.) Thus, $v \geq m$. Let now u be the greatest integer such that $um \leq v$. By the construction of F_1,

$$Y_0 \Rightarrow X_0 \Rightarrow P_m \Rightarrow P_{2m} \Rightarrow \cdots \Rightarrow P_{um}$$

is a derivation according to G'. If $um < v$, then $P_{um} \Rightarrow_{G'} P_v$. Consequently, by (4.16) and (4.15),

$$t_{G'}(P_v) \leqq u + 2 \leqq v/m + 2 \leqq 3v/m \leqq (c/k_1)v$$
$$= (c/k_1)\, t_{G_1}(P_v) \leqq (c/k_1)\, T_{G_1}(lg(P_v)) \leqq cf(lg(P_v)).$$

Since this estimate holds for any derivation (4.18), we have established (4.17). ∎

The construction in the previous proof is effective (provided that c is effectively given).

By definition, for any bounding function f, there is a constant $c > 0$ ($c = 1/k$) such that $cn \leqq f(n)$ for all n. Hence, if we denote by $i_0(n)$ the identity function defined by $i_0(n) = n$, we obtain by Theorem 4.4

$$\mathscr{L}_1(i_0) = \mathscr{L}_1(ci_0) \subseteq \mathscr{L}_1(f), \qquad \mathscr{L}_0(i_0) = \mathscr{L}_0(ci_0) \subseteq \mathscr{L}_0(f).$$

Therefore the following theorem is an immediate corollary of Theorem 4.4.

Theorem 4.5. Let f be a bounding function and c a positive number. Then for $j = 0, 1$,

$$\mathscr{L}_j(f) = \mathscr{L}_j(cf), \qquad \mathscr{L}_j(lin) = \mathscr{L}_j(i_0), \qquad \mathscr{L}_j(lin) \subseteq \mathscr{L}_j(f).$$

Theorem 4.6. Every λ-free context-free language belongs to the family $\mathscr{L}_1(lin)$. Consequently, for any bounding function f, every λ-free context-free language belongs to the family $\mathscr{L}_1(f)$. Every type-0 language is a homomorphic image of a language in $\mathscr{L}_1(lin)$. Consequently, for any bounding function f, every type-0 language is a homomorphic image of a language in $\mathscr{L}_1(f)$. For any bounding function f, the family $\mathscr{L}_1(f)$ contains non-context-free languages.

Proof. The second and the fourth sentence follow from the preceding sentences by Theorem 4.5. The last sentence is a consequence of the fourth sentence and the fact that $\mathscr{L}_2$ is closed under homomorphism. The first sentence follows by Theorem 8.5 in Part 2. Finally, the third sentence is an almost immediate consequence of Theorem 9.9 in Part 1. In fact, a slight modification in the proof of this theorem makes the grammar G_1 linear-time. To this end, one has to replace the exponent of Y by $lg(P) - lg(Q) + 1$ and introduce Y also in productions where $lg(P) = lg(Q)$. When going to the left, Y is transformed into Y^2. After these changes, every production of G_1 is either strictly length-increasing or deposits a terminal. (Note that we obtain the result first for λ-free type-0 languages only. This difficulty is easily overcome if we replace λ by a dummy terminal letter b which is then mapped into λ in the homomorphism.) ∎

By Theorem 4.6, the emptiness problem is unsolvable for all of the families $\mathscr{L}_1(f)$. Moreover, each problem which is unsolvable for context-free languages is also unsolvable for the families $\mathscr{L}_1(f)$. (Cf. Theorem 2.4.)

Our connectivity lemma, Theorem 4.3, is a useful tool in establishing closure results. One can show that for any f, the families $\mathscr{L}_1(f)$ and $\mathscr{L}_0(f)$ are closed under union, catenation, mirror image, intersection with regular languages, and λ-free homomorphism. They are not closed under arbitrary homomorphism (this follows by Theorem 4.6) and not in general closed under inverse homomorphism. One can also prove that

$$\{Pc\,\mathrm{mi}(P)cP\,|\,P \in W\{a,b\}\} \notin \mathscr{L}_1(f),$$

provided f satisfies the condition $\lim_{n\to\infty} f(n)/n^2 = 0$. Using this result, it is easy to see that $\mathscr{L}_1(lin)$ is not closed under intersection.

5. AXIOMATIC APPROACH. GAP THEOREM

We now discuss briefly some results which are valid for all complexity measures satisfying certain axioms. The theory is expressed in terms of (partial) computable functions. For an algorithm A_f that computes a function f, a complexity measure will show how many "steps" A_f takes to evaluate $f(n)$ where n is any specific argument value. Thus, to define a complexity measure, we consider a list

$$A_1, A_2, A_3, \ldots \tag{5.1}$$

of algorithms for the computation of all partial computable functions. To each algorithm A_i is assigned a *step-counting* function B_i which (intuitively) gives the amount of resource used by A_i on a specific input n. Thus, a complexity measure consists of two lists, (5.1), and

$$B_1, B_2, B_3, \ldots \tag{5.2}$$

which satisfy the two axioms given below.

For instance, the list of algorithms (5.1) could consist of all Turing machines and $B_i(n)$ could be the number of operations performed by A_i before halting on input n. Another complexity measure is obtained when we let (5.1) be a numeration of all Algol programs and define $B_i(n)$ as the number of instructions executed by A_i before halting on input n.

We want to emphasize once more that the complexity measures are associated with the algorithms rather than directly with the functions computed by the algorithms. This is natural because for each computable function there are infinitely many algorithms which compute it. Moreover, we cannot define the complexity of a function as that of its "best" algorithm since, as is seen below, there exist functions which have no best algorithm.

We now define a *computational complexity measure* as an enumeration (5.1) of all partial computable functions (of one variable) to which are associated the partial computable *step-counting* functions (5.2) such that the following axioms are satisfied.

Axiom 1. For all i and n, $A_i(n)$ is defined iff $B_i(n)$ is defined.

Axiom 2. There is an effective procedure which determines of any i, n, and m whether or not

$$B_i(n) = m.$$

Axiom 2 can be expressed also as follows. The function $C(i, m, n)$ defined by

$$C(i,m,n) = \begin{cases} 0 & \text{if} \quad B_i(n) \neq m, \\ 1 & \text{if} \quad B_i(n) = m \end{cases}$$

is computable. Note also that if (5.1) was originally considered as a list of algorithms such as Turing machines, we may in the formal definition consider it as an enumeration of partial computable functions with repetitions. Since different occurrences of the same function in (5.1) may be assigned a different step-counting function, we see that the complexity measure is associated with the algorithm rather than directly with the function. It is assumed that the enumeration (5.1) is such that the transitions from a function to its number and vice versa are effective.

The two examples described briefly above (the number of steps used by a Turing machine or an Algol program) each constitute a complexity measure. We consider now two examples which do not form complexity measures. Let (5.1) be an enumeration of all partial computable functions. Define the functions B_i as follows. If $A_i(n)$ is defined, then $B_i(n) = 0$. Otherwise, $B_i(n)$ is not defined. If Axiom 2 were satisfied, we could determine for any i and n whether or not $B_i(n) = 0$. But this would solve the halting problem (and the membership problem for type-0 languages) and consequently Axiom 2 is not satisfied. Define, secondly, the functions B_i by

$$B_i(n) = 0$$

for all i and n. Then Axiom 1 is not satisfied.

Our first theorem says that for any complexity measure, there exist arbitrarily complex computable functions. We say that i is an *index* for the function f iff $A_i(n) = f(n)$ for all n. (The equation means that A_i and f are defined for the same argument values, and whenever both are defined, they assume the same value.) In what follows, the expression "almost everywhere" (abbreviated a.e.) means "with finitely many exceptions."

Theorem 5.1. For any computational complexity measure $C = (A_i, B_i)$ and any computable function g, there exists a computable function f such that for any index i for f, $B_i(n) > g(n)$ a.e.

Proof. We define $f(n)$, as well as an auxiliary function $u(n)$, inductively as follows. First, $f(n) = u(n) = 1$ for $n = 0, 1$. Consider a fixed number $n \geq 2$. Then $u(n)$ is the smallest integer less than n such that

$$B_{u(n)}(n) \leq g(n) \tag{5.3}$$

and there is no m with the properties $u(n) < m < n$ and

$$B_{u(n)}(m) \leq g(m), \qquad A_{u(n)}(m) \neq f(m). \tag{5.4}$$

If no such integer exists, $u(n)$ is undefined. Moreover,

$$f(n) = \begin{cases} 0 & \text{if } A_{u(n)}(n) = 1, \\ 1 & \text{if } u(n) \text{ is not defined} \quad \text{or} \quad A_{u(n)}(n) \neq 1. \end{cases}$$

Clearly, f is total and computable since the conditions (5.3) and (5.4) can readily be tested. [Note that by Axiom 1 the condition (5.3) implies that $A_{u(n)}(n)$ is defined.] We claim that for any index i for f, $B_i(n) > g(n)$ a.e. Assume the contrary: There is an index j for f such that

$$B_j(n) \leq g(n) \tag{5.5}$$

for infinitely many values of n. Consequently, $j = u(n_0)$ for some n_0. [Such a number n_0 is found by considering values $n > j$ for which (5.5) is satisfied.] By the definition of f,

$$f(n_0) \neq A_{u(n_0)}(n_0) = A_j(n_0),$$

which implies that j is not an index for f. This contradiction shows that our claim is correct. ∎

The function f constructed above assumes only the values 0 and 1, and hence is bounded. From this we conclude that there exists no computable relation between functions and their complexities, since such a relation would give a bound on the complexity of any bounded function. This result is established in the following theorem, as well as the parallel result that the size of a computable function can, in fact, be bounded recursively by its complexity.

Theorem 5.2. Consider a computational complexity measure $C = (A_i, B_i)$. There does not exist any computable function g_1 such that, for each i,

$$g_1(n, A_i(n)) \geq B_i(n) \quad \text{a.e.}$$

There exists a computable function g_2 such that, for each i,

$$g_2(n, B_i(n)) \geq A_i(n) \quad \text{a.e.} \tag{5.6}$$

Proof. To prove the first assertion, we assume that such a g_1 exists. Choose in Theorem 5.1

$$g(n) = \max(g_1(n, 0), g_1(n, 1)),$$

and consider the function f as defined in the proof of the theorem. Then every index i for f satisfies

$$B_i(n) \leq g(n) \quad \text{a.e.},$$

which is a contradiction.

To prove the second assertion, consider the function

$$g_3(i, n, m) = \begin{cases} A_i(n) & \text{if} \quad B_i(n) = m, \\ 1, & \text{otherwise.} \end{cases}$$

The function g_3 is computable because (i) the condition $B_i(n) = m$ is decidable, by Axiom 2, and (ii) if $B_i(n) = m$, then $A_i(n)$ is defined, by Axiom 1. Now define g_2 by

$$g_2(n, m) = \max_{i \leq n} g_3(i, n, m).$$

Obviously also g_2 is computable. Assume now that $A_i(n)$ is defined and $n \geq i$. Then, by the definition of g_3,

$$g_2(n, B_i(n)) \geq A_i(n).$$

Consequently, (5.6) is satisfied. ∎

We have seen that there is no recursive relation between the size of a function and its complexity. However, there is a recursive relation between the step-counting functions of an algorithm in any two measures. Thus a function requiring "little" resource in one measure requires "little" resource in all measures.

Theorem 5.3. Let $C = (A_i, B_i)$ and $C' = (A_i, B_i')$ be computational complexity measures. Then there exists a computable function f such that, for each i,

$$f(n, B_i(n)) \geq B_i'(n) \quad \text{and} \quad f(n, B_i'(n)) \geq B_i(n) \quad \text{a.e.} \tag{5.7}$$

Proof. Define

$$f(n, m) = \max\{B_i(n), B_i'(n) | i \leq n, \text{ and } B_i(n) = m \text{ or } B_i'(n) = m\}.$$

[If, for some n and m, no numbers $B_i(n)$, $B_i'(n)$ are found, then we define $f(n, m) = 1$.] Then f is computable because by Axiom 2 the defining conditions can be tested and by Axiom 1 if one of the numbers $B_i(n)$ and $B_i'(n)$ equals m, then both of them are defined. By the definition of f, the inequalities in (5.7) hold whenever $n \geq i$. Thus we conclude that (5.7), with the restriction a.e. added, is correct. ∎

In the axiomatic approach, one can establish the following speedup theorem.

Proposition 5.1. Consider a computational complexity measure $C = (A_i, B_i)$ and a computable function $g(n)$. There exists a computable function $f(n)$ such that for every index i for f, there is an index j for f satisfying

$$B_i(n) \geq g(B_j(n)) \quad \text{a.e.} \tag{5.8}$$

The restriction "almost everywhere" in (5.8) means that although any algorithm for f can be sped up by the factor g, at the same time the set of exceptional values (for which the speedup result does not hold) might grow much larger. However, this speedup result shows that we cannot classify functions by their complexity since there are functions which have no best algorithms.

Our final result, the so-called *gap theorem*, asserts that step-counting functions are sparse relative to computable functions. For any computational complexity measure $C = (A_i, B_i)$ and for any computable function g, we define the *complexity class*

$$T_g^C = \{A_i | B_i(n) \leq g(n) \text{ a.e.}\}.$$

The gap theorem shows that there are arbitrarily large gaps in some complexity ranges where no new computation is performed. Thus there is no uniform way to increase a resource bound to guarantee an increase in generative capacity.

Theorem 5.4. Let $C = (A_i, B_i)$ be a computational complexity measure and g a computable function satisfying $g(n) \geq n$ for all n. Then there is a computable monotonically increasing function f such that

$$T_f^C = T_{gf}^C. \tag{5.9}$$

Proof. Define the function f as follows:

$$f(0) = 1,$$

$$f(n+1) = f(n) + m_n, \tag{5.10}$$

where m_n is the least number $m \geq 1$ such that, for each $i \leq n+1$, either $B_i(n+1) \leq f(n)+m$ or else it is not the case that

$$B_i(n+1) \leq g(f(n)+m). \tag{5.11}$$

We note first that m_n always exists since if $B_i(n+1)$ is not defined, then (5.11) is not satisfied for any m. By Axiom 2, m_n can be found effectively and consequently f is computable. By (5.10), for all j, the condition

$$B_j(n) \leq g(f(n)) \quad \text{a.e.}$$

implies the condition

$$B_j(n) \leq f(n) \quad \text{a.e.}$$

Therefore, (5.9) holds true. ∎

EXERCISES

1. Give an explicit example of a non-context-free language in $\mathscr{L}_1(lin)$.

2. Consider any bounding function f. Show that the infinity problem is unsolvable for $\mathscr{L}_1(f)$. Show also that it is unsolvable to determine whether a given language $L \in \mathscr{L}_1(f)$ is context-free.

3. Prove that for any bounding function f, the families $\mathscr{L}_0(f)$ and $\mathscr{L}_1(f)$ are closed under each of the operations of union, catenation, and mirror image.

4. Assume that f is a bounding function satisfying the condition $f(m)+f(n) \leq f(m+n)$ for all m and n. Prove that $\mathscr{L}_0(f)$ and $\mathscr{L}_1(f)$ are closed under substitution and λ-free catenation closure. (Cf. Book, 1969.)

5. Assume that f is a bounding function satisfying $f(n) \geq cn^2$ for some fixed $c > 0$ and all n. Prove that $\mathscr{L}_0(f)$ and $\mathscr{L}_1(f)$ are closed under intersection. (Cf. Book, 1969.)

6. Justify the last sentence in Section 4.

7. Prove that for any bounding function f, the families $\mathscr{L}_0(f)$ and $\mathscr{L}_1(f)$ are closed under neither left nor right quotient with regular languages.

8. Give an example of a complexity measure C and a computable function g such that the complexity class T_g^C is not recursively enumerable. [Cf. Hartmanis and Hopcroft (1971). In fact, the result holds in a slightly more general form.]

BIBLIOGRAPHICAL REMARKS

The material in Section 4 is due to Gladkij (1964) and Book (1969, 1971). The basic results concerning computational complexity belong to Rabin (1960) and Hartmanis and Stearns (1965), and the axiomatic approach to

Blum (1967). Our exposition in Section 5 follows Hartmanis and Hopcroft (1971). The work of Irland and Fischer (1970) is a comprehensive bibliography on computational complexity.

BIBLIOGRAPHY

M. Blum. A machine-independent theory of the complexity of recursive functions. *J. Assoc. Comput. Mach.* **14** (1967) 322–336.

R. Book. Grammars with Time Functions. Harvard Univ., Computation Laboratory Rep. No. NSF-23 (1969).

R. Book. Time-bounded grammars and their languages. *J. Comput. System Sci.* **5** (1971) 397–429.

A. Gladkij. O slozhnosti vyvoda v grammatikakh neposredstvenno sostavljajushchikh. *Algebra i Logika Seminar* **3** (1964) 29–44.

J. Hartmanis and **J. Hopcroft.** An overview of the theory of computational complexity. *J. Assoc. Comput. Mach.* **18** (1971) 444–475.

J. Hartmanis and **R. Stearns.** On the computational complexity of algorithms. *Trans. Amer. Math. Soc.* **117** (1965) 285–306.

M. Irland and **P. Fischer.** A bibliography on computational complexity. Univ. of Waterloo Res. Rep. CSRR 2028 (1970).

M. Rabin. Degrees of Difficulty of Computing a Function and a Partial Ordering of Recursive Sets. Hebrew Univ. (Jerusalem) Tech. Rep. 2 (1960).

GUIDE TO THE LITERATURE

References to work closely related to topics discussed have been given in connection with each individual chapter. They are by no means intended to be exhaustive. The bibliography by D. Wood in *ACM Comput. Rev.* **11** (1970) 417–430 exhausts the major western journals. Some of the books listed below also contain extensive bibliographies. *Information and Control, Journal of the Association for Computing Machinery, Mathematical Systems Theory, Journal of Computer and System Sciences, Acta Informatica,* and *Information Sciences* are among the major journals to look for new results. Besides, there is an annual *IEEE Conference Record of The Symposium on Switching and Automata Theory* as well as proceedings of the annual *ACM Symposium on Theory of Computing.* Reviews of published work can be found in the following journals (among others): *ACM Computing Reviews, Journal of Symbolic Logic, Mathematical Reviews, Referativnyi Zhurnal Matematika* and *Zentralblatt für Mathematik und ihre Grenzgebiete.*

The following *list of books on formal languages and automata theory* was compiled in March 1972. Books dealing almost entirely with switching theory or programming languages have not been listed. Only a couple of representatives of books on recursive functions have been chosen. Translations have been mentioned only in case the original is in Russian.

M. A. Arbib (ed.). "Algebraic Theory of Machines, Languages and Semigroups." Academic Press, New York, 1968, xvi + 359 pp.
M. A. Arbib. "Theories of Abstract Automata." Prentice Hall, Englewood Cliffs, New Jersey, 1969, xiii + 412 pp.

F. Bartholomes and **G. Hotz.** "Homomorphismen und Reduktionen linearer Sprachen." Lecture Notes in Operations Research and Mathematical Systems 32, Springer, New York, 1970, xii + 143 pp.

K. H. Böhling and **K. Indermark.** "Endliche Automaten I." Hochschulskripten 703, Bibliographisches Inst., 1969, 90 pp.

K. H. Böhling and **D. Schütt.** "Endliche Automaten II." Hochschulskripten 704, Bibliographisches Inst., 1970, 104 pp.

T. L. Booth. "Sequential Machines and Automata Theory." Wiley, New York, 1967, xiv + 592 pp.

C. Boucher. "Leçons sur la théorie des automates mathematiques." Lecture Notes in Operations Research and Mathematical Systems 46, Springer, New York, 1971, viii + 193 pp.

W. Brauer and **K. Indermark.** "Algorithmen, rekursive Funktionen und formale Sprachen." Hochschulskripten 817, Bibliographisches Inst., 1968, 115 pp.

R. G. Bukharaev. "Verojatnostnye avtomaty." Izd. Kazanskogo Univ., 1970, 188 pp.

E. R. Caianiello (ed.). "Automata Theory." Academic Press, New York, 1966, xiv + 341 pp.

V. Claus. "Stochastische Automaten." Teubner, Stuttgart, 1971, 184 pp.

E. F. Codd. "Cellular Automata." Academic Press, New York, 1968, ix + 122 pp.

J. H. Conway. "Regular Algebra and Finite Machines." Chapman and Hall, London, 1971, viii + 147 pp.

M. Davis. "Computability and Unsolvability." McGraw-Hill, New York, 1958, xxv + 210 pp.

P. Deussen. "Halbgruppen und Automaten." Heidelberger Taschenbücher 99, Springer, New York, 1971, 198 pp.

J. Dörr and **G. Hotz** (eds.). "Automatentheorie und formale Sprachen." Bibliographisches Inst., 1970.

E. Engeler. "Formal Languages." Markham, Chicago, 1968, vii + 81 pp.

F. Gécseg and **I. Péak.** "Algebraic Theory of Automata." Akadémiai Kiadó, 1972, xiii + 326 pp.

A. Gill. "Introduction to the Theory of Finite-State Machines." McGraw-Hill, New York, 1962, ix + 207 pp.

S. Ginsburg. "An Introduction to Mathematical Machine Theory." Addison-Wesley, Reading, Massachusetts, 1962, viii + 148 pp.

S. Ginsburg. "The Mathematical Theory of Context-Free Languages." McGraw-Hill, New York, 1966, xii + 232 pp.

S. Ginsburg, S. Greibach, and **J. Hopcroft.** "Studies in Abstract Families of Languages." Memoirs of the Amer. Math. Soc., No. 87, 1969, 51 pp.

A. Ginzburg. "Algebraic Theory of Automata." Academic Press, New York, 1968, ix + 165 pp.

A. V. Gladkij. "Leçons de linguistique mathématique." Centre de linguistique quantitative de la faculté des sciences de l'Université de Paris, Dunod, 1970.

W. M. Gluschkow. "Theorie der abstrakten Automaten." VEB Deutscher Verlag der Wissenschaften, 1963, 103 pp.

M. Gross and **A. Lentin.** "Notions sur les grammaires formelles." Gauthier-Villars, Paris, 1967, 197 pp.

W. Händler, E. Peschl, and **H. Unger** (eds.). "3. Colloquium über Automatentheorie" (Hannover 1965). Birkhäuser, Basel, 1967, 316 pp.

M. A. Harrison. "Introduction to Switching and Automata Theory." McGraw-Hill, New York, 1965, xvii + 499 pp.

M. A. Harrison. "Lectures on Linear Sequential Machines." Academic Press, New York, 1969, x + 210 pp.

J. Hart and S. Takasu (eds.). "Systems and Computer Science." Univ. of Toronto Press, Toronto, Canada, 1967, xi + 249 pp.

J. Hartmanis and R. E. Stearns. "Algebraic Structure Theory of Sequential Machines." Prentice Hall, Englewood Cliffs, New Jersey, 1966, viii + 211 pp.

J. E. Hopcroft and J. D. Ullman. "Formal Languages and Their Relation to Automata." Addison-Wesley, Reading, Massachusetts, 1969, x + 242 pp.

G. Hotz and H. Walter. "Automatentheorie und formale Sprachen. I. Turingmaschinen und rekursive Funktionen." Hochschulskripten 821, Bibliographisches Inst., 1968, 174 pp.

N. E. Kobrinskij and B. A. Trakhtenbrot. "Vvedenie v teoriju konechnykh avtomatov." Gosud. izd. Fiz.-Mat. Lit., Moscow, 1962, 404 pp.

Z. Kohavi and A. Paz (eds.). "Theory of Machines and Computations." Academic Press, New York, 1971, xiii + 416 pp.

V. A. Kozmidiadi and A. A. Muchnik (eds.). "Problemy matematicheskoi logiki. Slozhnost algoritmov i klassy vychislimykh funktsij." Izd. "Mir," 1970, 432 pp.

A. A. Lorents (ed.). "Verojatnostnye avtomaty i ikh primenenie." Izd. "Zinatne," Riga, 1971, 212 pp.

R. McNaughton and S. Papert. "Counter-Free Automata," Research Monograph no. 65. M.I.T. Press, Cambridge, Massachusetts, 1971, xix + 163 pp.

A. I. Maltsev. "Algoritmy i rekursivnye funktsij." Izd. "Nauka," 1965, 391 pp.

S. Marcus. "Gramatici si automate finite." Edit. Acad. Republ. Popul. Romine, 1964, 255 pp.

"Mathematical Theory of Automata," Polytechnic Inst. of Brooklyn. Proc. of a Symp. held in New York 1962. Wiley, New York, 1963, xix + 640 pp.

H. Maurer. "Theoretische Grundlagen der Programmiersprachen." Hochschultaschenbücher 404, Bibliographisches Inst., 1969, 253 pp.

M. Minsky. "Computation: Finite and Infinite Machines." Prentice Hall, Englewood Cliffs, New Jersey, 1967, xvii + 317 pp.

E. F. Moore (ed.). "Sequential Machines: Selected Papers." Addison-Wesley, Reading, Massachusetts, 1964, v + 266 pp.

R. J. Nelson. "Introduction to Automata." Wiley, New York, 1968, xii + 400 pp.

A. Paz. "Introduction to Probabilistic Automata." Academic Press, New York, 1971, xxv + 228 pp.

B. Reusch. "Lineare Automaten." Bibliographisches Inst., Hochschulskripten 708, 1969.

H. Rogers, Jr. "Theory of Recursive Functions and Effective Computability." McGraw-Hill, New York, 1967, xix + 482 pp.

A. Salomaa. "Theory of Automata." Pergamon, Oxford, 1969, xii + 260 pp.

D. Schütt. "Überblick über die algebraischen Theorien in der Automatentheorie." Gesellschaft für Mathematik und Datenverarbeitung, Bonn, 1968, 78 pp.

C. E. Shannon and J. McCarthy (eds.). "Automata Studies." Princeton Univ. Press, Princeton, New Jersey, 1956, viii + 285 pp.

R. M. Smullyan. "Theory of Formal Systems." Princeton Univ. Press, Princeton, New Jersey, 1961, vii + 142 pp.

P. H. Starke. "Abstrakte Automaten." VEB Deutscher Verlag der Wissenschaften, 1969, 392 pp.

B. A. Trakhtenbrot. "Algorithms and Automatic Computing Machines." Heath, Boston, Massachusetts, 1963, 101 pp.

B. A. Trakhtenbrot and Ja. M. Barzdin. "Konechnye avtomaty (povedenie i sintez)." Izd. "Nauka," 1970, 400 pp.

Subject Index